Reading the Landscape of Europe

READING THE *L*ANDSCAPE OF EUROPE

by May Theilgaard Watts

ILLUSTRATIONS BY THE AUTHOR

HARPER & ROW, PUBLISHERS

NEW YORK, EVANSTON, SAN FRANCISCO, LONDON

1817

The chapter "Reading the Rooflines of Europe" first appeared in a different form in *Landscape Magazine*. Another version appeared in *The Subversive Science: Essays Toward an Ecology of Man* published by Houghton Mifflin.

The quotation on page 8 is from "The Peaceful Shepherd" from *The Poetry of Robert Frost* edited by Edward Connery Lathem. Copyright 1928, © 1969 by Holt, Rinehart and Winston, Inc. Copyright © 1956 by Robert Frost. Reprinted by permission of Holt, Rinehart and Winston, Inc.

Grateful acknowledgment is made to Alfred A. Knopf, Inc., for permission to reprint excerpts from *Poets in a Landscape*, © 1957 by Gilbert Highet, and from *The Landscape of Europe*, copyright 1953 by Hans Cloos.

Dedicated to the students who have walked with me
to read the landscapes of our Midwest

Note: This book, originally in the
R. Public Library, was purchased
and paid for ($ 9.50) by me
with the permission of the
Director.

A. L.

Contents

v

Switzerland

Germany

Denmark

Norway

Britain

Acknowledgments

Many have helped with this book. Most steadfast have stood the members of my family: my husband, Raymond Watts, who did not live to see the book published, and our children, Erica, Nancy, and Tom. From them, in varying combinations, the "we" of the personal experiences recounted here was recruited.

Next come special friends who have given unflagging support throughout: Helen Turner, Marlie Moulton, and Barbara Adams. Others who furnished some indispensable ingredient are: Paul Sears, Johannes Iversen, Peter Glob, Ruth Kroscher, Eleanor Himmelfarb, Alice Barkhausen, Miriam Fry, Floyd Swink, and Edna Jones.

Finally, the whole has been firmed and shaped by the sensitive touch of my editor, Nahum J. Waxman. Should you find some errors or omissions that may have escaped even his scrutiny, consider Europe and what a thick, old manuscript it is, magnificently illuminated and embellished, but how full of cross-outs, changes, and blurred erasures.

It would be best of all, reader, for you to go and turn some pages there for yourself.

READING THE LANDSCAPE OF EUROPE

Prologue

THE ROOFS of Europe, the old roofs, at least, have some interesting things to say to travelers. The rooflines of a region can serve, for example, as a prologue to reading the local landscape. They offer a record of how men have come to terms with rain and wind and heat and cold and, of course, other men. Roof materials may point to local quarries or clay pits or forests or reed-fringed swamps. Roof forms, their structure, their pitch, the overhang of their eaves, their chimneys, their very mosses add further comments, until the environment is so dependably indicated that a confirmed roof-reader may even be equipped to predict the quality of the native oak leaf: big, small, leathery, harsh, prickly, silky, thin, or thick. He may also be able to guess certain qualities of the local humans as well, including a thing or two about their gods, and their gardens.

Roof-reading began to be a part of our traveling as we made our way across Normandy toward Paris. (Normandy proved a good starting point, a place of comfortably undramatic weather and responses to weather, from which to branch outward to all sorts of modifications and extremes: southeast to Italy and Switzerland, east to Germany, north to Denmark and Norway, and west to Britain.) Our attention happened to be caught by a willow seedling sprouting in the gutter of a cottage, and we stopped to look at the roof more closely. We noticed the black-green mosses on the north-facing slope of the roof and found, in an especially sheltered angle where the mosses were piled like cushions, a delicate fern unrolling. Then our attention was diverted to a roof on the opposite side of the narrow lane. The sunny orange tiles of that south-facing slope held a

1

few stonecrop plants, showing yellow bloom and fat, gray-green leaves. Already, in those three microclimates—the north-facing slope, the sheltered angle, and the south-facing slope—we had seen a hint of the differing landscapes of Normandy, then the Black Forest, and, finally, sunny Provence.

In Normandy we saw rooflines of moderate pitch—no need there, evidently, for steep slopes to get rid of heavy rains or snows. Their eaves showed only a moderate overhang—no need for them to be extended to offer shelter, and no need for them to be retracted to avoid ripping winds. Their chimneys were of moderate importance —no need for roaring fires.

In that landscape, where men have elected to build roofs having neither response to nor insurance against weather, nature and time have elected to build forests of beech trees.

Of all the forest leaves of Europe, a beech tree leaf speaks most clearly of a long line of peaceful existence in equable circumstances, with neither a surplus nor a deficiency of those leaf-shaping qualities of weather: warmth, humidity, wind. As with the roofs, it is not the features that are present but the features that are absent which are revealing.

Northwestern France

The beech leaf has no:

> leathery surface nor hairy covering to lessen the outgo of water;
> reduction, by lobing or rolling or folding, of the surface exposed
>   to the thirsty sun;
> drooping habit, or dripping point, to let excessive rain run off;
> aromatic fragrance from protective oils;
> grazing deterrents, such as bristles or bitter taste.

marronnier	robinier	platane
Aesculus Hippocastanum	Robinia pseudo-acacia	Platanus
horse chestnut	black locust	occidentalis
		plane

tilleul
Tilia
grandifolia
linden

saule
Salix
willow

Paris

The beech leaves felt thin and silky and vulnerable between our fingers, as did the leaf of the chief plant of the forest floor, the pink oxalis, and the leaves of two other forest trees, the hornbeam and the English oak. The weather was certainly not bland, nor enervatingly constant (the forest leaves all retreat before winter's advance). Evidently it provided those continual changes which seem so necessary for developing a vigorous, active people. The tiles of the roofs looked tightly fitted, and window shutters were usually closed against the night air. Every fallen twig in the forest had been collected, and every willow had been pollarded for firewood. Bent working backs were a part of the landscape. The climate seemed to prevent inhibitions from thawing: we heard no one sing aloud out of doors in the daylight, and no Normandy child would return our waves. But the wheat with its company of red poppies and cornflowers waved. And there, where apple orchards were setting their fruit and cows were starting the production of cheese, we lunched on crusty French bread and apple cider and Camembert.

As our road widened and straightened toward Paris we found that, for the moment, the roofs were having less and less to say about weather. And in Paris roofs are as divorced from environment as is city life itself. The handsome mansard roof, with its two slopes on every side, told us next to nothing about rainfall or wind or crops, but it dictated that we, who seldom wore gloves, would put them on in broad daylight, in summer, and would abandon, regretfully, our flat walking shoes, to corset our feet in fashionable shoes with heels. That is because the mansard roof belongs to the realm of style, and to the realm of that supreme stylist, Louis XIV.

The associates of this roof are the typical eclectic assemblage of a city: horse chestnuts from the Balkans; black locusts and blue spruces from America; geraniums from Africa; the oriental plane tree, because it endures city life so well; and the native linden, because it endures shaping.

The food, too, is eclectic. We ate trout from the north with almonds from the south, and beef from the Argentine, and Danish butter, and oranges from Africa.

Southward from Paris we watched the roofs flatten and broaden, displaying wide eaves that shaded the windows. The windows were smaller there, with shutters that were often firmly closed against the heat of the day. These roofs of curved, rust-colored tile, while too hot and dry to give a foothold to mosses, supported drifts of sturdy stonecrop plants, with their plump, water-storing leaves. As we traveled among terraced vineyards to visit châteaux that gave their own proud names to their vintages, we saw more and more leaves that were paler green or were smaller, thicker, or narrower, or had a holly form.

Here, where Nature had selected warm yellows and hot reds for its flower colors, men had chosen cool blue for painting their doors and shutters.

Bent working backs were no longer a part of the landscape; they were replaced by backs bent to conform to the curves of the chaise longue. Here a French child might return a friendly wave, people might sing outdoors, even before sundown, and nightingales performed out of the dark. There were many chestnut trees, and many scrubby oaks, and many fat geese.

Around the roots of the oaks we knew that there might be truffles

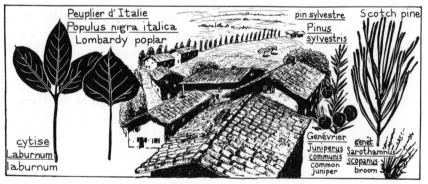

Southern France

growing, but these we did not see until lunchtime, when we found
black truffles in the pâté. There were chestnut pastries, too.

As one travels south in Europe he meets a number of changes that
run parallel with changes seen as one travels southwest in America.
Here are a few:

SOME PARALLEL CHANGES

TRAVELING SOUTH IN EUROPE		TRAVELING SOUTH IN AMERICA
	flatter roofs	
	smaller windows	
	more shutters	
	more red flowers	
	flat-topped trees	
	thicker leaves	
	smaller leaves	
	grayer leaves	
	holly-form leaves	
example: kermes oak, holm oak		*example:* Emory oak, desert holly
	more aromatic leaves	
examples: rosemary, lavender, thyme		*examples:* sagebrush, desert lavender
	more legumes (especially the yellow-flowered ones)	
	more improbable birds	
examples: hoopoe, bee eater		*examples:* roadrunner, hummingbird
	louder music	
	wider balconies	
	bigger guitars	
	more reclining seats	
example: chaise longue		*example:* rocking chair
	more tanned skins without a hat-line or a sleeve-line (people who *work* in the sun wear hats and sleeves)	
	more water in religious rituals (as compared with more hell-fire in religion as one travels north)	
example: for sprinkling Catholics		*example:* for dipping Baptists
	more dogs asleep on their sides	

As we continued south, into Provence, we observed one change that has no parallel in the American Southwest. Something had happened to the roofs. They had pulled in their eaves. Windows, even small ones, were absent from the north walls of houses, and some roofs had rocks on them.

We were in the area of the mistral, that fearful northwest wind that comes off the Alps each winter and spring, blowing strong and bitter cold for days on end, scourging the towns and farms of Provence and the Rhone valley.

Every small field was barricaded against the mistral with a closely woven fence of tall reeds. Vincent van Gogh, who is said to have ventured out into the mistral, even though it keeps most people indoors, painted the fences into his pictures. Perhaps it was the mistral that caused him to see the cypresses of San Remy undulating against a great pinwheel sky.

There were umbrella pines, too, flat topped, presenting a thin edge to the drying wind. Many plants had small, thick, gray foliage, often with hairy or waxy surfaces. While vacationers put on dark glasses and rubbed their skins with oil, the trees here wore thick corky bark and were full of oily sap. They stood widely spaced, as in America's mesa country; and it was hardly possible to walk among them without pressing out a richness of rosemary, thyme, and lavender, with a tinge of garlic. There were goats feeding on the sparse gray-greenness, and there were many artists painting. This country has long belonged to the artists, not only van Gogh, but Cézanne, Matisse, Picasso, and many others.

At lunchtime we sat beneath the canopy of two of the local trees, grateful for the tight armor they wore against sun and drought. We pulled the cork (from a local cork oak) out of our wine bottle and relished a salad tossed in oil from the olive trees. We finished with Roquefort cheese, made from the milk of warm ewes and ripened in cold caves.

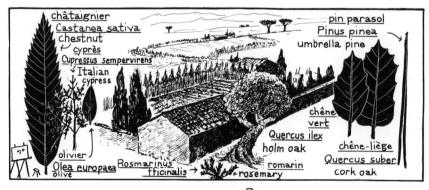

Provence

As we traveled west into Italy's watery Po valley, we saw that the tiled roofs of the two-storied farmhouses had extended themselves into L shapes and taken on added responsibilities. One wing of each house, often decorated with a Madonna or saint, accommodated cattle downstairs and the family upstairs, and was provided with an outside stairway. The other wing was open except for its roof and one side, which was built up with openwork brick lattice. The open wings were empty when we passed that way in June, but were filled with baled hay when we came again in September, before the rainy season.

From the productive croplands spread flat under the sun, we soon turned south. The hill towns and the long slopes of olive trees and grape vines beckoned. We stopped to eat pasta made from products of the flat croplands, with Gorgonzola cheese from the cows (who were fed on the hay sheltered under the long roofs) and Chianti from the slopes ahead.

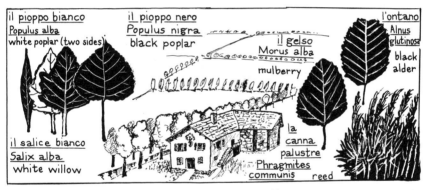

Po Valley

The rooflines of Italian cities displayed records of human conflict, pride, and hope. Castle battlements presented rows of teeth, standing for the Guelph party with its allegiance to the pope, or rows of fishtails for the Ghibellines, with their allegiance to the emperor. Spires and domes raised bells, and columns raised soldiers and statesmen and wolves and horses and gods. And mingled with these against the sky we enjoyed the lighter note of many dovecotes and decorative chimney pots, and lines of laundry flapping from high balconies.

In southern Italy the roofs finally became completely flat, and remained that way across Greece and the other Mediterranean countries. In these warm lands, now shorn of all but the most sparse covering of drought-resistant and goat-resistant plants, the flat roofs have long been popular places in the night breeze, places offering unbroken views of the stars over the sea and the treeless hills. They served the ancients as places to trace out the sky pictures and to retell and embellish the tales of Phoenicia or Babylonia, or of other lands to the east.

Creatures of these hills are mentioned as constellations in writings as early as the sixth century B.C. *Capricornus,* half goat and half fish, may have been suggested partly by the pastures and partly by the Mediterranean. The Ram, *Aries,* woolly looking with no bright stars, wears a long fat tail. He is of an ancient breed, and his immense tail is thought to have furnished a reserve of fat that was insurance against long seasons of drought and poor pasture. *Taurus,* the Bull, is there. And *Auriga,* the Charioteer, holds the star Capella, called "The She-Goat," as well as the three small stars called "the Kids." *Boötes,* called "the Herdsman," is there. The ancient Sumerians described the stars as "the heavenly flock" and called the sun "the old sheep" and the seven planets "the old-sheep stars."

We all still gratefully use the friendly handholds to the night skies supplied by the ancients when they aligned the stars into pictures of their world. Anyone still fortunate enough to have access to a dark night sky can profit from the flat roofs and the night breezes along the Mediterranean. Robert Frost, unconsciously profiting by them, in New England, wrote, "On the pasture bars/I leaned to line the figures in/Between the dotted stars."

Constellations named from flat roofs

Boötes   Capricornus Auriga
     Taurus   Aries

Mediterranean countries

From the flat Mediterranean roofs we turned northward again, and westward, and skyward into the Swiss Alps. The roofs sloped there, but shallowly. Thick slabs of slate were used for shingles, and boulders anchored them against the wind. During the winter thick featherbeds of snow provide additional warmth. The eaves were wide and spread like the wings of brooding hens. We soon found ourselves taking advantage of them to get out of the frequent mountain showers. We ate lunch under them. We slept up under them. And we even got permission to attempt to dry our small washing up there under the eaves.

Switzerland

For us in our wet raincoats and rainhats it was easy to understand why the roofs had been built so wide, and why porches and balconies were tucked up under the eaves. There is plenty of lumber for balconies in the forests that thrive in the heavy rainfall, and there is plenty of time for wood carving in the winter isolation in the mountains. The balconies were carved and decorated with red paint and red geraniums.

And the roofs themselves supported a rich community of plant life. One extended at our eye level, a veritable rock garden on its gentle slope. Its slates and boulders were encrusted with a gray and green community of lichens, mosses, ferns, harebells in bloom, and seedling Norway spruces. We looked across that roofscape to a meadow where Brown Swiss cattle were eating bright green grass laced with flowers; and then we stooped in under the roof to eat a hearty fondue, product of the high meadows.

As we descended from the Alps and entered the Black Forest, we saw roofs that were still made of slate and still glistened with the frequent rain. But they were different from Alpine roofs. The slates were fitted and shaped and had no need for boulders to hold them in place. The roof ridges rose high, and the roof slopes were long and steep. The rain dripped from the dangling twigs of the Norway spruces and gurgled in the gutters, but it made no sound in the beech forest as it filtered down to sink into cushions of moss. In the towns the roofs were often so steeply pitched that several tiers of dormer windows interrupted them. On the farms there were barns with roof slopes that reached almost to the ground.

By contrast, on the heights overlooking the Rhine, the castle roofs, notched for weapons and slotted for pouring hot oil and molten lead, recorded response to men rather than weather. We were glad to be there in one of the Rhine's more peaceful interludes, as we sat beside the river enjoying trout and venison from the Black Forest and a Rhine wine from the slopes below the castles.

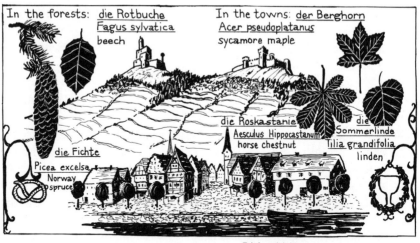

Rhine Valley

In Denmark, and in England as well, many cottages wear their roofs like stocking caps, pulled low around the ears. Thatching speaks of an equable, relaxed climate, without excess of wind or rain or sun, but dependably humid. Thatch is too fire-vulnerable for use in an area with summer droughts and wind. Even then, for safety's

stilk-eg
Quercus robur
English
oak

bøg beech
Fagus
sylvatica

ask
Fraxinus
excelsior
ash

kodriver
Primula veris
cowslip

hvidtjørn
Crataegus
hawthorn

Parts of Denmark and England

sake, a rake or a pitchfork may be kept handy for throwing off burning thatch, and sometimes the area around the chimney is treated with a mixture of lime and salt to reduce the danger of fire. The best protection, however, is dampness. Old thatch is usually such a thick mass, after having had new layers added right over the old ones, that most of the time its interior is moist.

The use of thatch generally indicates that the area is not too wet to grow wheat straw; or that there are slow rivers and shallow bays enough to supply reeds. These watery places also provide good fishing to that photogenic wading bird, the stork, which often builds its nest on the roof ridge.

The thatch has a life of its own. It is a teeming community of insects and molds and more. *The Village Gardener* by J. C. Loudon (second edition, 1850) warns of earwigs and spiders in the thatch and of Virginia creepers and ivy, which tend to grow around the chimneys and to harbor snails and slugs. Mr. Loudon warns that a family keeping two servants under ordinary circumstances would require three in such a cottage.

Thatched roofs belong with the weather that makes beech forests and velvet lawns and gardens where tall spiked flowers such as delphiniums, foxglove, and hollyhock open their buds slowly and stand stately, not bent by wind nor bleached by hot sun nor beaten by downpour. In such a garden we ate another product of the equable climate, fat strawberries in big blue-and-white bowls, with thick cream from the cows that grazed in the wet meadows.

We traveled as the Vikings once did, from one landscape of slow rivers and high humidity to another, and we were fortunate to be able to see people practicing the ancient craft of thatching, first in

Cotswolds

Denmark and then in East Anglia and Kent. The thatchers we watched worked in pairs, one man on top of the roof, the other beneath it. They passed a long needle back and forth between them and seemed to be tailoring their roofs as they stitched the reeds in place, pulling strands of twine from the bundles dangling from their belts. Later, in Devon, we saw them working with wheat-straw.

From the soft roofs of Devon we moved northward to the hard roofs of the Cotswolds. Stone is the only native building material available in that landscape, shorn of its timber by man and his sheep. Rain has shaped the layered limestone into wide bony hills, now mantled in the merest skintight tissue of green, and even this tissue is unceasingly subdued by sheep.

Here people had quarried and relayered the limestone into stout walls, which straggled across broad pastures, and into thick walls and chimneys for cottages, huddled like flocks in the lee of a hill beside a stream, and even into roofing for the cottages. This last was not easy. The villagers sought out an especially thin-layered limestone, which they had to quarry before Christmas. Then they laid it aside held firmly in clamps, to wait until the first sharp frost should expand the quarry water imprisoned between the layers. When the frost came there was not a moment to spare; churchbells were sometimes rung to call workers out into the frosty night to come finish the job that the frost had started. They released the clamps, pried apart the thin sheets of stone, and spread them about to await warmer weather, when they would be shaped into roof tiles.

After the stone houses of the Cotswolds, the wooden houses of Norway were a great contrast—too great, we thought, to be justified by any difference in the weather of the two areas. Norway's houses and churches looked too thinly built for its northern cold and its fogs and long winters. But in Norway as in the Cotswolds it was a matter of using the available local materials. Not that Norway lacks stone, but it lacks softer, easily worked stone, and does have ample supplies of pine and spruce trees. Usually the pitch of roofs was steep enough to let the snow and rain slide off. The old stave churches were built so that they offered the rain and snow a series of descending slopes.

Farmers have put another kind of roof on their barns in the high summer pastures. They gave it a low pitch so that they could cover it with sod. Such sod roofs were green and often flowery, and from time to time we saw a goat grazing there.

There was intricate carving on frames and lintels and beams, and even on shingles. This was especially so on the stave churches, but we saw it on many houses, too. Evidently long winter nights and the isolation of the mountains were a stimulus to handiwork. Damp cold did its work too, stimulating hell-fire in the religion and banning baptism by immersion.

For the most part, today's roofs do not speak, as did the old ones, of wind, rain, and snow, or of deep, dripping forests or sun-scorched landscapes. They speak instead of style and solvency, being, somewhat like the roofs of Paris, primarily expressions of fashion.

Norway

Modern urban roofs do serve certain functions, of course. They serve for clothes drying, swimming pools, roof gardens, heliports, and penthouses. And now a radical suggestion has made its appearance. In the June 1969 *New Scientist* a planner, David Stephens, suggests that in the future roofs may double as roads, freeing the

ground level for broad walks, homes, shops, and handsome plantings. An original plan, but not one promising rooflines that will
make comfortable reading. The landscape of which I write is one
shaped by man and nature—in consort.

France

The Limestone of France

$\approx$ 1

THE SEA laid down the limestone layers of France slowly, with variations.

Sometimes the sea was active and restless. Then it let larger shells accumulate in thick masses. *Calcaire grossier*, this limestone was to be called one day, when blocks of it were cut and hauled by chanting multitudes to make the portals and transept of Chartres Cathedral.

Sometimes a more quiet sea shaped a layer so compact and resistant that it would one day be sought to form the silvery-white framework of the rose windows of Notre Dame. *Cliquart*, this kind of limestone would be called.

Sometimes a placid sea let the whiteness settle dreamily down, over long slow ages, only microscopic creatures leaving their fragile cases behind to form a layer of fine chalk that hardened until it could one day be cut for Reims Cathedral and Amiens.

The sea spread its limy layers over as much of France as it could reach. But it could not cover the higher masses of older, harder rocks that were the relic-stumps of ancient mountains. The rivers eroding those masses deposited their loads of stony grains and flakes on the sea floor, where they were cemented together to form softer strata between the limestone layers.

Then came a period of upheaval, called the "Alpine storm." That was about sixty million years ago.

As the Alps were raised high to the southeast of France, the Pyrenees were uplifted to the southwest. And the ancient central mass, the Massif Central, was raised, too, pushing up through the limestone cover, which it wore as its *causses,* its skirts.

At the same time long parallel fractures, or faults, dropped a long block down between the Alps and the Massif Central, forming the Rhone Graben, or rift valley, which was one day to become a main route for trade, and conquerors, and Christianity.

During the Alpine storm, layers of limestone, too, were uplifted. In the area between the hard mountain relic-stumps of Brittany on the west and the Vosges Mountains on the east, the edges of the layers were raised slightly higher than the centers. And the resulting stack of saucer-shaped layers was tilted up toward the east.

Time and erosion worked on the layers. And because the stack was tilted up toward the east, the rivers flowed toward the west, toward the center of the upcurved layers, toward the place that would one day be Paris.

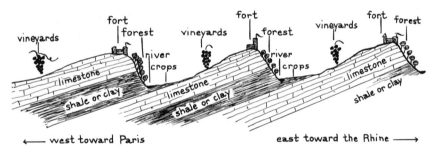

The basic rhythm of the côtés of the Paris basin
(not drawn to scale)

The edges of the saucers in the graduated stack formed a series of abrupt east-facing escarpments, each overlooking a river valley and a long west-tilted slope. Such edges have been, inevitably, sites for forts. On the steep faces of the escarpments forests have grown, surviving longer here than on the flat croplands. The west-tilted surface of each saucer has been the naturally appointed site for vineyards.

Because the western edges of the saucers were lower and easier to attack, it was inevitable that Germany, to reach Paris, would over-run Belgium.

While the surface of northern France was being thus molded for vineyards and for war, and for other developments, such as Paris, the limestone plateaus of the south were being shaped as well. There, the rivers carved straight down through the limestone, forming steep-walled gorges in the flat heights. And up on the plateaus the rain found its way into cracks, and slowly dissolved and worked its way through the limestone, finding an outlet somewhere on a wall of the Vézère River. It carved many caves, including the first art galleries of France.

One special cave was being prepared with gleaming walls and ceiling. The walls of the main parts of this cave were not dripping. Their hard surface was slowly oozing moisture filled with calcite. Slowly, the cave was being hermetically sealed with a glassy white coating.

Above, on the plateau, a Neanderthal man may have shambled, bowlegged, through the rich mosses and the deep green ferns. He may have gathered branches and twigs on the plateau to make a shelter, branches of magnolia and sweet gum, perhaps. Probably his was the first human use of the limestone when he picked out its embedded flints for making his fires and simple weapons.

Up there on the plateau the hippopotamus roamed, and the rhinoceros. They had no memories of the three glacial periods that had come and gone. No premonitions of the fourth one that was coming.

The climate grew steadily colder. No longer was this a place for the hippopotamus. The thick-fleeced mammoth took its place, and the huge cave bear came down from the north and a different rhinoceros appeared, adapted to cold by its thick woolly fleece.

No longer was this the place for magnolia and sweet gum. These did not make an escape to the south as the animals did. Caught between the cold from the north and the cold extending down the mountains in their path, they were extinguished in Europe. It was thus that the flora of Europe became pauperized, left without many of the species that would persist in North America, where they were able to move south down between the north-south mountain chains.

On the plateaus along the Vézère, pine trees stood in a thin open forest, and there were great stretches of swampland and steppes and tundra. Everywhere was the gray of reindeer lichens.

There were reindeer feeding on the lichens, and browsing on birch twigs.

Hunting the deer came a man of upright stature, with a high forehead. This was Cro-Magnon man, *Homo sapiens* like us. His period was the Aurignacian, the time of the reindeer hunters.

One important day the smooth-walled cave in the Vézère valley reverberated to the thunder of a section of falling roof. A narrow beam of light entered. The reindeer hunters found the opening, and as they felt their way along the cool dark wall they might have been surprised at its icy smoothness. Perhaps, however, their chief concern was the possibility of lions lurking in the dark.

The hunters went away but returned with lamps, pieces of exfoliated limestone from the plateau, slightly concave, the best of them, so that animal fat could be burned in the centers. Several of these lamps with blackened centers were found in the caves fifteen thousand years later, when this shining-walled series of caves was to be named "Lascaux." The reindeer hunters continued to come to the caves. They painted animals on the calcite walls and ceiling.

Obviously they painted with tradition and learning and familiarity with the art of other caves. They had no need to start at the beginning of learning. Their heritage included records of those beginnings, when men had held their hands against the wall and drawn around them as stencils, or when men had traced with their fingers or with flints the simple lines archaeologists call "macaronis." Here their starting point seems to have been simple animal silhouettes done in yellow or red or black.

Presently they were filling in the outlines with black or red and doing the outlines themselves with bolder lines. They learned to make the manes of horses with a blurred edge, perhaps using dry powder puffed through a crude "spray gun" made of a hollow reed.

They made some fine engravings without colors, some of small size.

They emerged from the cave into a landscape that was still warm enough for some of the fierce cave lions to linger. In one part of the cave the reindeer men engraved six of these lions together.

But they painted the ibex as well, which may have come down from the mountains during the glacial period to feed on the sunny slopes.

They also painted the aurochs, *Bos primogenius*. Sometimes they painted the smaller cows or the much larger bulls. In the great Hall of Bulls they painted them with great curving horns. The aurochs was a beast of the forest, the thicket, the grassland, capable of enduring intense cold.

They painted stags and seemed to enjoy letting themselves go, embellishing the horns as children sometimes do. Deer must have passed up the valley of the Vézère in great herds as they moved north in the spring, following the opening up of fresh pastures, and also escaping the clouds of gnats, when the southern extremity of the ice sheet retreated in its seasonal seesawing.

They painted horses. These must have come drifting in herds from Russia, through the corridor between the great ice sheet of the north and the ice sheet of the Alps.

They painted animals whose presence indicated the deepening cold. They painted the woolly rhinoceros.

One animal represented no existing creature at all. It was drawn from the imagination, decorated with spots, given a blunt nose and two long horns. Because it is imaginary it is known as "the Unicorn."

They painted or engraved lines in lattice formation that may have been intended to represent traps.

Many pregnant animals are shown.

What was going on in the caves? Was it a sympathetic magic, hunting magic? Or was there some other religious significance? There is a mystery about the number of stone lamps found at a deep and inaccessible part of the cave, and about the polish on the lip of the entrance to the deep shaft, a polish that suggests the passing of many men. Certainly the cold, damp cave was not a place of physical comfort. When a lamp was lighted, the smoke must have been choking, blinding.

Presently the cold retreated to the north. The reindeer followed, nibbling the reindeer lichen. The reindeer hunters followed their meat. The caves and their paintings were left behind.

We guess that the cave painters worked in the Lascaux caves for about a thousand years, since they recorded only the animals of one period. Another cave, nearby, called Font de Gaume, was probably in use for thousands of years; the animals there record the advancing and the retreating ice sheet. An inspired guide traced with his cane the dim forms of animals upon animals, showing us animals that must have come up from Africa during the warm periods between the glaciers: a lioness, four antelopes. There were animals from the Siberian tundra: forty horses, eighty bison. And there were animals of the extreme cold of the north: twenty-three mammoths, two woolly rhinoceroses, seventeen reindeer.

The Lascaux paintings might have been erased long ago but for a lucky accident that occurred after the reindeer hunters left. Somehow, no one knows how, the entrance was closed. The outside air was virtually cut off.

A forest grew over the cave. In that birch and pine forest men hunted elk and deer and aurochs. Then the forest of the pine gave way to hazel and elm and linden. The deepening shade nursed seedling beech and hornbeam.

But the cold crept back and the pines came back, too.

Then it grew warmer, and the mixed forest replaced the pine and made deeper and deeper shade, where only the beech could flourish. Slowly the gray smooth trunks of beech trees took over the best of the land that lay on the limestone. The more difficult places wore oak forests.

In the beech forests above the Lascaux caves the aurochs and deer looked the same as the pictures of their ancestors waiting in the dark below.

It was silent there, in the cave, but above there was a new sound, a sound that stopped the call of the cuckoo and froze the aurochs in its tracks. An ax made of flint was swinging, in short, quick strokes. A tree fell. The chopping began again. Soon there came the smell of fire, and the aurochs fled before the smoke. A man was clearing with stone ax and fire to raise his grain. After a time he moved on and cleared another space. His clearings were only a pinprick in the vast forests of France in 3000 B.C., and for the next three thousand years the beech and oak still stood in almost solid formation across the valleys and hills. But it was only a matter of time; the end had been foretold.

South along the Mediterranean there was change. The Greeks had come. They had founded Massilia (Marseilles) and then Nicaea (Nice) and Antipolis (Antibes). And they had brought the olive, the cypress, the fig, the pomegranate, and—the beech forests could shudder for their tenure of the limestone—the grape. That was about 600 B.C.

Meanwhile a new animal had been introduced into the clearings and was nibbling at the forest. On the plateau above the Vézère River an aurochs must one day have met this man-herded woolly sheep. And an aurochs must have been killed by a spear that was tipped not with flint but with iron. The Celts, tall, light-skinned, fair-haired, had wandered in from the area of the Danube. These men, whom the Romans were to call "Galli," knew how to forge two-edged iron spears.

Below in the caves, the water percolating through from the old entrance probably was covering, with a crust of calcite and mud, the flint that the reindeer hunters had left on the floor.

The forests still stood in close formation across France. The new plantings of olives and grapes hardly broke the ranks of oaks and beeches. This we know, because in 50 B.C. Julius Caesar described Gaul. He told of the clearings where the Gallic tribes had built fortified enclosures against invaders and where the huts were built of reeds thatched with straw. These men wore breeches and jackets of deerskin. Some wore wooden shoes.

He told how dense the forests stood, and how they had become associated with the religion of the Gauls. The Druids were cutting the mistletoe from oak branches and were setting sacrificial fires on Midsummer Eve. The mistletoe is still given a place of hopeful importance, and fires still burn on hilltops in France on June 23.

Caesar knew the aurochs of the forests. He called it *urus*.

Below in the Lascaux cave, a big flake of limestone loosened from a frieze in the great hall, and fell, damaging the likeness of a bull and the head of a horse.

Above the caves the limestone was moving, not in large flakes but in man-cut blocks. The Romans were building with it, cracking their conquerors' whips over the Gallic slaves who had cut and hauled it for their use. Arenas, they built of it, forums and public baths, aqueducts, triumphal arches, and roads.

The Christians, moving up from the south, were soon building the limestone into churches. At first these, and the monasteries with their calm cloisters, were formed of the rounded Romanesque arches.

A new people began hunting the aurochs, and each other. The Franks, the Visigoths, and the Burgundians had moved in violently after the Romans. Clovis, chieftain of the Franks, conquered other barbarians. So rare had the aurochs become by that time that only Clovis the King had the right to hunt it.

More and more limestone was needed for more and more

churches, which served, in that violent time, not only for worship but as places of asylum.

From the south, once again, a new terror moved in. The Saracens slaughtered and kidnapped and plundered as they came in along the Mediterranean. But they brought new plants with them, especially a kind of purple crocus, from whose golden, aromatic stigmas is made saffron, so essential to the flavor of bouillabaisse. If they hunted the aurochs it must have been in the Pyrenees. There were still a few left there, and in the Vosges of northeastern France.

Men were using limestone to build dungeons, and fortresses against each other, and to wall their moated towns, and to build castles for their lords, and—always—to build churches.

The age of the great cathedrals arrived. Men called them "white prayers in stone" and "the book of the people without books." The monk Glaber wrote that France gradually came to be covered with a "white robe of churches." Centuries later, Victor Hugo wrote, "In the middle ages, human genius had no important thought which it did not grave on stone."

Men came to the stone with new ideas. They had discovered not only how to use stone as bulging massive muscles but also how to draw it out into sinews. They had learned how to support walls with buttresses, and thus to lighten it. They had learned how to make a ribbed vault, and now the arches that had formerly been rounded took on more the shape of two hands, fingertips pressed together, uplifted in prayer. The Gothic arch, this came to be called, unreasonably. But that name was applied during the Renaissance, when men wanted to belittle it.

There was no such name for the structure that was started on an island in the Seine in 1163.

A huge block of limestone was set down where others had raised their temples. The men of Gaul, of the tribe of Parisii, had raised a wooden shrine there, and had probably brought to it a spray of mistletoe from one of the Druid oaks. Roman conquerors had replaced the wooden shrine with a temple in limestone, with Jupiter, Mercury, and Vulcan on their altar, and one Gallic Druid god, Esus. The well-cut stones of this Roman temple were probably taken down and used for making a stone wall for the island after the Romans left, as were other stones of the Roman town, Lutetia—stones from an amphitheater that had seated sixteen thousand persons, from triumphal arches, from the great public baths and the aqueduct.

Christianity came. The only well-cut stones in the crude church raised to St. Stephen were those shaped by the Romans.

During all these years the dense forest still surrounded Paris. Wild boar, wolves, bear, and stags came close to the city. So things were on that day in 1163 when the first stone was laid for the cathedral of Notre Dame of Paris.

To the quarries on the left bank of the Seine, and to many other quarries as far as ten miles away, men went to cut limestone. Teamsters cracked their long whips over the heavy oxcarts that creaked across the bridge to the island.

Chalk, too, was brought, to cover the tables where the workers in glass were making their designs. And limekilns were active.

The forests were being cut. It required much timber to fire up the foundries where the bells were being cast.

That first block of stone was a massive one, made of *lambourde ferme* from the quarries of Montrouge. The master builder had selected it himself, and marked it, so that it might be laid down just as the sea had laid it down ages before. It was beautifully dressed, as the Romans might have treated it, even though it would never be seen once the cathedral was built. A prelate, perhaps the pope, came to bless the cornerstone. Then other great pieces were brought. Ten yards deep the stone was laid, as if the very bottom of the ancient sea had been moved for the foundation.

For the pillars to form the grand colonnade, the stonecutters sought a limestone famous for its hardness, in the old sea bottom at Bagneux and the Butte Saint-Jacques.* They cut mammoth drums of rock, and set them on top of one another, twelve of them to make each pillar.

The builders went to other quarries for the material for the famous facade. For its statues they chose a limestone that formed thick belts and could be easily carved; *lias tendre*, it was called. For the fine work that needed to be of great strength, small columns, cornices, and the framework of rose windows, they chose *cliquart*, the hardest, silvery-white limestone of all. The stone framework of the north rose window, with its Old Testament stories and its old

---

* "The stone itself is as hard and resistant as any in France: the bedrock of Bagneux and the Butte Sainte-Jacques." (*Notre-Dame of Paris*, Allen Temko, p. 128.)

blue glass, has stood firm for 700 years, with only a few minor repairs. (The glass was stored in the cellar of a castle during two world wars.)

And so, presently, while the Lascaux cave waited within the

How would Lascaux Cave
artists interpret the art
of cathedral caves?

earth, France had another cave also built of limestone, dim with flickering lights of animal fat, bearing man's art on the walls and ceiling, and all dedicated to hope.

How would a Lascaux man have interpreted this cave? Would he have seen evidence of hunting magic and deduced that the men of this cave hunted sad-faced thin men with empty eyes and well-combed beards, and rounder, well-draped women, and lambs and doves? Would the unicorn-dreaming artist of Lascaux have felt that a kindred spirit had created the angels, with their extra set of limbs? What would he have thought of the man who had invented those oak leaves and grape leaves and wheat because he himself had never seen the like of them? Would he have interpreted the cross, the halo, as a totem, or a trap? Would he have explained the many lost heads and hands as the work of time and seeping water? Could he have conceived of the angry mobs that destroyed the sympathetic magic of their fathers? Or would he have believed that men had invented spears that they could hurl mechanically from such a distance that they no longer saw, or knew, or cared, what they speared? What would he have thought of a rose window? He must have seen sunsets and stars caught in icicles, and known such blues in the gentians of the tundra. Would he have appreciated the sculptor's pleasure in folded draperies, having himself enjoyed elaborating on the theme of reindeer antlers?

Possibly the man-made cave and its symbols would not have surprised the Lascaux visitor as much as the forest that surrounded Paris. The marching ranks of beech trees had nothing in common with the spare stands of stunted pines through which he had pursued his reindeer. But the beech forests, with long aisles between uniform columns of stone-gray trunks supporting the high ribbed canopy, were being thinned, as they had been thinned since Caesar described them and as they continued to be thinned, until they were finally destroyed.

Just as the life of the tundra and swamp and pine forest was captured and held by the Lascaux caves, so has the pulse, the rhythm, the light, and the architecture of the beech forest been captured and held in the man-made limestone caves. Chartres, most of all.

I should have scoffed at the idea that anything could approach the spirit of a virgin forest. But I found Chartres greater than any of the forests that I have known. It holds all that is best of the forests, selected, simplified, emphasized, and directed by all that is best in the spirit of man.

This limestone, perhaps more than any other, has been handled by devoted believers. From five miles away they brought the limestone, from the quarries of Berchères-l'Evêque. "Men of all walks of life," it is written in a record of that time, the account of an abbot, "have bent their proud and haughty necks to the harness of carts . . . [and] dragged to the abode of Christ these wagons loaded with wines, grains, oil, stone, wood, and all that is necessary for the wants of life, or for the construction of the church."

Once France had its great cathedrals, limestone was not again cut and hauled as an act of devotion. Now it was cut by serfs, for castles and châteaux, and soon it resounded to the clatter of armor, of horses clashing in tournaments, to songs of troubadours, and to the twang of longbows.

Inside the castles the limestone walls wore tapestries, showing deer in the surrounding forests, wild boar, oak leaves and beech trees, and lilies of the valley.

In the Rhine country, the last herds of the aurochs still lingered.

For hundreds of years the serfs cut the limestone below and raised it for a line of kings, for an emperor, for a pope at Avignon. And from the least to the greatest, all refreshed themselves from the same source—the vine from the limestone slopes of France.

In the Paris basin the grape is cultivated wherever there are such sunny slopes. In Herault and Bas Languedoc, loose soils and long sunny autumns and limy subsoils make the good wine. In the Loire valley the chalk slopes produce the sparkling wines of Vouvray. On the limestone slopes of Barois are the vineyards of Chablis. In Champagne the warm chalk slopes of the Marne valley produce other sparkling wines. On other limestone slopes are the wines of Beaujolais, Chambertin, Beaune, and Mâcon. In Alsace, on the loess soils over the limestone, at the foot of the Vosges, are Tokay, Muscatel, Reisling. Around Reims, to draw a line from one vine village to another, would be to draw the edge of the limestone escarpment.

With his wine, of course, every peasant, every king, broke off a chunk of a crusty French loaf. The important wheatfields of France lie, as well, on the limestone plateaus.

And while the surface nourished the grapes and the wheat, caves in the limestone offered places of unchanging temperature where wine could mature, where the sparkling wines could wait out their allotted years; this was especially so in the caves around Reims and Epernay and Vouvray.

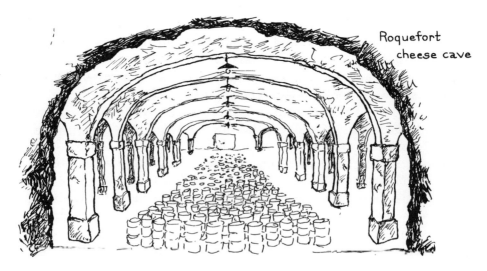

Roquefort cheese cave

And the limestone had one more offering. It was discovered once, by accident, that a simple cheese made of ewes' milk would be transformed, vibrantly, by a certain blue-green mold that throve in certain cold limestone caves. Since then the wine and the French bread have been enhanced by the robust company of the Roquefort cheese.

In 1627 the last aurochs, an old female, died. One painting of an aurochs, made in the sixteenth century, was discovered in 1827; it has been treasured and extensively redrawn. No one could suspect that other drawings of this now-extinct animal, made fifteen thousand years ago, were waiting in the pitch dark of sealed caves under the limestone plateaus.

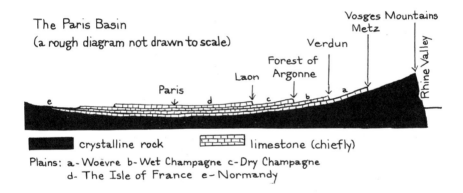

The Paris Basin
(a rough diagram not drawn to scale)

crystalline rock   limestone (chiefly)

Plains: a- Woëvre b- Wet Champagne c- Dry Champagne
d- The Isle of France e- Normandy

In the Paris basin men were killing each other more efficiently than ever. The stack of limestone saucers offered its high edges as vantage points to such fortifications as Château-Thierry, Vimy Ridge, Verdun, Saint-Mihiel.

All of those places that were so well known during the First World War peered from perches on such limestone escarpments. The Forest of Argonne and the Forest of Compiègne were on the same saucer edges. The French name for these edges of the great stacked saucers is *côte*, probably because of their resemblance to old coastlines. Reading east from Paris, these edges are named in Côte de l'Île-de-France, Côte de Champagne, Côte de Meuse, Côte de Moselle. On one *côte* along the Meuse, an ancient Gallic fortress gave place to the Roman fortress, Virodunum Castrum, and later became the Verdun that endured the siege of the Prussians in 1792, then again in 1870, and then again in 1914.

World War I passed, and the limy soil of France was left enriched with the bones of many young men. One day, as a second world war was adding its further enrichment, a tree fell quietly down.

Falling, it tore out its roots and left a hole. Scrubby plants grew, and tangled above the hole. But air found its way in, and began to erase the pictures that had been so long undisturbed.

Then a dog came running and fell into the hole.

In a moment a boy, above the opening, called him: "Robot, Robot!"

The voice sounded strange echoing from the hole.

The boy and his companions pulled out the scrubby plants. They dropped a stone, and listened. Then they cut more plants, moved what loose stones they could, so that the eldest boy, Ravidat, could squeeze, writhe, and slither his way in. He fell the last part.

Ravidat saw that he was in a cave and called the others. The boys twisted down, with loose bits of limestone clattering along. They had matches, and saw enough to make them slap each other on the back and dance for joy. They knew about prehistoric cave paintings, as did all French schoolboys. Swearing to secrecy, they returned the next day with a better light, a lamp that they had improvised from a grease gun and a rope.

Then they told their teacher about the cave. He was dubious but finally came. He quickly summoned Abbé Breuil, the chief authority on cave painting.

The great archaeologist brought his knowledge of other caves to his interpretation of the new-found one. He pointed out the way in which the Lascaux painters, while showing the animal in profile, also showed both horns and both parts of the cleft hooves (as children do because they know so little and Picasso does because he knows so much). Abbé Breuil compared this "twisted perspective" with paintings done in the age following the reindeer hunters' time. In this age, called the Magdalenian, animals were shown in true profile, as they might be shown by a camera, which is incapable of looking—or imagining—around corners.

Some answers began to come in. Lumps of charcoal found near the stone lamps far back in the caves, near the only picture of a man, were investigated. They proved to be conifer charcoal. That was to be expected, since open stands of stunted pines would have been the only trees associated with the tundra of the reindeer hunters' age.

Some of the charcoal was sent to the University of Chicago for radiocarbon dating. The answer came back: "The charcoal was burned about sixteen thousand years ago."

In a small alcove of the caves was found a piece of rope, carbonized, the first piece of plaited rope found from the reindeer hunters. Close to the rope were two reindeer bones. On the floor of the pit near the drawing of the man were some flint chips and spears of deer horn. At the end of a tunnel nearby were some horse bones.

Many of the questions about Lascaux were still unanswered, and will, perhaps, remain so. Does the association of certain animals with each other, the horse and the cow, for example, or the bison and the horse, not only in this cave but in others, indicate that some ancient myth is being depicted? Do the latticed signs indicate traps, or tribal emblems? Why are these signs more numerous in connection with the dangerous animals, and why are they placed in front of an animal more often than behind it? If this art was "hunting magic," why are so few animals shown with darts or spears? How were these darts or spears propelled, since no bow has been found in

Lascaux Cave deer

Chartres Cathedral sheep

Embellishments of the limestone

fact or in drawing in any cave of the period, though there is some evidence of a spear-throwing device?

There are many other questions.

There has not been much time. Older history books and encyclopedias do not even mention Lascaux.

Now the Lascaux caves are sealed again. A human-borne fungus, which entered with their opening, spread rapidly and threatened to destroy all the fine paintings. The fungus has finally been brought under control, but only as long as the caves are kept dark and closed.

We wondered, when we heard the sad news, whether the Lascaux paintings might not be destined for another long sleep within the earth, while the beech woods slowly covered the plateau again, and then perhaps retreated again before cold and stunted pine trees and tundra. We wondered what manner of survivor might find the paintings next time, and whether all the animals would be extinct and improbable to him, and whether he would know how to date with carbon 14 the lump of chewing gum stuck in a crevice near the entrance. Would he be able to reconstruct us from that clue?

The Sharp-edged Tools of France

≋ 2

In PARIS, an American woman on a guided tour muttered to herself as she looked at the pruned trees. Then she spoke to the guide, scornfully.

"Crucified trees, that's what I call them."

"Madame," the Frenchman said firmly, "those trees have been *directed.*"

One needs preparation for the directed landscape of France. He can get it in part by reviewing the words he uses for precisely molded forms. First of all, there are the words we use in connection with our own directed shapes; corset, brassiere, coiffure, modiste, masseur, svelte, chic, soignée. Then there are the words that belong to foods of shapely elegance: hors d'oeuvre, petits fours, meringue, charlotte russe. And the words for rigid forms to hold poetic ideas: triolet, villanelle, sonnet. Or the words for firm dance forms: minuet, cotillion. Especially there are the words that are shaped with such precision that we find ourselves relying on them when our own tongue provides no substitute: etiquette, insouciance, éclat, en rapport, esprit de corps, roué, bon mot, nuance, soupçon, naïveté. And finally, there are the cutting words, sharp edged: cliché, déclassée, gauche, bourgeoisie, faux pas.

After such setting-up exercises, we are ready to view the French landscape (preferably not through our eye-glasses but through a lorgnette or pince-nez). We are prepared for seeing common things take rigid shapes in that country where

— this becomes this —

— this becomes this —

—this becomes this—

—this becomes this—

— this becomes this —

— this becomes this —

— this becomes this —

— this becomes this —

We had no sooner started across Normandy from Le Havre when we saw our first evidence of FIRM CONTROL. The cows grazed under a system, no "wandering lowing here and there." They were tethered in a row that would be moved gradually across the meadow.

In the next field we saw at work the first of the three form-making tools of France, the three sharp-edged tools that shape the landscape, and are themselves of most definite form. At a distance one might have thought that another line of cows was proceeding systematically across another field. But this was a line of peasants with bent backs, each grubbing with a short-handled hoe. No tool here to lean on in order to rest and ruminate at the row's end. The shortness of the handle bows the back and brings the eyes close to the revered soil, so that no weed can escape detection. The sight of those weedless rows of spaced uniformity took me back to summer afternoons on our front porch, long ago, when I learned to embroider with French knots, uniform, spaced, neat.

Farther along the road, the second tool was at work. A scythe was being swung at the plants along the edge of the road. It was a narrow strip but wide enough—two or three feet—to be green with plants that are "weeds" to Americans, enemies to be vanquished with weed-killer. To the French peasant these "weeds" are hay, and it is cut and gathered into wheelbarrows, or onto bicycles or the backs of old men or women, to be taken into town for the rabbits. Never does one see a road edge being cut by anything other than a swinging scythe—probably the world's most shapely tool—and never will one see the mown hay left unused.

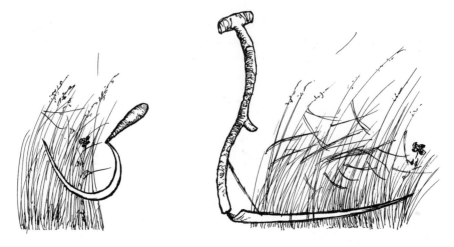

While the short-handled hoe and the scythe help shape the landscape of France, it is the third of the sharp-edged tools, the mighty pruning shears, that has the most conspicuous effect.

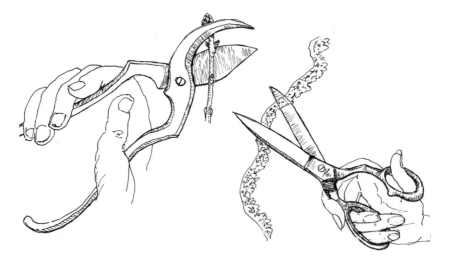

Down the roads of northern France we drove between long lines of trees such as we had never seen, miles and miles of them, raising gangling trunks to high, small, tufted tops. Certainly they did not obstruct our view from the road, but it is conceivable that they may once have served to cover troop movements, or so, at least, a Frenchman explained their original function to us.

Along the streams were willows, as along our streams at home, but what a difference! In America the willow is the most relaxed and abandoned of trees, ever leaning with the wind and dipping its twigs in the streams. Here the willows were all pollarded. The twigs had been harvested, as yet another crop, for firewood or basketry.

Then we saw the "pressed vegetation." Not pressed flowers in some old book, but flat pressed trees dividing vegetable plots. The branches of these trees did not shade the beans or the strawberries, nor did they interfere with the workers. They had been trained into one plane.

We stopped to buy a brown-paper sack full of ripe, fragrant strawberries and stayed to look at the garden where the strawberries grew. The trees there seemed to have been cut into shapes just for the fun of it, the way one might cut shapes in Christmas cookies. The fun must have been passed down through several generations. There were cubes, cones, spheres, layered disks, roosters, peacocks, arches, and tunnels. This was a functioning garden, however, not a showplace.

One day we walked in the rain and appreciated a long double row of linden trees that had been carved into a compact tunnel.

Another day we saw, against a south-facing whitewashed wall, a row of trees that had been espaliered. They were shaped like angular candelabra. We wished that we might be there at harvest time to see plump pears against that gleaming wall turning pink cheeks to the sun. We were beginning to appreciate the "directed trees" of France, a little.

At Versailles the direction seemed powerful and unrelenting, not only in tree shapes but also in patterned gardens. Here, where plants became architectural materials, was the master plan that, for many years, influenced and shaped the world's gardens. Here was the formality that crossed the channel to dominate the gardens of English manor houses, that shaped the cookie-cutter flower beds of the rows of semidetached villas, and then crossed over to America, to peter out, in the midwest, in a star-shaped bed or two.

At Villandry, garden showplace of the Loire valley, the geometric designs were incredibly rigid. Looking down on the pruned and tortured shrubbery arrangements, which could not be walked through lest the raked gravel be disturbed, one could only think of security, adjustment, conformity, tyranny, dictatorship, martial law, and wonder why living material continues to be used, why not some synthetic, which could be simply dusted off instead of being pruned.

To recover from this display of right-angled greenery, we took to the smallest of roads, where we presently happened upon a piece of fun-with-pruning-shears. A gardener had shaped a fruit tree to form a woven basket that contained its own flowery self. That gardener must have chuckled as he started wielding his pruning shears toward the creation of this living *rondeau*.

It was in the grape country that the pruning shears had really taken control. Here were none of the rambling grape vines of our garden pergolas, none of the long ropes that make natural swings on our river bottoms. Anyone who did not know that it is the nature of a grape vine to pour itself out into long shoots, would not have suspected it from looking at those French vineyards. Each old trunk lifted up a round head of leaves and stood unsupported, like a dwarf tree just three feet tall. Later in the season, direction would be provided for a controlled number of shoots, and support for the steadily increasing weight of the grapes.

In the evening, when the peasant goes home from the vineyard, he evidently takes his pruning shears with him and spends his leisure pruning his roses. Every cottage, every fence, wears roses on a well-trained vine. Some are fashioned into pillars, some into

arches, some into lollipop shapes, some into trellises made of themselves.

How fitting that the Frenchman with his eager pruning shears should have a country so favorable to the two plants that, perhaps of all the plants of the world, thrive best under vigorous pruning, the rose and the grape.

Or, perhaps, it worked the other way around. The constant shaping of roses and grapes, to say nothing of such other amenables as boxwood, yew, Italian cypress, and the willing fruit trees, may have shaped the French spirit. The sense of control and pattern in his daily surroundings may have helped to give the Frenchman the assurance that we admire and resent almost in the same breath.

We saw a strange tree. It had evidently been pollarded all its life, and then been suddenly abandoned to its own way, possibly when the pruner had gone off to war. What a monstrous pair of limbs the mighty spurt of its long-inhibited energy had exploded into! (So, it seems, have monstrous new branches of art and philosophy ruptured the patterned, pruned ways of French thought.)

It is hardly surprising that this land that is so compactly square in outline, that keeps its rivers almost entirely to itself, that painfully laid the egg of cubism, that shapes its countryside with three sharp-edged tools and has had its destiny continually shaped by a fourth sharp-edged tool, the sword, would be a land that pruned its rulers with the guillotine.

Nor is it surprising that this land would combine its "divine concern for form" with another sharp-edged tool, the dressmaker's shears, and shape the clothes of the world.

And then there is the bread knife, for handling that most distinctive French form, the long, slender loaf of bread. But most of the warm loaves that we saw going home along the streets and boulevards and byways, under arms, in bicycle baskets, in pockets, in briefcases, projecting from bus windows and baby buggies, had not succeeded in waiting for the bread knife. The end crust of that fragrant loaf had proved too enticing. Consequently most loaves looked like this:

Hunger ignores the niceties of form, even in France.

The Flowers of France

ᴥ 3

THE FLEUR-DE-LIS AND OTHER FLOWERS

THE SMALL hostelry at Nogent-sur-Seine seemed still asleep when I came downstairs. But tight bunches of freshly picked cornflowers and daisies waited stiffly on each table in the freshly scrubbed dining room. I quietly unlocked the front door and crossed the garden, past a parade of German irises and the old espaliered pear tree.

There beyond the garden gate lay the Seine. On the opposite bank the compact row of houses, facing the morning sun and the river, no longer looked so coolly, aloofly French gray as they had on the previous evening. They seemed to be unfolding from their reflections in a sort of gaily colored Rorschach design.

Two stout rowboats had been nosed into the near bank. In the V between their bulky prows there stood one yellow iris, tall among the saluting spears of its leaves. It shone in the early sun as gold as its countless representations in Saint Louis's Saint Chapelle, and the river beneath it was as silken blue as many a royal banner that has carried the fleur-de-lis.

This is the Flower of France, the flower the traveler already knows by its French name, the flower that we meet most often in stone, glass, metal, tapestry.

In the sixth century Clovis I, king of the Franks, was engaged in battle with the Goths near Cologne. His banner carried a strange coat of arms, consisting of three toads. Before the battle Queen Clotilde had wrested a promise from him. She had already accepted Christianity. He had not, but he had promised her that, if he won this engagement, he would be baptized.

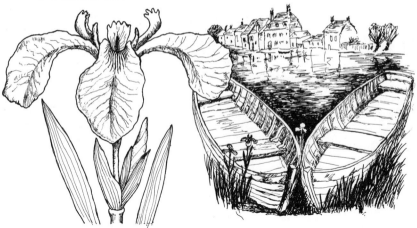

Iris pseudacorus — fleur-de-lis

That day Clovis found his army outnumbered by the Goths. There came a moment when he desperately needed to get his men across the Rhine, but he was unfamiliar with the river. He looked downstream and up, and suddenly he noticed a yellow gleam at the bend, which he recognized as a patch of iris. That flower, he knew, waded only in shallow water. Perhaps it marked a place where the army could ford the stream successfully. They tried and succeeded.

The victorious Clovis kept his promise to his queen. He accepted her God, whose help he had asked during the battle. He was baptized at Reims, where all the kings of France have since been crowned, and instead of the three toads, he adopted three yellow irises for his emblem.

There are those who belittle this tale, but their substitute explanations of the fleur-de-lis are uninteresting and consist chiefly of explaining what is *not* true. You are welcome to believe with them that this design represents a cluster of spearheads, or a gathering of bees, or an arrangement of letters, or nothing at all. But however you may feel about it in the cool evening, if you follow a footpath along the Seine by morning light and come upon a clump of yellow iris, you will believe the story of Clovis and his toads and the yellow gleam on the Rhine. You will feel certain that this flower was the inspiration for the fleur-de-lis that shines in the north rose window at Chartres and against the blue background of Saint Chapelle; that was carried to the Crusades on the banner of Louis VII and was called, after him, Fleur de Louis, which became fleur-de-lis; that crossed the channel to appear on the royal coat of arms of Edward III of England, as a symbol of his claim to the French throne through his mother; and that remained a part of the English coat of arms until it was finally, during the reign of George III, crowded off by the Irish harp, the Scottish lion, and the arms of Hanover.

There is another bright yellow flower that has kings in its background. This one gleams on dry hillsides. The plant forms a bush of stiff green stems, covered with pea-shaped flowers. "Broom," we call it. *Genêt* is the French name, or *planta genêt,* and thereby hangs a tale.

A certain Geoffrey, count of Anjou and Maine, one day plucked a flowering sprig from a steep bank, which was held together by the stout roots of this shrub. Thrusting the sprig into his helmet, he declared (in story language), "This golden plant shall be my cognizance, rooted firmly amid the rocks, yet upholding that which is ready to fall. I will maintain it on the field, in the tourney, and in the court of justice."

Broom had long been considered an emblem of humility, because Mary had rebuked it for snapping its pods so loudly around the place where the infant Christ was concealed from Herod's soldiers; and also because the stiff twigs were often bound together to be used for sweeping lowly cottages.

According to an old "language-of-flowers" book, Alfred the Great thought that the broom betokened humility. Such manuals, now consistently out of print, were, in the past, essential equipment for sending coded floral messages in the form of nosegays, or tussymussies. Using old Saxon flowers and the book as a guide, one could convey such complex messages as, "Your humility and constancy and purity of heart claim my affectionate remembrance." *The Poetical Language of Flowers, or the Pilgrimage of Love* by Thomas Miller (London, 1847) relates the broom, humility, and King Alfred in one somewhat speculative little story:

Who can tell the thoughts of the Saxon Alfred when, wandering alone crownless and scepterless, he stretched himself on the lonely moor beneath the shadow of thy golden blossoms, sighing for the fair queen he had left behind? When he bowed his kingly head and, musing on thy beauty, buried in a solitary wild, thought how even regal dignity could be advanced by humility.

According to the same book, Geoffrey of Anjou had learned this legend from "the fair Saxon he had espoused" and, thinking of

Alfred the Great, "that brave and houseless king," had "mounted the humble Broom in his haughty helmet."

A symbol of humility must have been conspicuous in that family, especially when Geoffrey, count of Anjou and Maine (later to be crowned duke of Normandy) brought in the Empress Matilda. This "fair Saxon he had espoused" was, according to Churchill, "fierce, proud, hard, cynical, living for politics above all other passions." Her father was Henry I of England, and her mother was Matilda, daughter of the King of Scotland. Her grandfather was William the Conqueror, and her grandmother was another Matilda, direct descendant of Alfred the Great. It is possible that, starting with Alfred's Rowena, this royal line of mothers and daughters had recounted in an unbroken line the story of the scepterless Alfred's lonely musings on humility beside the blossoming broom. But no matter whether it all started with Alfred, or with Geoffrey of Anjou, we know that the yellow broom began to be named in the same breath with royalty only after Geoffrey wore it in his helmet. Geoffrey and Matilda had a son, who became Henry II of England. And this Henry and Eleanor of Aquitaine had a son, whose name was Richard Plantagenet. He was also called Richard Coeur de Lion.

And where, all this time, was the tough yellow shrub, emblem of humility? Right there, in the name *Plantagenet,* which is simply *planta genêt,* the French name for broom. The sprig in Geoffrey's helmet had given its name to one of the proudest lines in English history. It faded, finally, on the day when Richard III died at the Battle of Bosworth.

There are several other plants bearing yellow, pea-blossomed flowers in France. The one that Geoffrey of Anjou picked wore its yellow flowers on leafy shoots with crowded tripartite leaves. Had Geoffrey walked instead on an acid southern heath and picked a stout stalk without leaves among its flowers, he would have immortalized the shrub called Spanish broom. Or had he plucked his sprig from a low, green-twigged shrub with a leafless stem but with a bract at the base of each flower, then he would have worn dyer's greenweed. Had he pricked his fingers in many places as he tried to pluck this spray of destiny, he would probably have given up, for that would have been gorse. If he had reached up and plucked his yellow flower from a small tree, the laburnum or golden chain tree, known in France as the *bois d'Arc,* then the royal family would have had a droopy symbol.

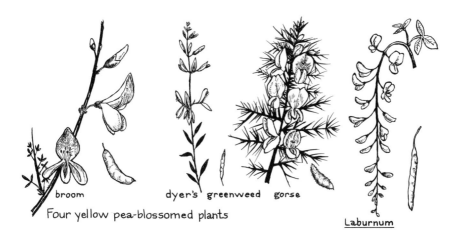

broom   dyer's greenweed   gorse

Four yellow pea-blossomed plants

Laburnum

These two royal flowers, the broom from the dry bank and the iris from the river, were intermingled on the collar that was the insignia of an order formed by Saint Louis in 1234. *Colle de Genêt,* it was called, and its motto was *Deus exultant humilis,* "God exalteth the lowly." To belong to this order was considered the highest honor.

Another plant with royalty and humility combined in its background is often seen on the tiled or thatched roofs of cottages. This is the houseleek, or hen and chickens, *joubarbe des toits.* Its scientific name, *Sempervivum tectorum,* indicates both its toughness and its habitat; *sempervivum* means "live forever," and *tectorum,* "of the roofs (*des toits*)." This plant grows naturally on exposed ledges in the Alps, where it faces many an electric storm. Noticing this, the peasants assumed that it must be impervious to lightning. And Charlemagne himself ordered it planted, for protection, on every roof. It resides on such hot tiles that it is hard to understand how it stays alive, at least until one inspects the thick succulent leaves, which store the rain as it falls. Seldom do we see a plant in bloom; to allow it to flower is considered unlucky. Another gay succulent of rooftops and dry walls is the little stonecrop, or wall pepper (*poivre des murailles*), *Sedum acre,* with its profusion of yellow star-shaped flowers.

While Charlemagne's lightning rod thrives on the rooftop, nearby in the garden blooms the flower of another emperor. But so inconspicuous is the greenish spike that it is best located with the nose. Napoleon liked the smell of this *mignonette.* From Egypt, while on

Flowers of walls and roofs

one of his campaigns, he sent seeds home to Josephine for the garden she was making—with help—at Malmaison. She grew it as a pot plant in her drawing room, and soon it appeared in other drawing rooms and in sunny window boxes, and gradually it became a part of gardens. (There are wild mignonettes growing along the roadsides, but these only *look* like the garden plant; they are hardly fragrant.)

The flower most often associated with Napoleon (except perhaps for the rose) is the violet. Josephine wore violets on her wedding day, and Napoleon was sometimes called "Corporal Violet." When he was sent to Elba, he said, "I will return when the violets bloom again."

During Napoleon's exile the violet became a secret sign by which his followers could identify each other. When he did return as he had promised, the gardens of the Tuilleries were filled with violets to honor him. For a time then, violets and violet-colored gowns were much worn, but when the Bourbons were restored, the wearing of a violet was considered treasonable. It is told that an actress was hissed off the stage for wearing a bunch of violets. A few pressed violets gathered from Josephine's grave were found in a locket worn by Napoleon when he died.

One must come early to France, in late March or April, to smell the sweet violet, *violette odorante*, that Napoleon liked so well; but the woods violet, *violette des bois*, and the dog violet, *violette des chiens*, bloom through May.

Another little flower, more modest even than the violet, must surely have had its share of association with royalty. This is the ivy-leaved toadflax, *ruines-de-Rome,* which drapes the walls of every château. Clinging to the massive masonry that lifts Châteaudun above the Loire valley, it undoubtedly felt the breath of molten lead poured on the enemy from the apertures above and received many a misdirected arrow from below. On the other side of the wall other ivy-leaved toadflax plants must have been present at the flourishing arrival of gilded barouches and the cracks of whips and the swish of silks. At Amboise, we examined an old established colony of the toadflax and wondered whether it might have been brushed by the sleeve of Leonardo da Vinci, or spattered by the carriage wheels of Catherine de Médicis. At Villandry, the toadflax on the walls that surrounded the geometric greenery seemed indecorously relaxed and abandoned.

This plant is a part of every medieval city wall. You will look down into its thriving growth from the top of the hill town of Cordes, and see it reflected in the moat of Richelieu, and find it in the crevices of Carcassonne. After its introduction into Britain it climbed the walls of Kenilworth Castle so vigorously that it earned the name "Kenilworth ivy."

Be sure to examine the flower stem when you look up, or down, at this plant on a French wall. It turns the spurred lilac flower away from the wall in a receptive position for some pollinator; then it reverses direction so that the ripening seed capsule may be inserted into a crevice where the seeds are shed and can make new plants.

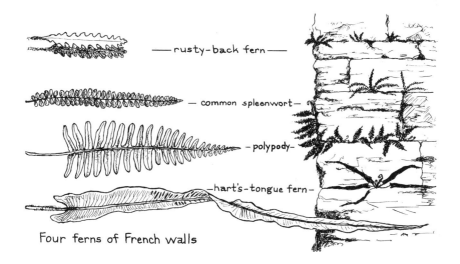

rusty-back fern

common spleenwort

polypody

hart's-tongue fern

Four ferns of French walls

France's limestone walls also wear several ferns. Among these, four are sure to be noticed. One that demands attention by its rusty-scaled undersurface is rusty-back, *Ceterach officinarum.* Another is a delicate miniature with polished stems, common spleenwort, *Asplenium trichomanes.* The third, common polypody, *Polypodium vulgare,* is familiar from rock walls and canyons in America. The last, hart's-tongue fern, *Phyllitis scolopendrium,* does not look like a fern at all, until we see the spore dots on the underside of the frond.

The first time you investigate the plants that grow in a French wall, you will meet the nettle, the curse of botanizing in France. You will feel it sting your ankles again and again, but the irritation doesn't last long. Take a hard look at it the first time it stings you, and after that try, if you can, to circle it so as to avoid brushing against it and breaking off the tips of its hairlike tubes, which are filled with irritating fluids. Be thankful that Europe has no poison ivy at all, and no poison sumac. Be thankful, too, if this is the only way you are nettled in France.

The nettle thrives on nitrogenous soils. Thus, it gathers thickly at the base of Ailsa Craig, off the coast of Scotland, where it flourishes

Nettles and a flowery French wall

breaking point

acid exuding

Each hair is like an acid-filled hypodermic needle

in heavy deposits of bird excrement from the great assemblages of water birds; it also gathers in farmyards, especially around manure piles. In France, it seemed, we were nettled at the base of *every* wall, but in England we felt their pricks only where the wall was somewhat secluded—around a bend, or somewhat screened. Could the nettle distribution be indicating a difference in the relative sense of propriety with which Frenchmen and Englishmen relieve themselves?

In Denmark nettle clumps are said to grow where innocent blood has been shed. In the Scottish Highlands they are said to grow from the bodies of dead men.

Nettles clearly are weeds, but, to a degree, weeds are a matter of definition. There are some plants, for example, that do not look like weeds to an American traveler, although a French farmer sees easily through their airs and graces. To him, plants like poppies, cornflowers, and scabiosas are simply weeds. One gardener-traveler stopped beside a wheatfield and exclaimed with indignation, "Weeds? How can anyone call those flowers weeds? I grow them in my garden!" She did admit, however, that they looked perhaps better in the wheat than in any garden beds that she had ever seen.

For many foreigners the poppy is the one flower, above all others, that is associated with France. The one that grows in American gardens is a more delicately tinted version, owing to the work of an English preacher, the Reverend William Wilks, of Shirley, in Cornwall. Reverend Wilks one day noticed a field poppy with white-edged petals, carefully selected seeds for several generations, and gave us finally the Shirley poppy.

The French name for poppy is *coquelicot*. Edmond Rostand wrote that when the cock crows the poppy moves as though it heard its name called. Peasants say that it is good for the wheat to have poppies in it, which may simply be wishful thinking, or perhaps it is another of those old wives' tales that will turn out to be true after all.

In the wheatfields, together with the red of poppies, the white of oxeye daisies, and the shining yellow of buttercups, there is the dusty lavender of scabiosas, the pale blue of forget-me-nots, and the deep blue of the flower that Americans call "bachelor's button" or "cornflower" and the French call *bluet*. "Hurt-sickle" is an English name that hints at the plant's toughness, and *casselunettes,* "break spectacles," is another French name, which may allude to the flower's bright color but more likely refers to an eyewash concocted from the flower, once alleged to be so effective that one may break his no-longer-needed spectacles.

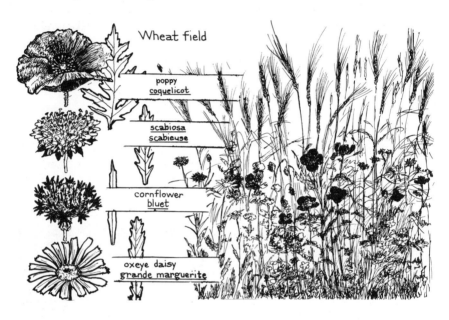

Wheat field

poppy
coquelicot

scabiosa
scabieuse

cornflower
bluet

oxeye daisy
grande marguerite

Along the roads of France we met not only the plants that were invited into gardens in the United States, but also many that came without invitation, crossing the ocean in shoes, trouser cuffs, and luggage, and becoming naturalized. There were butter-and-eggs, *linaire vulgare,* and mullein, *moline,* and bouncing bet, *savonnaire,* and shepherd's purse, *bourse à pasteur,* and dandelion, *dent de lion,* to name but a few.

In addition to these stout peasants, there were plenty of other familiar plants to welcome. We met these along the sheltered, shady roadsides: veronicas, forget-me-nots, blue salvias, wild pansies, and occasional tall spikes of foxglove. On the forest floor were great colonies of lily of the valley, *muguet de mai,* and carpets of sweet woodruff, *reine des bois,* or oxalis, *pain de coucou.*

Along the sunny border of a forest, we ate the winy, fragrant little wild strawberry, *fraisier des bois*—the one sold in small baskets on the streets of Paris in the springtime. Later, in a garden, we ate great bulging strawberries, another product of France, but one that is not really French at all. The big strawberry is thought to have originated in France from a chance hybrid between two foreigners living there: the American wild strawberry, *Fragaria virginiana,* and one from Chile, *Fragaria chiloensis.*

While we saw many plants in France that had become part of the gardens and roadsides of America, we caught an occasional glimpse of a plant that had crossed in the other direction. A clump of Amer-

Three flowers of the shady forest – and one of the forest margin

ican goldenrod grew tall in a choice position in one garden, and brown-eyed Susan in another. Standing alone in the middle of a lawn was a Colorado spruce or a Douglas fir, and we traveled for miles along roads made fragrant by the American black locust.

These were invited and coddled, but we also met some migrants that were as unwelcome there as the dandelion is in America. Most unwelcome is the Canadian waterweed, *Elodea canadensis,* which has spread explosively up and down European streams.

We found some familiar plants when we walked on the hills along the Mediterranean. There in the hot sun our feet stirred up whiffs that transported us to our herb gardens, our kitchens, our linen chests. But rosemary, thyme, and lavender are in their true homes here on these sun-beaten hills.

THE ROSES OF FRANCE

After the fleur-de-lis, the most important flower of France is the rose.

I was prepared for the roses of France, even for the warm breath of the fields near Grasse. I had been prepared by June mornings at home, mornings when opening the living room door was like lifting the lid of a potpourri jar, because our long, old-fashioned windows stood open above the cabbage roses that have perfumed midwestern mornings for a hundred years.

"Cabbage rose" is the prosy name that everyone in our town gives to this buxom beauty that sprawls over our fences and into alleys and spills heaps of pink petals over the clasped hands and heaven-directed forefingers of the old marble tombstones. It can be depended upon for graduations, and June weddings, and sometimes even for Memorial Day. And that is probably the reason why it is the flower most often (with the exception of the pansy) found pressed in Bibles and albums. The "cabbage" in its name must have been suggested by its deeply-cupped sphere of layer upon layer of petals, as was its scientific name, *Rosa centifolia,* "hundred-leaved rose." It was described and given the name *centifolia* by Theophrastus in 350 B.C.

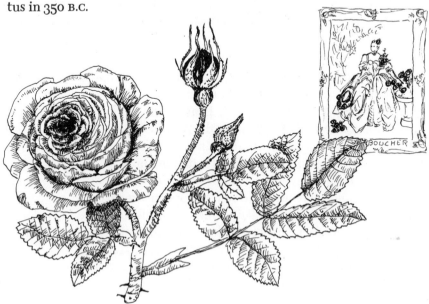

Long before the fragrant morning when I met these same roses at Grasse, I had learned to call them "Provence roses." The Chicago gardener who taught me this name had to open his mouth, and take a rose out of it, before he could speak. He had just popped it in for a minute, he explained, to warm up the volatile oils and release the fragrance. He was demonstrating what had been learned by chance long ago, in a Persian garden. A favorite sultana had thrown many rose petals into the bath that she was preparing for her master. The sun was hot on the water. The sultana noticed oily droplets on the surface. She skimmed them off, and then discovered the rich fragrance they released.

Out beside our fence there grows one of the varied offspring of the Provence rose, the moss rose, with the encrusted bud that is so much a part of old lace valentines. It was used in the era of gentility to convey, by means of the delicate language of flowers, this message:

> Your youthful charms [indicated by the bud state of the rose]
> and your retiring modesty [indicated by the mossiness]
> inspire loving thoughts [represented by a pansy].

(An ardent suitor, well versed in the annals of such sweet symbolism, might have added a Canterbury bell to express his constancy, a sprig of hawthorn to signify hope, heather to describe his solitude, and lily of the valley to plead for a return of his happiness.)

The language of flowers used the bud of the moss rose

The mossy variety of the Provence rose is thought to have originated in Carcassonne about 1696, according to Fréard du Castel of Bayeux, a French writer-horticulturist who obtained a plant from Carcassonne and wrote about it in 1746.

But the rose of Provence is not usually rated as the leading rose citizen of France, although it may appear to be so when one looks at the garlanded ladies of Fragonard and Boucher. That honor belongs to *Rosa gallica*, the rose of Provins, called "the French rose" or "the apothecary's rose." The last name was earned in the thirteenth century, when it was discovered that this rose's petals kept their delicate perfume even when dried and reduced to powder, and could be used for conserves and confections. It is a red rose, with about twelve petals. I have met it clambering robustly down a road-bank in front of an abandoned farm in Wisconsin, and almost filling a Vermont cellarhole.

These two, the rose of Provence and the rose of Provins, together with one other, garland the history of France. The third is, of course, the damask rose, *Rosa damascena*. This one we have all met—in rose water.

Saladin, when he returned to Jerusalem in 1187, ordered five hundred camel-loads of rose water to wash the floor and walls and ceiling of the Mosque of Omar, to purify it after its use as a Christian church by "those infidels, the crusaders." One of those crusaders has long been credited with having carried the damask rose back to France, in 1270. No one is certain about this, but there is no uncertainty about the distinctive fragrance of the damask rose, and its importance in the making of attar of roses and rose water. Perhaps its greatest contribution, however, came through the French hybridizers, who made use of its occasional habit of second blooming.

A fourth French rose, a minor one, is the white, or York rose, *Rosa alba,* the one that links French history and the English War of the Roses. I found one of these in an old cemetery in Indiana, a great bush of clustered white roses sprawling over a row of three small tombstones, each with its white lamb, each bearing the date 1883.

French roses, incidentally, followed the fleur-de-lis and the broom as insignia of English royalty. After the War of the Roses the red rose of Lancaster, which was *Rosa gallica,* and white rose of York, which was *Rosa alba,* were united into the red-and-white rose of the Tudors.

There was one more rose that furnished a preparation for the roses of France. This one sprawls against the east wall of my house, bearing an abundance of purplish-red flowers of no special distinction. But its name has distinction. *Rosa L'Heritiereana,* it was named by the botanist, C. A. Thory, in honor of Charles Louis L'Heritier. The dedication of the rose said:

Nous avons donné à cet abrisseau le nom de L'Heritier (Charles Louis) magistrat distingué et savant Botaniste, né à Paris en 1746, Mort assassiné pendant les troubles de la revolution français.

When that "wise botanist" L'Heritier, many years before he was to be "killed by an assassin during the troubles of the French revolution," sought an illustrator for his botanical writings, he found a remarkable young man who not only drew exquisitely but was eager to learn all that the botanist could teach him about the flowers to be drawn. This was the young Pierre Joseph Redouté. Some years later he was to illustrate the most famous rose books in the world. The three-volume set, called *Les Roses,* had a text written by Thory, but its fame comes because of its illustrations by Redouté.

Actually, although the books are rare, there is probably hardly a tourist who sets out for France without having met Redouté's roses somewhere. There are soft-toned reproductions made by printers who delight in accepting the challenge to their craftsmanship, and who succeed in reproducing in halftone everything except the translucence, the "lighting from within" for which Redouté's stipple engravings are famous. There are tawdry prints in glossy inks, cheaply framed and sold in variety stores; there are prints in gardening books, in books about printing, in books about Napoleon and Josephine, and in nursery catalogues; and one can also buy a collection of chocolate bars, each one wrapped in a tiny replica of a Redouté rose print.

In a rare complete three-volume set of *Les Roses* at the Morton Arboretum I turn to one old-fashioned rose after another. They are all there—if they grew in Josephine's garden they are there—the Provins rose, the moss rose, the damask rose, the L'Heritiereana, and many, many more.

Les Roses begins on a strong note:

. . . le lion est toujours le roi des animaux, l'aigle, le monarque des airs, et la rose, la reine des fleurs.

Redouté was accustomed to other royalty beside the "queen of flowers." He gave lessons in floral painting to several royal ladies. Charles X awarded him the Légion d'Honneur, and Louis XVIII gave him a medal.

In France we met the Provins rose not far from Nancy, where Marie Antoinette slept one night on a bed of Provins rose petals. She was on her way to marry the Dauphin, and the natives of Provins, on learning that she was to stop overnight at Nancy, had spent the day gathering red rose petals for her pleasure.

Later, as Queen of France, after the Dauphin had become Louis XVI, Marie Antoinette found retreat from court splendors in her own gardens at the Petit Trianon. When she heard of a man who painted flowers more exquisitely than anyone else could do, a man who had illustrated the works of L'Heritier, she sent for him, and there in those quiet gardens, where the queen played at the bucolic life, Redouté studied and painted her flowers.

In 1792 the Revolution put an end to his pleasant retreat, and to his patroness as well. All of Redouté's pictures were burned, so we could not see his records of Marie Antoinette's flowers. However, we did walk about the gardens of Le Hameau and the Petit Trianon and wonder whether he had also tried his hand at drawing the thick candles of pink bloom on that horse chestnut, or sketched the water lilies in the pond beside the ivy-covered mill; and whether he had ever set up his easel on the mossy instep of that ancient linden, or under the long, arched pergola; and whether his ankles had been stung by the ancestors of the same nettles that were stinging ours.

Although the pictures of Marie Antoinette's flowers were destroyed, her roses must have provided good practice for Redouté. In 1805 he was appointed Court Painter to the Empress Josephine, and it is the roses of Josephine's Malmaison that make up the plates of *Les Roses*.

In her garden, Josephine had not one cabbage rose, but 27 varieties of them, and 3 moss roses, 167 Provins roses, 9 damask roses, 8 albas, and many others. Surprisingly, she had even obtained the prairie rose of the western United States, *Rosa setigera*, the gangling robust native whose arching sprays tore at the oxen when they broke the prairie. This, and another American wild rose, *Rosa carolina*, were probably brought to France by returning missionaries. In this rose garden Napoleon is said to have spent his last night as emperor of France, before embarking for Elba.

Interest in Josephine's rose garden surmounted even political barriers. Once, when a French trading ship had been seized, the captors
discovered that their booty contained some seeds and plants ad-
dressed to Malmaison. They promptly and carefully forwarded
them. After Napleon's defeat in 1815, the victorious British troops
entering Paris were given instructions to protect the roses of Malmaison.

Walking where Josephine's collection used to be (it was finally
destroyed during the Franco-Prussian War), we felt that the paths
were haunted by a distinguished company. The botanist Jussieu was
bending over a flower to count the number of petals, to examine the
stamens. Redouté was selecting a full-blown rose for a new plate.
Strolling there was Aimé Bonpland, companion of that great world
traveler, Alexander von Humboldt. He was looking to see whether
the seeds that he had brought from the tropics for Josephine to try
in her garden were still growing. André Dupont, chief horticulturist
of the garden, was busy transferring pollen with his camel's-hair
brushes as he embarked on the venture of creating new roses by
artificial pollenation. Later hybridizers have followed in Dupont's
pioneering footsteps: Pernet, Cochet, Vibert, Descemet, Vilmorin
were among them, world-famous creators of new roses.

A French catalogue of 1791 offered 25 varieties of roses. Then
came the influence of Malmaison. An 1829 catalogue offered 2,562
varieties.

We talked about Napoleon and Josephine and their roses on our
way back to Paris. We passed a Provins rose and recalled that, while
Marie Antoinette had slept on a bed of its red petals the night
before her marriage, the Archduchess Marie-Louise of Austria had
not fared so well when she made her last overnight stop on her way
to become Napoleon's second wife. The Provins population had
plied her with rose confections, rose preserves, rose wines, until, it is
sad to say, she had become sick.

As Napoleon had turned from Josephine in search of an heir, his
new, more fertile Empress turned from him, and then France itself
turned away. It all made little difference to the bees, who were
placidly busy on the roses.

In a garden near Lyons, a certain bee gathered pollen from a deeppetaled pink damask rose. He bumbled over to a more open-faced red rose, a variety of the Provins rose, and collected some more pollen. But his hairy body left some pollen from the first rose behind. A seed grew, and by luck lived to make a plant. When the plant bloomed it attracted notice. It was intensely fragrant, semi-double, well-shaped. Because France had a king now, Louis XVIII, it was named "Rose du Roi."

Hybridizers, noting the new rose's long season of bloom, took over where the bee had left off to make more of this same kind of rose. They called the new roses "hybrid perpetuals," *hybrides remontants.* Soon another creation was given a royal name. This was "La Reine" (1842). By 1884 there were eight hundred *hybrides remontants.*

And the French bees were still at it, greedily scooping up more pollen from one rose while they messily left behind a part of what they had gathered from another, paying little attention to the human hybridizers who were hovering busily over the roses with their little camel's-hair brushes. One bee visited one of the new hybrid perpetuals and then bustled into a tea rose. A seed of this chance union grew and flowered. It was noticed, and heralded, and finally adjudged an entirely new class of roses. The first "hybrid tea" had been born. It was christened "La France," and introduced in 1867 by the House of Guillot, of Lyons. Guillot reported that it had appeared in a bed of seedlings of unknown parentage.

Soon after the appearance of the La France rose, Joseph Pernet-Ducher, who was to become the leading rose hybridizer of the world, began his experiments. Year after year he dreamed of breeding yellow into his *hybrides de thé.* Finally he achieved success—a sunflower-yellow rose. But personal sorrow prevented complete joy in his triumph. While he was still considering what name to give his new rose, there came word that his eldest son had been killed in action; within the week he heard that his other son had been taken as well. In 1920 Pernet-Ducher named the yellow rose for his eldest son, "Souvenir de Claudius Pernet." The few good yellows among the hybrid teas have all descended from this rose. "Soeur Thérèse" is one of the outstanding descendants.

The great Pernet-Ducher had as a student one hybridizer whose son, Francis Meilland, made for the world a fabulous new rose. This rose is known in Germany as "Gloria Dei," in the rest of Europe as "Mme. Meilland," and in the United States as "Peace."

Choice roses, like fine fashions, often bear the label "Made in France," and wear French names as well.

Many are named for titled people:

> Duchesse D'Angoulème
> Comtesse de Murinais
> Baron Girod de L'Ain
> Cardinal de Richelieu
> Grande Duchesse Charlotte
> Baronne Prévost

Many more are named for plainer people:

> Mme. Caroline Testout (a Paris dress designer)
> Mme. Cochet-Cochet (a rose hybridizer's wife)
> Antoine Rivoire (an early rose hybridizer)
> Félicité et Perpetueté (twin daughters of a hybridizer)
> Violonellista Albert Fourès

Some are named for places, especially for Lyons:

> Beauté de Lyon
> Belle Lyonnaise
> Gloire Lyonnaise
> Rose de Trianon
> Souvenir de Malmaison
> Gloire de Dijon
> Pompom de Paris

Some names are descriptive, especially when the rose is yellow or white:

> Soleil d'Or
> Perle d'Or
> Rêve d'Or
> Neige d'Avril
> Neige Parfum
> Étoile d'Or

Some are triumphant:

> L'Idéal
> Belle des Jardins
> Élite
> Rosette de Légion d'Honneur

Many more French names may be seen attached to roses in the gardens of Bagatelle, outside Paris, and many names that are not French. Side by side with such English names as "Mrs. Miniver," "Lisbeth Prim," and "Clovelly," one might find such German names as "Vater Rhein," "Kaiserin Auguste Viktoria," "Geheimrat Duisberg," "Frau Ida Munch"; American names such as "Will Rogers," "President Herbert Hoover," "Chrysler Imperial," or "General MacArthur"; a rare Spanish name, such as "Padre Pedralbes"; and plenty of Dutch names, "Mevrouw Welmoet van Heek," "Jonkheer Mr. G. Sandberg," "Veluvezoom," and "Mevrouw van Straaten van Nes." (In America, for some reason, this last rose was named "Permanent Wave.")

While the assemblage of roses at Bagatelle is international, the gardens are trimly French, and Marie Antoinette is again in the background. She made a wager with her brother-in-law, the Comte d'Artois, that he could not, within two months, raze the old hunting lodge and rebuild a new château, complete with furnishings and planted gardens. She lost the hundred thousand-pound wager (what a lot of cake that would have bought). After the revolution Napoleon restored the estate, planning to have his son occupy it. But Napoleon fell, and his son died in exile. Then the Comte d'Artois returned as Charles X, and lived there until he, too, was forced to flee into exile.

Such historic misery makes a fitting background for the strained faces of all the hopeful hybridizers who bring their best creations to Bagatelle each year, for the famous Bagatelle International Rose Contest. Only two of the contestants will be awarded the precious Bagatelle medals, one for the best French rose, one for the best rose of another country.

After one has paid his respects to old-time roses and old memories at the Petit Trianon and at Malmaison, and to their essences at Grasse, and to newer roses and their hybridizers at Lyons, and their growers at Antibes, and seen the trial gardens and the public park at Bagatelle, then he is ready for a resumé and a comparison and an abundant reliving of all these experiences, and much more, at the greatest rose garden in the world, La Roseraie de l'Haÿ-les-Roses outside of Paris.

An outstanding French rosarian, J. H. Nicolas, tells how the inspiration for this garden came about in his own father's beautiful rose garden. His father, a cotton merchant, received regular business visits from Jules Gravereaux, the owner of a large Paris department store, Le Bon Marché. After business hours the two men spent long summer evenings in the Nicolas rose garden. The department-store owner so often expressed longing for a garden of his own that, one day, his host finally said to him, "Gravereaux, if I had your fortune I would retire from business and devote my life to the rose."

That was in 1885, and Gravereaux finally did make up his mind to follow this alluring advice. By 1902 his garden had 6,059 varieties of roses, which continued to accumulate as Gravereaux acquired all the new roses created each year. He was the authority called upon to find the old roses for a token restoration of the gardens of Malmaison, and to help Bagatelle build up its collection. After he died, in 1916, it was decided to add each year only those roses given awards in major contests.

The arches of roses, the standards, the botanic collection, the Malmaison border of Josephine's roses, the plan of the whole, and the pleasant use of statuary (a splendid dragon at the beginning of the display of China roses, for example), all make La Roserai de l'Haÿ-les-Roses a unique rose experience. But in France there is no need to hunt down roses to their special lairs. If one visits only historical sites, the rose is there, done in plaster, in stone, in oil, in clay, garlanding the ornate ceilings of Versailles and of every château.

The rose was the favorite flower of Madame Pompadour, and of Victor Hugo. Hugo used to express the hope that he would die in the season of roses. When he died, on May 22, 1885, friends heaped roses on his coffin and arranged for the carving of roses at the base of his tomb.

Peasants have their roses, too. Actually, that is where roses look best of all—on a peasant cottage, or in a small garden.

Women on their wedding morning used to throw petals of roses into a stream, saying, *"Rose de ma jeunesse ne quitte pas ma vieillesse* (rose of my youth do not forsake me in my old age)."

The Land Itself

 le massif—the block mountain, composed of uplifted ancient crystalline rock, of the northwest corner of France (Brittany); of the northeast corner of France (Vosges Mountains); and of the south-central part of France (*le Massif Central*)

 la côte—the coast; or the escarpment at the edge of a layer of sedimentary rock, especially around the Paris basin, as *Côte de l'Île-de-France* (edge of the island of France)

 le calcaire—the limestone, or the calcareous rock

 les Causses—the high calcareous tableland of southern France

 les Landes—the flat, sandy wastelands of the southwestern coast

The Covering of the Land

 la forêt or *le bois*—the forest

  forêt des hêtres—forest of beeches

  forêt des chênes—forest of oaks

  forêt d'épicéas—forest of spruces

  forêt des aroles et des mélèzes—forest of cembra pines and larches

  forêt des chênes verts—forest of evergreen oaks

   (*le maquis*—the scrubby, aromatic area of the Mediterranean coast)

  forêt des bords des rivières—forest of the borders of rivers

 le bocage—hedgerow country of Britanny and Normandy

 la culture—cultivated land

 le pâturage—pasture

 le vignoble—the vineyard

 le champ—the field

The Flora:

 fleurs des bois—flowers of the forest; many include *bois* (forest) in their names as:

  violette des bois—violet

  fraisier des bois—wild strawberry

anémone des bois—anemone

flore des marais—flora of the swamps; many names include either *marais* (swamp) or *eau* (water) as:

lentille d'eau—duckweed

quenouille d'eau—cattail

populage des marais—marsh marigold

fougère des marais—marsh shieldfern

fleurs des champs—flowers of the fields as:

pensée des champs—wild pansy

liseron des champs—wild morning glory

moutarde des champs—wild mustard

fleurs des bords de la route—flowers of the edges of the road (many are familiars of American roadsides) as:

dent de lion—dandelion

chicorée sauvage—wild chicory

molène—mullein

To Prepare for The Limestone of France

There are many splendid books about the Lascaux caves, with color reproductions of the cave paintings, but I found the clearest presentation of the cave paintings and their various interpretations in *Lascaux* by Annette Laming, translated by Eleanore Frances Armstrong (Penguin Books, Baltimore, 1959).

The structure of the Paris basin is graphically shown in *Things Maps Don't Tell* by Armin K. Lobeck (Macmillan, New York, 1956); and the structure around Paris is fully developed in a book written during the First World War by one of Lobeck's pupils, *Typography and Strategy in the War* by Douglas Wilson Johnson (Henry Holt, New York, 1917).

To read about the use of limestone in the cathedrals, one must surely read *Mont Saint Michel and Chartres* by Henry Adams (Houghton Mifflin, Boston, 1913); and *Notre Dame de Paris, The Biography of a Cathedral* by Allan Temko (Viking, New York, 1959). From Temko's book I learned and retold the part of this chapter dealing with various kinds of limestone. For a discussion of the depiction of nature in the cathedrals, read *The Gothic Image* by Emile Male (Harper, New York, 1958).

To Prepare for The Sharp-edged Tools of France

Gardens and People, by Fletcher Steele (Houghton Mifflin, Boston, 1964) has a chapter called "The French Must Calculate," pp. 127–143, which one can best appreciate who has read the preceding chapter, "Englishmen Care"; and goes on to read the following chapter, "The Italian Feels." *The Age of Louis XIV,* by Will and Ariel Durant (Simon and Schuster, New York, 1963) in Chapter III, "The King and the Arts," pp. 87–103, sums up the art of the sun king as having been "a disciplined and academic art, majestic in its orderly splendor." *Great Gardens of the*

Western World, by Peter Coats (G. P. Putnam's Sons, New York, 1963) displays and describes five famous French gardens: Villandry, Vaux-le-Vicomte, Versailles, Courances, and Bagatelle.

To Prepare for The Flowers of France

If the stories, legends, superstitions of the flowers interest you, there is one book above all others that will give what you hope to find, and much more. That is *Plant Lore Legends and Lyrics* by Richard Folkard (Samson Low and Co., London, 1884). This book is long out of print, but can be found in many libraries. The only one that I know that approaches it in scope is *Myths and Legends of Flowers, Trees, Fruits, and Plants* by Charles W. Skinner (Lippincott, Philadelphia, 1925), but it is also out of print. An excellent one has recently been republished: *The Folklore of Plants,* by T. F. Thiselton-Dyer (Chatto and Windus, London, 1889), republished by Singing Tree Press, a division of Gale Research, Detroit, 1968.

For use in identifying the flowers of France, there is a pleasant series of small colorful books, called *Les Petits Atlas Payot Lausanne.* From the series you will need: No. 12, *Fleurs des Alpes I;* No. 27, *Fleurs des Alpes II;* No. 13, *Fleurs des Champs I;* No. 20, *Fleurs des Champs;* No. 14, *Fleurs des Bois;* No. 26, *Flore des Marais.* These are in French, but the pictures are all in color, and the scientific names are there (Librairie Payot, Lausanne, n.d.). They are available at most French bookstores, and many variety shops.

To Prepare for The Roses of France

Try to find a place where you can sit quietly, alone, with Redouté's three-volume *Les Roses* (P. Dufart, Paris, 1835). It is not easy to find, but worth a lot of effort. The following institutions have copies: The Arnold Arboretum, Boston, Mass.; The Brooklyn Botanical Gardens, Brooklyn, N.Y.; the New York Public Library; the Massachusetts Historical Society, Boston, Mass.; the Missouri Botanical Gardens, St. Louis, Mo.; the Library of Congress, Washington, D.C.; the Library of the U.S. Department of Agriculture, Washington, D.C.; The Morton Arboretum Library, Lisle, Ill. If you simply can't find a copy, see *Redouté's Roses* by Pierre J. Redouté, preface by Eva Mannering (Van Nostrand, New York, 1965); or, preferably, *The Best of Redouté's Roses,* folio, by Eva Mannering (Ariel Press, London, 1958).

For accounts of the old-fashioned roses, read *The Old Shrub Roses,* by Graham Stuart Thomas (Charles T. Branford Co., Newton Center, Mass., 1956). Read especially the chapter "Old Roses of Paris." For accounts of rose hybridizers, try to find a copy of *A Rose Odyssey,* by Jean Henri

Nicolas, which is now out of print (Doubleday, Doran, & Co., Garden City, N.Y., 1937). For the story of roses read *The History of the Rose* by Roy E. Shepherd (Macmillan, New York, 1954), especially Chapter 5, "The French Rose and Its Relatives."

Italy

The Hills of Italy

Most of the Italian landscape records its stories in braille—a gigantic braille of hilltops. A traveler, reading the stories, finds himself going from hilltop to hilltop:

to a
castled hill

from a
forested hill

to a
gardened hill

to a
templed hill

to a hill
with a shrine

to a
volcano

to a hill with
a monastery

to a walled
hill town

to a
marble quarry

A FORESTED HILL

Wine casks stood along the narrow streets of a small hill town, and a free taste of the local wine was offered to us, in green plastic cups. It was September, and the wine harvest was being celebrated.

The casks, dark, old, and massive, must have received the harvests of many autumns. Their thick staves were of oak.

From the end of the street we looked across to adjoining hills. They had no oaks, no trees at all, except for the cypresses of a graveyard and an occasional crooked roadside camp follower. The colors of the landscape were gray-brown and tan, with some low, spreading masses of black-green and some brighter patches of the yellow and green of broom.

These hills, and all the hills of Italy, were once forested. The hill on which we drank wine out of green plastic is at an altitude to have produced deciduous oaks. A higher hill, there in the distance, probably once had a forest of chestnuts, perhaps beech.

The following cross section shows the ancient covering of the land.

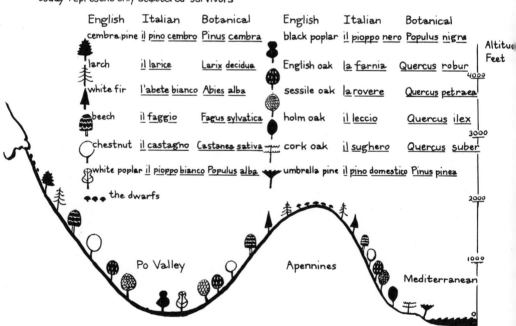

The Forests of Italy — a cross section

Each tree symbol represents many of a kind in the original forest, but may today represent only scattered survivors

English	Italian	Botanical	English	Italian	Botanical
cembra pine	il pino cembro	Pinus cembra	black poplar	il pioppo nero	Populus nigra
larch	il larice	Larix decidua	English oak	la farnia	Quercus robur
white fir	l'abete bianco	Abies alba	sessile oak	la rovere	Quercus petraea
beech	il faggio	Fagus sylvatica	holm oak	il leccio	Quercus ilex
chestnut	il castagno	Castanea sativa	cork oak	il sughero	Quercus suber
white poplar	il pioppo bianco	Populus alba	umbrella pine	il pino domestico	Pinus pinea
the dwarfs					

Altitude Feet

4000

3000

2000

1000

Po Valley   Apennines   Mediterranean

The forests of antiquity are well documented by the classical writers. Eight hundred years before Christ, Homer was already describing the first signs of deforestation as he compared the sounds of battle with "the din of woodcutters in the glades of a mountain." Thucydides, in the fifth century B.C., wrote of "the spontaneous conflagrations sometimes known to occur through the wind's rubbing the branches of a mountain forest together." Theophrastus, in the fourth century B.C., writing of the uses of trees of Greece, Crete, Corsica, and southern Italy, specified certain trees as suitable "for shipbuilding, housebuilding, rafters, beams, yardarms, masts, keels, charcoal." Strabo's *Geography*, in the first century, told that the mountains near Genoa furnished "plenty of wood for construction of ships"; and mentioned mast-fed swine being supplied for Roman banquets. He told of pitch works, and the making of large casks for wine.

The cutting of trees in order to use them made little impression on the forests. But then the farmers came, cutting trees to be rid of them, to make place for vines, and meadows for cattle, and plots for wheat, and orchards.

The poets loved the clearings, with meadows and vineyards and open groves. Horace, at about the time of Julius Caesar's assassination, wrote "The choir of poets all loves woods and shuns the city," but his own favorite spot seemed to be Tivoli, which already had gardens and temples and fountains.

Virgil, writing at about the same time as Horace, describes the landscape:

The farmer cleaves the earth with share and curving plough. There is his yearly work: that makes food for his home and little ones, for his cattle and well-deserving oxen. Without delay the year's yield burgeons out in fruit or in young creatures or in nodding heads of grain, loading the furrows with the crop, overflowing the bins. Comes winter: Then the generous olive yields its juice; the pigs come home jolly with acorns; berries flourish. . . . his chaste home guards its modesty; the cows let down their generous udders; plump on the luxuriant turf the kidlings cross their hostile horns, butting and struggling.

Virgil mentioned also wide-spreading trees, beeches and oaks, giving shade to grassy pastures where sheep and goats grazed.

Tibullus, a friend of Horace's, wrote about a farmer who fashioned a flute out of oat straw, who led the dance and won the prize, "the best of the herd, a he-goat."

The gamboling sheep and kids moved into the forests so gently that no one noticed the seedling beeches that the ewes ate off at the ground, or the sapling chestnuts that the goats girdled; nor did anyone stop to listen to the louder splash of the rain on the stripped forest floor or to observe the muddy runoff from the forest. Certainly, no one blamed the gentle ewes and their lambkins when the harbors began to silt up, and when Pisa and Ravenna were cut off from the seacoast by vast deltas.

I saw the destroyers in action one early October day, in the mountains. We opened the door to step out of a small shop we had been visiting and found that we could not make our way into the narrow street. Sheep filled it, jostling, arguing, as far down the street and as far up the mountain as we could see. The rams wore flattened and curved horns almost too handsomely gesturing to be true. The whole mass shoved itself past, complaining that there was nothing to eat there in that cobblestoned street, no saplings to strip, no twigs to prune. The shepherd, with mustache and black eyes as gay as the horns of the rams, stepped buoyantly along at the end, with his dogs and his heavily laden donkey. The herd was on its way to winter pasture.

Later in the day we passed the same flock, several miles down the mountain. The shepherd was busy commanding the dogs, and the dogs were urging the sheep to keep moving. It would have required a dog apiece to keep those sheep from stripping every green mouthful along the way. They stood there on their hind legs, with forelegs braced high on tree trunks and their necks stretched, to reach leaf, young bark, or living twig.

But some forests do still exist in Italy, covering now about 15 percent of their original area. I was permitted to enter a tall, ferny forest, preserved by generations of one family. I lifted a patch of moss carefully and used my pencil to investigate what lay beneath. There was only a film of dark humus over the yellowish-tan clay. And beneath the clay, my pencil probed easily to bedrock. How tenuous is the foothold of the forest on these hills! There is neither enough rain to assist the formation of humus, nor enough frost to help crack the rocks and let roots enter. Sheep and goats change such a forested hill into a desert hill in three stages.

Forest, sheep, and goats

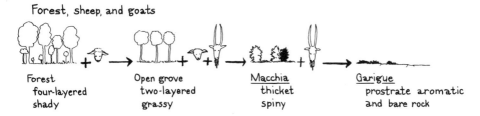

Forest	Open grove	Macchia	Garigue
four-layered	two-layered	thicket	prostrate aromatic
shady	grassy	spiny	and bare rock

The first stage is the open grove. The dappled grassy grove with widely spaced trees and no underbrush is a model for parks and gardens all over the world. One of the most thoroughly tamed landscapes, it served as a bucolic setting of castles for lords and ladies, who craved a return to nature with none of the hardships of agriculture. It was also the scene always visible through the windows of Madonna paintings. The shepherd and his sheep entered religion in other goat-stripped landscapes a very long time ago; consider the Twenty-third Psalm, The Lamb of God, the Good Shepherd, the lost sheep, the fold, the pastor. The three Wise Men might have had more difficulty following the low-hanging star to Bethlehem had the goat not first removed the forests.

The second stage is the maquis, *la macchia*. When mature trees have died, only the toughest, spiniest, bitterest-tasting trees and shrubs persist. These are goat-pruned dwarfs, forming tangled thickets and interspersed with tough grasses. Poets and lords and ladies are gone, but there have been useful hiding places for certain guerilla fighters, who have adopted the name of this setting.

The third stage is the garigue, *la gariga*. Here the plants are prostrate masses. Many are prickly, many are evergreen, many are aromatic. The bare rock shows through in more and more places as the goats seek the last tough nibbles.

The last stage is desert.

Alexander von Humboldt, from his observations in many lands, wrote in 1849 that civilization sets bounds to the increase of forests, and that "the youthfulness of a civilization is proved by the existence of its woods."

It has taken eight thousand years for the Mediterranean, known as "the Cradle of Civilization," to become practically stripped. America is showing signs of becoming civilized, too.

The god Pan symbolized Italy well: half man, half goat, seated on a fallen tree trunk and playing on shepherd's pipes, his feet pressing out the aroma of rosemary "that's for memory."

A TEMPLED HILL

When drought blasted the land, men raised their eyes not to the unyielding blue of the sky but to a hill where a cloud often rested.

A powerful god must surely inhabit that hill—a god who had become displeased and was sending the drought in punishment. The psalmist of one Mediterranean country had sung:

I will lift up mine eyes unto the hills, from whence cometh my help. My help cometh from the Lord who made Heaven and Earth.

That was a land where droughts were bitter and the god who inflicted them was severe.

The droughts of the Roman world were less harsh than those of the Holy Land, and the god who controlled them was not as stern. He was known as Jupiter Pluvius, the rain-giver; or Jupiter Imbricator, the shower-sender; or Jupiter Fulgar, wielder of power over lightning; or Jupiter Tonitrualis, hurler of thunderbolts. His rain was called *aqua Jovis*.

Jupiter dwelt in a sacred grove on top of the highest of the Alban hills. Each spring when the winter rains were stopping and the summer drought was threatening, a white heifer was sacrificed and many other offerings were made.

There were many hills sacred to Jupiter. The best known group was originally a part of a great plateau of volcanic ash and tufa. The Tiber River, coming down from the mountains, was slowed as it neared the sea. It skirted the plateau on its left, and rivulets found their way across the plateau and down to the Tiber. The tributaries tongued their way deeper and deeper, until the plateau had been carved into several hills, the classical "seven hills of Rome."

Most famous of the seven is the Capitoline Hill. Romulus came here to consecrate the spoils of war on a sacred oak tree, and Augustus came to build the temple to Jupiter Capitolinus. Still later, when Roman kings wanted to celebrate a victory, they came here to put on the symbols of Jupiter's greatness: the eagle, the oak, and the laurel.

The laurel leaf is perhaps the most Mediterranean of them all—in form, in finish, in pungency, in story. Even the tree's dark fruit is characteristic of what drought has selected for these hills, seeds buried safe from desiccation in a rich pulp of dark flesh, as in the grape, the olive, the fig.

The laurel has lived so long with a story-telling people that it has acquired more than its share of tales. The earliest is that of Apollo and Daphne. Cupid had wanted to play with Apollo's bow and arrows, and when Apollo forbade him to do so Cupid revenged himself by shooting Apollo with a golden tipped arrow, compelling him to fall in love with the first woman he should meet. Then he shot a second arrow, one with a leaden tip, at Daphne, the wood nymph, which served to create fear and repugnance in her heart. Apollo and Daphne met, of course, and Daphne fled from Apollo's advances until she could run no more, then implored the gods to change her form into one that would not attract Apollo. Ovid (as translated by Dryden) tells what happened:

> Scarce had she finished when her feet she found
> Benumbed with cold and fastened to the ground.
> A filmy rind about her body grows;
> Her hair to leaves, her arms extend to boughs.
> The nymph is all into a laurel gone,
> The smoothness of her skin remains alone.

When Apollo realized that Daphne had been transformed, he declared to the tree:

I espouse thee for my tree:
Be thou the prize of honor and renown;
The deathless poet, and the poem, crown;
Thou shalt the Roman festivals adorn,
And, after poets, be by victors worn.

Dante-drawn from Signorelli

laurel
l'alloro
Laurus nobilis

Daphne -Apollo- Cupid   c.286-305

coin   c.350 B.C.

Roman centurion's helmet

Caesar was crowned with laurel leaves. Generals sent victorious dispatches encased in laurel leaves to their emperors. Diviners wore laurel leaves and slept with them under their pillows to bring dreams revealing the future. Rhymesters too slept on them that they might become great poets. Laurels are an ancient protection against lightning and evil spirits. The custom of fastening a laurel bough over a doorway to drive away death gave rise to the custom of crowning young doctors with laurel berries, called *bacca lauri,* and thus the students became "baccalaureates." Because those students had, supposedly, no time for matrimony, the same word was adopted for all males who did not marry, and who thereby remained "bachelors." Nero showed so much faith in the efficacy of the laurel that he fled to Laurentium during a plague, so that he might breathe the air that the laurels had purified.

The Capitoline Hill has looked down on as many changes as has any hill in the world. It was, of course, once covered by dense forest, which obscured the view of the swampy valley that separated it from the hill beyond. Wolves must have lurked in that forest, and we read that one of them suckled Romulus and Remus. Gradually men cleared the forest and built the temple to Jupiter. It is recorded by Petronius that in times of drought noble matrons walked barefoot up the long slope of this hill to the temple of Jove the Thunderer to pray for rain, and that "the rain came down in bucketfuls, and all the women smiled though wet as rats."

Recalling the splendidly arranged classical hair styles from friezes and paintings, we find those smiling, wet matrons difficult to visualize. It is recorded that they made their hair lustrous by using maidenhair fern in wine with celery seed and oil. Below, in the Forum, their strolling husbands probably slipped under some colonnade so as not to lose the creases in their purple-bordered white wool togas. A senator who lost his crease no doubt reviled against the rainmakers as bitterly as some moderns rebel against our cloud-seeders.

Then came a time when the Forum was called the Cornfield, and Jupiter's hill was called Goat's Hill. The names themselves explain why the forest was not to return.

We saw a lizard sunning himself on marble and happened to notice a handsome leaf showing its intricate pattern against the face of the stone. The leaf looked somehow familiar but somehow wrong. It was an acanthus leaf, and because we identified it from the only specimens we had met, on the capitals of Corinthian columns, we somehow expected it to grow curled over.

The idea for those curled-over leaves is said to have come to the young architect, Callimachus, in a strange way. A little girl had died. Her grieving nurse put her charge's favorite trinkets into a

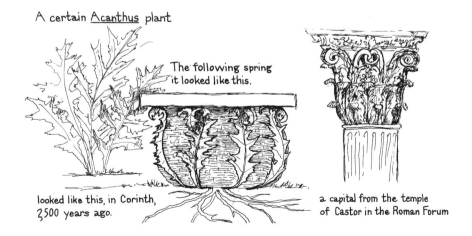

A certain <u>Acanthus</u> plant

The following spring it looked like this.

looked like this, in Corinth, 2,500 years ago.

a capital from the temple of Castor in the Roman Forum

basket and placed the basket beside the tomb; she then covered the basket with a tile. When the growth period came, an acanthus plant broke through the ground and sent vigorous leaves growing upward. The leaves were obstructed by the tile, and curved back. The architect happened to observe this accidental curving of the intricate leaves. He copied it, and others, many others, have been copying it ever since.

A HILLTOP MONASTERY

Asceticism was to be expected of a monastery. But we didn't expect the site of the monastery to look so ascetic.

Volcanic ash rose, deeply eroded, looking like an especially grim example in a conservation book. Ahead we saw cypress trees topping the mountain. Close-ranked, compact, they presented a mere knife edge to the sun and wind. The sides of the mountain wore only tattered rags of vegetation, gray-green as if leaves, too, wore sackcloth and ashes.

That stark hill was especially surprising because we had come to it across the green croplands and warm reddish soil of Tuscany. Only a few minutes earlier we had passed on the road a cart drawn by two white oxen. The cart was softly pink, and decorated with painted flowers. The driver was singing. The cart was empty, but surely it had been loaded with grapes and was returning for another load. From the spreading horns of the oxen to the two big wheels with sky-blue spokes, it had seemed too gay to be true. Somehow we had managed not to follow him when he turned down a narrow side road.

By contrast, the eroded hill of the monastery seemed too harsh to be true. No wonder that it had been called *deserto di Accona,* the desert of Accona, when the first hermits came here. Now it is called Monte Oliveto Maggiore, named after an even more ascetic hill, the Mount of Olives, which bears Golgotha, the place of skulls.

But in Italy gaiety somehow erupts. The monastery was built of pink brick, and its doorway, decorated with terra cottas by della Robbia, showed his characteristic sky blue.

On the walls of the loggia around the cloister were paintings of the life of San Benedetto. The ones painted by the great Sodoma offer special escapes from asceticism. Through the windows he supplied in his backgrounds, we could see into pleasant Italian landscapes. And when we found the self-portrait that Sodoma introduced into one of the scenes, we suspected that those windows were his own joy overflowing. With a haircut he might have been the man singing in the pink cart.

Another traveler, Hilaire Belloc, in his *The Path to Rome,* wrote about windows:

. . . would you not call your architect up before you and say . . . "Sir, see that the windows of my house are *tall, narrow, thick,* and have a round top of them"?

Of course you would, for thus you would best catch in separate pictures the sunlit things outside your home.

Everywhere in his great travel book, Belloc found many windows into the landscape, through the thick ascetic walls of his pilgrimage.

Cicero wrote that he had his architect provide narrow windows for him to enjoy his pleasure grounds.

We went out into the landscape, with Sodoma, Belloc, and

Old olive trees

Cicero, and looked at the monastery olive orchard. Here the trees stood in clean ground, finely cultivated to contain the rain. From that little rain and from volcanic dust, from the Mediterranean sunshine and from air vibrant with bells and masses, they were making olive oil.

The olive tree could have been designed by great Mediterranean personalities. Scientists, gods, poets, and others could have had a hand in its design.

Athene is credited with having had the first hand in it. The tree was born at her command during her contest with Neptune for supremacy over the Greeks. Neptune had tried first; he struck the rock of the Acropolis with his trident and produced a salt-water spring. Athene produced the olive tree, and won. Athens was given her name.

King Solomon might have designed the olive's stout timber for use in building the doors, the posts, and the cherubim of the Temple at Jerusalem, not foreseeing that the olive timber would be so lasting that a certain beam, rejected for the temple and thrown into a morass, would furnish a foothold for the Queen of Sheba, who would see a dreadful vision of the Crucifixion as she crossed on the timber. The timber was much later withdrawn from the morass and used to fashion the Cross.

Malpighi might have designed the strong plumbing system with tubes extending from the wide-spreading roots up to the leaves, evergreen for using the winter sun, but small and gray-green for facing the summer sun.

Galileo might have filled the cells of the fruit with oil to keep them from being dried out during a drought.

Bernini might have designed the shape of the whole tree, to delight him by fitting it within the circumference of a circle.

Giotto might have designed the humble functional form and unassuming garb as background for his people.

Michelangelo might have sculpted those muscles and sinews in the old trunks.

Machiavelli might have designed the whole tree to his ideal of strength terminating in success.

Verdi might have orchestrated that dense canopy of leaves into a chorus forming a background for the epic tragedy and struggle depicted by the trunk.

An ecologist, of course, would maintain that the designer was time and change and circumstance. And a monk up there on that mountain would credit yet a different Designer.

In the grove adjoining the olive orchard the ground was not

cultivated. Here, under oaks, we saw many clear yellow flowers that looked like crocuses. They proved, on closer inspection, to be *Sternbergia,* considered by some students to have been "the lilies of the field," which "toil not, neither do they spin, yet Solomon in all his glory was not arrayed like one of these." This bright flower has become adjusted to summer drought with an adjustment different from that of the olive. It does not face the drought at all, but simply waits in the security of its well-packaged bulb until the autumn rains trigger its sudden growth. The drought-shaped Italian hillsides conceal many such packages, equipped with a great adaptation— the ability to wait.

We looked back at the mount, back to the top, where the dark cypresses stood with every part directed heavenward. Then we looked down the road, hoping for another pink cart.

A HILL WITH A SHRINE

If all the Saint-Francis-preaching-to-the-birds statues from American gardens were to be carried on a pilgrimage to be blessed at the shrine of Saint Francis of Assisi, the line of gardener-pilgrims might stretch a long way up the western slope of the Apennines. The line might start at the level of the umbrella pines; mount through the level of the evergreen oaks, and through deciduous oaks and chestnuts; pass the too-impressive temple raised over the body of the forthright saint, and the woods where he competed all night with a nightingale at singing the glory of God, and the woods where lived the famous wolf before its conversion; pass the thornless rose bushes that wore their share of thorns until the day when Saint Francis threw himself into their thorniness to subdue the "Brother Ass" of his own body; and arrive at last at the simple hermitage with its venerable oak that is said to have known Saint Francis. The line might then continue right to the top of the Apennines, past beeches and firs, and start down the steeper slope toward the Adriatic Sea.

Unfortunately, there are no good statistics on American-garden Saint Francises, but as we climb the Apennines we can take pleasure in imagining such a pilgrimage of statuary—stone, cement, wood, plastic—with or without their commonly attendant garden flamingoes.

Assisi itself, thirteen hundred feet high, looked a bit stark from the outside, but not when we entered and followed the narrow streets up and down between the old stone buildings. It was garlanded with vines, window boxes, and potted plants on every balcony and windowsill. We emerged at the town piazza, which the young Francis knew so well in his more carefree days. He must have been familiar with the relics of an earlier Roman town, Assisium, which give evidence of Minerva and Jupiter, the earlier gods on this hilltop.

We looked across to Perugia, Assisi's close neighbor and ancient enemy, where Francis was held as a prisoner of war for a year. On another nearby hill perched a third walled town, Spoleto, where Francis had his first vision, after which he returned to Assisi for solitude and prayer.

The rest of his story is told by the basilica and monastery of Saint Francis, which rises from the edge of the hilltop, supported on many arches. We went first of all down to the crypt to see the hiding place deep within the limestone of the Apennines where the body of the saint was concealed for so many years lest the Perugians steal it so that their hilltop might receive the benefits of a saint's body.

We learned that the lamps in the crypt burn oil that is furnished by a different Italian region each year. Each October 4, on the anniversary of the death of Saint Francis, branches are placed on the altar, branches of the two characteristic trees of the Mediterranean, the olive, symbolizing peace, and the laurel, symbolizing honor.

We ascended next into the light and abundant color of the Upper Church to read his story as it was told for people who had no books, certainly no colored picture books. The Italians admire these great paintings and revere their saint and his little brothers the birds. We purchased from a friar in the Franciscan shop a print of one of the scenes in Giotto's twenty-eight frescoes from the Upper Church—the one in which Saint Francis preaches to the birds. Later, unwrapping that print, we looked at it and wondered about Italians and their saints.

Earlier in the day, stopping in a town at the foot of the hill, we had happened to look into a store window. It was full of rifles, except for the center, at which there was a strange apparatus. A flat piece of metal, about a foot long, was rotating slowly, erratically, above a box that looked like a battery. The flat piece was set with glittering bits of glass. A man stepped up to look into the gun window, and we managed to ask him to identify the object. *"Pour l'alouette,"* he explained, using French for our benefit and making a flying motion. Then he lifted an imaginary rifle, sighted, fired, and dropped his hands like dead wings. (We learn a lot from the articulate hands of Italians.)

There at the foot of Saint Francis's hill they were selling a device that must look to a bird like water stirring or like another bird bathing—and guns to shoot any bird who comes down to investigate.

One Sunday morning in Siena, we noticed that something was happening up on the fort wall. Up on the wall, which is as wide as a street, we were greeted by bird song, varied, wild. But these were not gaily colored birds in gilded cages being sold to ladies for their parlors and balconies; only one small section of the wall was offering that kind. All the rest of the market was offering small brown thrushlike birds in simple wooden cages. The customers were men, working men who paid out their money with hard hands. We sought an explanation from a young English-speaking Italian woman. She told us, "It is the hunting season. All Italian men are going hunting. At this time of year I seldom see my husband. When he comes home he brings a brace of pheasants. My husband and his friends are able to lease the hunting rights on a big estate. Those men you see on the wall cannot afford to lease a place. They hunt the small birds. They cook a pot full of them and eat the whole bird, sucking out the skulls and smacking their lips. They hang the caged birds in the woods; other birds come and are shot."

As we talked about the bird market, another traveler recalled her experiences near Hamburg in 1912: "I stayed at a farm. The only meat that was ever served was either sausage, or a plate of small birds. The old grandfather at the head of the table had his big dog always beside him. IIis head rested on the grandfather's knee. The old man sucked the bird bones with relish, and then spit them into the mouth of the waiting dog."

Plutarch records that once, when Pompey was ill, his doctor ordered him a dish of thrushes.

In Chartres we were once served lark-liver pâté with brandy and pistachio nuts. It was delicious.

Thrushes, larks, blackbirds, tits, pipits, finches, nuthatches, warblers, nightingales

HILLTOP GARDENS

Two kinds of gardens garland the hills of Italy: gardens with rain only and gardens with water laid on. The gardens with rain only are skeletons of a grander past when they, too, had water brought to them.

The first garden that we visited, on a hill near Siena at a former monastery, was a small one, no bigger than an average room, and dry. Probably the water that had first made a garden there had been carried in a watering can by a monk. A woman who lived with her family in one side of the central court brought a key to open the door into the walled square and presented us with a big branch from a rosemary shrub covered with blue flowers. The shrub survived when the gardening monks left, for it had survived on the dry hill long before the monks came. There were two trees—a fig and a pomegranate—left in the square, at two of the four corners. The rest of the brown earth was bare, but the woman made a tender gesture with both hands, starting at the soil and rising about six inches. She smiled and said, "*Flora,*" and we understood that there must be many bulbs underground waiting for release by winter rains.

One of the largest unirrigated gardens we saw was once copiously watered by an engineer-emperor, the great Hadrian. Some colossal cypresses still flanked the avenue, descendants of those that once stood to hear the sound of chariot wheels when Hadrian arrived on his cool Sabine hill, retreating from the dust and heat of Rome. The trees seemed not to have noticed when the water supply failed; their roots were plunged deeply into the volcanic hillside. In a deep excavation where Hadrian had his canal, or his pool, some water must still be trapped, for reeds were crowded there.

A redbud was growing against a wall. According to legend the redbud was at one time a straighter, taller tree, but Judas hanged himself from it, after betraying Christ. The tree blushed with shame through all its small flowers and begged God to give it a form that could never be so used again. That is why the redbud is called the Judas tree and is always small and crooked. We realized that the emperor Hadrian, or his slave, if he planted the ancestor of the redbud must have planted it not so very long after its magical transformation. The villa beside the garden was built between A.D. 118 and 138. The redbud, *Cercis siliquastrum*, is known as *il siliquastro*, and, except for the blunted tip of its leaf, it looks much like the redbud of the eastern United States.

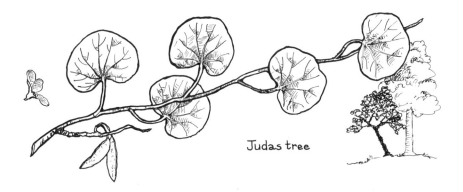

Judas tree

Around the ruined villa many hardy pioneers were blooming: mullein, a mallow, a silene, a mustard, and many, many more. We searched for signs of the return of the forest, realizing that this return would be slow, first because of sheep and later because of tourists. We found some young oak trees, deciduous oaks, and knew that the trees had not forgotten their place in the zones of a mountainside. They would, however, have to bide their time.

The villas of the ancient Romans lay within reach of Rome, by chariot, usually. Cicero had seventeen villas. Pliny the Younger left an account of his suburban villa at Laurentium and his country estate in Tuscany. He recorded that around a certain basin, beneath a vine-covered arbor, there was a broad brim to hold the plates for a banquet, and on the surface of the pool, in boat-shaped dishes, floated the banquet foods.

No doubt some of the guests reclining on couches around the pool wore wreaths of roses on their heads. The wearing of crowns of flowers and leaves was important to the Romans, who had acquired the habit from the Greeks. The Greeks had approached their altars with wreathed hair and had led animals with garlands around their horns to the sacrifice. Boys wore garlands of roses or hyacinths in religious processions, and a young man might stroll about with a rosebud behind his ear. The Romans conferred crowns as rewards for military successes. Most desired was the *corona obsidionalis,* made of grass and flowers from the land on which an army had been beleaguered, and presented by the soldiers to the general who had come to their aid. The *corona civica,* made of oak leaves, was worn by one who had saved the life of a Roman soldier. The *corona triumphalis,* made of laurel leaves, was awarded to a general who had achieved a signal victory. Julius Caesar valued the special dispensation by the Senate that allowed him to wear his laurel wreath every day, though other Romans were permitted to wear them only on special festive occasions. He may have appreciated it especially because it screened his baldness, which the Romans considered a deformity. Poets wore coronets of ivy. There were also chaplets made of olive, parsley, myrtle, or garden flowers and worn by the family for the evening meal.

We met a horse in Genoa in the early summer, pulling a delivery wagon and wearing a straw hat with a big bunch of cherries on the front.

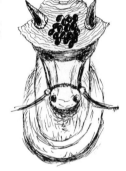

One of the grandest garlanded heads belongs to a certain Sabine hill above Tivoli (ancient Tibur). That hill is intoxicated with water; since the Renaissance, when Cardinal Ippolito d'Este took possession, it has been having a debauch of water.

At the foot of the hill, the river Aniene (the ancient Anio) hurries down to join the Tiber and to stroll with it through Rome. But first it has a final fling. The waters are piped to the top of the hill, where they are disgorged from the mossy heads of beasts, birds, and fish, even sprayed from the plump breasts of matronly sphinxes, and spouted from the horns of sea gods. They curvet, splash, gurgle, bounce, spray, and spit, subside into reflection, and flow down to the Aniene again, resigned.

The visiting waters leave behind a changed hillside. The changes that man has made with their help are not very different from the kinds of exotic plantings that mark all public gardens and parks; but the plants that have come naturally with the introduction of abundant water are interesting, because they show something of what the Mediterranean world would achieve in vegetation, had it a more abundant rainfall.

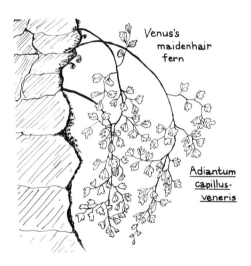

Venus's maidenhair fern

Adiantum capillus-veneris

A stone channel running the whole length of the second terrace is deeply encrusted with liverwort, that most primitive of land plants, which has achieved the historic step of coming ashore but has not advanced so far as to lift its green ribbons off the surface of the drenched rock. Its encrustations of blue-green are draped by the most delicate of maidenhair ferns. The harts tongue fern extends its green tongues on wet rock. Mosses fill all crevices, and algae thrive in the pools. An assemblage from the first pages of the book of evolution, from the foggy youth of the world, has come together here in its ancestral wetness. And wherever the society of primitives leaves a gap, there the ivy fills it.

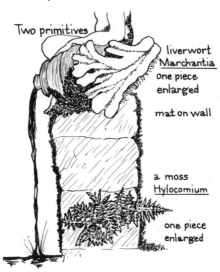

It was a shock when we turned from the blue-greenness and looked out to a neighboring hill, gray-green in the sun, with widely spaced mounds of trees or shrubs. That sopping hillside of ours must at one time have looked like that gray-green hill. That was before the sixteenth century, when a former Benedictine monastery was transformed into the Villa d'Este.

One of the most pleasant of the Italian gardens is an extension of a lived-in home on a small hill in Tuscany. From the high dignified central hall of the villa we stepped through a wide door to two or three broad steps that faced the garden theater. Before us, across an open area, was a dense block of clipped trees, mature ilex trees, probably tonsured by generations of gardeners singing "Figaro." The face of the block had been clipped into a flat wall of shining green; and the tops were sculptured into a row of identical scallops.

Then we realized that the block was not flat but shallowly horse-shoe shaped. What a background for a play! At the end of each arm of the horseshoe an arched entrance had been shaped. We entered and walked underneath in the dense shade, looking out now and then to the brightness and emerging at the arch in the opposite arm. The dark horseshoe must offer usable wings during a play, and a cool place to stroll during the summer heat.

The ilex, clipped, is probably the most important building block of Italian gardens. This is the holm oak, *Quercus ilex*, called *il leccio* by Italians. Virgil put the darkness of an ilex tree and the whiteness of an ox into two fine lines:

> Ille, latus niveum mollifultus hacintho
> Ilice sub nigra pallents ruminat herbas.
>
> He, with his snow-white side resting upon the soft hyacinth,
> Ruminates the pale herbage under the black ilex.

The garden extended down, by a succession of parterred terraces, to a balustrade and a view of a hotter, drier landscape.

A CASTLED HILL

A hill may be an island—especially in Italy.

Islands, because of their isolation, have long held special interest for biologists. The Galápagos revealed to Charles Darwin the giant reptiles and now-famous finches, which had split into a swarm of species, each one fitting into a special ecological niche. Australia, in similar isolation without mammals, filled its empty niches with the exotic marsupials. New Zealand, in the absence of large predators, produced flightless birds.

Of course, isolation may result from barriers other than water; lack of communication is the important element. Islands, real ones and figurative ones, offer a special interest when their barriers are breached and their stabilized self-sufficiency is invaded by tension and change. When communication is established between inbred varieties of a plant, for example, the result is often a vigorous hybrid. On the southern beaches of England a new marsh grass, *Spartina townsendi*, is taking over. It was first noticed in 1870 and is a hybrid between the American marsh grass *Spartina alternifolia* and the European marsh grass *Spartina stricta*. It marches in solid ranks across the beaches, heedless of tradition and the establishment.

On a hill in Tuscany, bearing the Castle of Brolio, we saw barriers being breached and tension replacing the peace of long isolation. The record was being written before our eyes.

We stood before the castle and looked up at its stern battle-mented face. "Completed in the ninth century, with ramparts and a ditch around it," we had read. "In 1141 it became the property of the noble Ricasoli family," our book went on. We turned to look down across a scene interwoven of grape vines, olive trees, and wheat. The diet of Italy was growing there: wine, olive oil, and pasta. Surely there had to be tomatoes somewhere, to complete the larder.

All parts of the scene, productive, self-sufficient, combined to give a feeling of security. Changelessness, timelessness. The stronghold appearance of the castle helped, and so did the sight of three people around a tea table at its foot, and the glimpse of a young girl on a tall white horse galloping down a forest lane.

Nothing seemed out of harmony, not at the first appreciative look. But further examination revealed an area to our left that was different from the rest. A vineyard contained nothing but grape vines, no olive trees. And a newly plowed field was square instead of being, as elsewhere, a long strip between vines and olive trees.

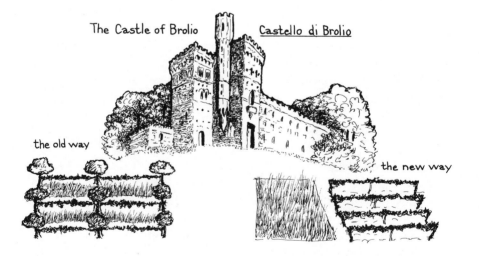

The Castle of Brolio Castello di Brolio

the old way   the new way

We stood and talked about the difference between the areas. Probably we gestured from one area to the other. Perhaps that was why the Baroness Ricosoli left the tea table and came down to us. She explained the difference to us, in English.

She spoke first of the idyllic scene, the major part of the view, with its mixed crops. The plowed strips, she explained, were areas from which the wheat had recently been harvested.

"All that," she waved a hand toward the right, and then over the hills to right and left, "all that is the old Tuscany."

She talked about the generations of peasants who had created the shapely scene of old Tuscany. They had lived on the place, sometimes well, but sometimes, when a crop failed, far from well. They needed to have the crops succeed, and sometimes sprayed, or pruned, or cultivated far into the dusk. Then they would go downhill to their small homes and their own fruit trees and vegetable patches and herb plots.

"There are some down there who still prefer to serve in the old way."

She told, on the other hand, of the sons of the peasants, who have gone, on their Vespas, down the hill to the highway and made contact with the outside world by way of radios, movies, meetings, speeches, political groups, and have come back demanding changes on the land, and in their lives.

"They demand a salary, paid on a certain day, whether the vines are sick or well, whether the rains come or not."

She told of other demands. The crops must be planted so that they can be efficiently handled by power machinery. No hoeing. No mixed crops. Long evenings, weekends, good roads for the motor bikes.

"The government backs them up, firmly. You have read, perhaps, that we have a leftist government?"

She told it all without rancor, not voicing regret, but expressing hope that the new men would find their futures better than the past in which their peasant fathers lived.

"Who is right?" She shrugged. "Who is wrong? Who is to say?"

Who knows whether the hybrid marsh grass on Britain's beaches will prove a boon or a nuisance?

We asked about a sawmill we had passed earlier. There had been impressive logs of oak and chestnut waiting. She explained that the forest on these hills had always been selectively cut; the mature trees were removed systematically, leaving space for others to mature.

We went, then, to enjoy the forest. Would the young men demand presently that sheep and goats be turned into the ferny, four-layered forest, to clean it up and make forestry easier?

On the forest floor we found a cyclamen in bloom. This wild relative of the full-bodied matronly cyclamens grown by florists was slight, and the flowers danced on naked stems. The leaves come in the springtime and die down during the summer drought, but send up their blossoms after the autumn rains. Evidence of the fat storage root, which makes possible such a sudden flowering, is recorded in its popular names: sowbread, swinebread, and panis porcinus. The distended shape of the root probably suggested its time-honored use in confinement cases. Because of the cyclamen's reputed potency in this regard, the herbalist Gerard recorded that he fenced the plants with sticks, lest some matron should chance to step over them and thus bring on a miscarriage.

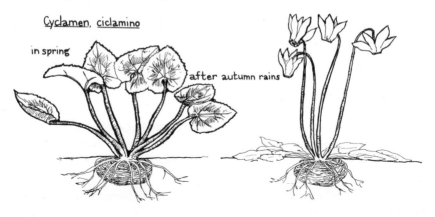

Cyclamen, ciclamino

in spring

after autumn rains

The bambinos of the new generation will probably be delivered without the benefit of the cyclamen root's powers, unless some crone from the older generation sneaks out to get it by the light of whatever phase of the moon happens to be accepted as propitious. That is not incredible. I know one big business man who habitually carries a horse chestnut in the pocket of his meticulously tailored suit to protect him from rheumatism; and *everyone* knows about four-leaf clovers.

After seeing two methods of growing grapes at Brolio, we looked at many vineyards. Some held only grapes, and had finely cultivated soil for the conservation of moisture. Virgil, in his second Georgic, told how the soil must be broken "thrice and again," and described "wheeling the steaming oxen between the vineyard rows." There were vine rows interrupted by trees other than olives. There were poplars, elms, and mulberries. The vines sometimes clambered up to the very tips of these trees, and had to be gathered with long ladders.

We saw other castled hills, many others. But they all had lost the character of islands, as they established communication with other hilltops and with the valleys. For most of them that happened long ago. The Roman *castelli* of the Alban hills became a summer retreat for the patricians of ancient Rome. The castle-topped hill of Ischia, a true island, was tied to Naples by a bridge long ago, and is thoroughly invaded by hybrid cultures.

At Brolio one might arrive almost in time to watch the curtain rising on a new landscape and a new way of life. Which way will the new life turn for security, downhill to gatherings of men from many hilltops, or uphill to the castle?

A HILL OF MARBLE

Along a road in Tuscany we came to a surprising hill. It appeared to be composed chiefly of marble, and the clean vertical face of the hill was being cut off in great chunks like a giant cheese, a cheese veined with red-brown mold.

We inspected a mill where the big blocks were being sawed into layers not much more than an inch thick and stacked on edge like so much lumber. We walked through deep marble dust and marble chips to inspect those leaning stacks that held enough travertine marble for a thousand coffee tables, or for the floors of palaces, or for curving staircases in marble halls.

Next day, in Siena, we saw an outstanding assemblage of all the colors that marble may be stained during its formation. The Cathedral of Siena, with its facade in alternate bands of light and dark marble, was a reminder of the stratifications of shell life laid down under the sea, where marble had its rough beginnings. And it recorded an evolution in architecture, just as the sequence of the rock strata beneath the sea records the evolution of life. The lower part of the facade is Romanesque; the upper parts are Gothic.

The floor of the cathedral glows with the soft colors of many marbles. They have been used to make inlaid pictures of Old Testament stories, of various sibyls, and of the emblems of Siena. Many artists, from 1372 to 1562, made the drawings and sent them to master stonecutters, who prepared the stones and fitted the pieces together over the old brick floor.

On a later day, between Pisa and Genoa, we saw from far off the face of a hill gleaming. We were approaching Monte Sagro and the famous Carrara marble, as white and shining as a lump of sugar. No wonder that geologists sometimes refer to such marble as "saccharoidal."

One of the most famous blocks of marble ever to be quarried in the Carrara district contained Michelangelo's *David*.

Cross section of Monte Sagro - at Carrara
(with hints of potentials of the four layers)

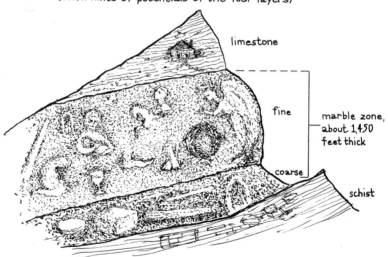

The creation of *David* could be said to have started in the Triassic Period some two hundred million years ago. It started at the bottom of a shallow sea, where abundant shell life slowly built up layers of limestone. The metamorphosis of that coarse, porous, grayish limestone came millions of years later, when the Alps were formed. In the region where the town of Carrara now lies, the former sea bottom was heaved up into great folds. The force and pressure and heat of the sharp folding metamorphosed the gray limestone. As it cooled it formed the crystalline, pellucid, homogenous, cream-colored marble called "statuary marble."

The folded mountains contained zones of schist, zones of banded limestones, and zones of coarser "architectural marble," as well as the zones of statuary marble. Some of the zones became violet-veined and mottled with red-brown streaks of iron oxide; others became green or almost black with organic impregnations.

Eventually forests covered the surfaces of the upfolded sea-bottom, and, in time, the forests were inhabited by a warlike tribe, the Apuans. The Romans subdued the Apuans in 180 B.C. and found the marble under the forests.

The Romans had learned about using marble from the Greeks. The Greeks had had their own famous "Parian marble," from the Isle of Paros in the Aegean Sea. They had built the Parthenon of it. The Romans needed a lot of marble for columns and colossal statues and triumphal arches.

One day, more than a thousand years later, quarrymen carefully lowered a splendid block of marble down to the sea. It was carried by boat to Pisa and then up the Arno to Florence. It was a column seventeen feet long.

Michelangelo ran his hands over the column. He could not know that the stuff of it had been assembled in the sea and uplifted and refined by the forces of mountain-building, but he felt that the block had a David in it. He chiseled him free.

A WALLED HILL TOWN

One tube of paint was all that I bought at that artists' supply shop. That should be, I thought, enough for sketching in Siena. (I already had paper and a brush.)

The label on the tube read *Terra di Siena, bruciata,* "earth of Siena, burnt."

I continued to the end of the narrow street, where it opened, as the main streets of Siena do, on the famous center of the town, the Piazza del Campo. At the edge of the Campo I ordered enough food to justify getting a glass of water for painting, and to provide an excuse for lingering at one of the host of small tables. They and their

Siena

attendant awnings curved around the perimeter of the great open space on which windows, balconies, buildings, people faced. The focusing fronts formed a second city wall, facing inward, within the long town wall, which has faced outward toward the sieges of many centuries.

The shell-shaped Campo conformed to a dip at the junction of the three hills of red clay that are enclosed by the city walls.

I looked across to the tall bell-tower and the Palazzo Publico with its slightly-curved facade shaped to the edge of the shell and let my eyes ride the curved window tops and angled battlements and chimneys, past the massive Palazzo Sansedoni, and back to the tower again. My tube of burnt sienna would suffice, with a bit more water for the brick of one building, or the paint on one set of shutters, and a bit less water for certain balconies. Perhaps, though, I would have been better equipped had I bought a tube of raw sienna as well, for the buildings of a yellower tinge.

I had not been working long, moving from table to table, and sitting on the edge of the Fonte Gaia, the Gay Fountain, before I realized that something more was needed—black and white. The white of my paper would do for the white marble of the cathedral, which rose beyond the red-brown roofs and walls. Black was needed for the zebralike bands of dark marble striping one building; and black, too, for the fanlike ribs of stone radiating from the center of the brick-paved shell of the Campo; and for the dark, narrow streets opening from the edge of the shell; and for the old woman who had come out to the center to sell tight bunches of rosemary and bouquets of pale wild cyclamen in rings of ferns; and for the wide robes of the priest who silently led a procession, to which no one seemed to pay the slightest attention, across the Campo; and for the

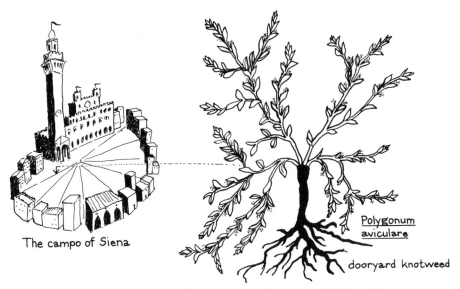

The campo of Siena

Polygonum
aviculare

dooryard knotweed

Drawn from the Greek Herbal of Dioscorides
illustrated by a Byzantine, A.D. 512

tapering banner borne high behind the priest. And suddenly more white was there—in a team of oxen drawing a heavy cart.

These, then, were certainly the colors of Siena: its own earth color (in a few shades), together with the black and white used in the town's official symbol to commemorate the black horse of Ascius and the white horse of Senius. A statue of those two sons of Remus, being suckled by a she-wolf, as were Romulus and Remus, tops a column at the Town Hall. Another legend about the black-and-white combination recounts that Senius and Ascius, when fleeing from Rome and their uncle Romulus, made burnt offerings to Diana and Apollo; white smoke rose from the altar of Diana while black smoke rose from the altar of Apollo.

Black, white, and burnt sienna. . . . Suddenly, the town started to wake up. Carts were pushed past, bearing colors of every sort in small replicas of the large silk banners used by the various divisions of the town, the *contrade*. On Siena's two great days of horse races, called the Palio, color absolutely explodes, not only on banners but in medieval costumes as well. Color dominates on balconies and in the crowds of cheering thousands. Children practice at waving and throwing banners in the game called *sbandierata*, and there is a colorful banquet day, at which the winning horse is guest of honor.

Thinking about the days of the Palio, I walked around the Campo in the direction that the pounding hoofs take. Suddenly I realized that the Campo, in fact, the entire town, was bereft of one color—

green. I had seen only one tree that day, a small, crooked one. The square itself seemed utterly stripped of plant life.

Then, at the very edge of the shell, I saw a bit of green, gray-green. It formed a diffuse, pressed mat. It was tough, but not conspicuous enough to have earned itself a scornful name like "stinkweed" or "ragweed." It was not prickly, not smelly, not poison-ous; it was simply able to endure drought and many treading feet. It survived. The same creeping plant grows year after year close to home plate on the baseball diamond at Lincoln Park in Chicago, where other immigrants from Italy, as well as those from Germany and Ireland and Boston and Mississippi, slide home. The common name of this plant is "knotgrass"; the botanical name is *Polygonum aviculare*. The species name, *aviculare*, was given to it because someone, long ago, observed that its leaves and seeds were eaten by birds.

This plant was described in the Greek *Herbal of Dioscorides*, compiled in the first century and translated in 1655. Its uses, it seems, were many:

But ye juice being drank, hath a binding refrigerating faculty. It is commodious for ye blood-spitters, & ye fluxes by the belly, & for ye sick of choler, & ye strangury. It moves ye urine also manifestly, & helps ye venomous-beast-bitten, being drank with wine, & ye circuits of agues, being taken one hour before ye fit. It stops also ye womanish flux taken as a Pessum, & it is good for ear-griefs & ye mattering of them, being dropt in. But being sodden with wine & withall taking honey, it doth excellent well for the ulcers in ye privities. But ye leaves are laid on for ye burning of ye stomach, & ye casting up of blood & for ye Herpetes, & Erysipelata, & inflammations, & wounds newly made.

I stood above the slight, gray-green mat there on the bricks of the Campo and reviewed the hazards that must have threatened it.

The seed must have germinated during the spring rains. Then the plant faced hungry birds and summer drought on the shadeless brick. Then came trucks bearing loads of clay, which was dumped on the track and firmed for the race. Then came the day of the Palio. The knotgrass might have been trodden to death under the five preliminary trial races; or it might have been wiped out by the thousands of feet of the cheering crowds; or it might have been worn out under the feet of parade horses, grooms, mace bearers, trumpeters, pages carrying laurel wreaths; or it might have been ground to dust under the pounding feet of the racehorses in their three laps around the Campo. But it survived, flat, gray-green, diffuse, unimposing.

Such conditioning in the crowded places of Europe has selected out the immigrants that became the tough weeds that have captured the beaten, worn places in America.

I found another tough plant in Siena, also decribed in the *Herbal of Dioscorides,* growing on the city gate called the Porta Romana. It grew also on top of the city wall in the wide space where the bird market was held on Sunday mornings. This one, small, flattened, and as inconspicuous as the knotgrass, is called "pellitory-of-the-wall" in England. Its genus name, *Parietaria,* is an ancient one, from the word *paries,* meaning "wall." This is the most common plant of all the walls of the walled towns of Italy. I found it growing, with a splendid view before it, on the walls of Perugia and of Assisi. The complete name *Parietaria officinalis* indicates that this plant was used by the herbalists and sold in their shops. Since an Italian botany book also lists *Parietaria judaica* and *Parietaria lusitanica* and *Parietaria cretica,* it seems, in varying forms, to be a part of many Mediterranean walls. Probably, when the "walls of Jericho came tumbling down" a *Parietaria* tumbled, too.

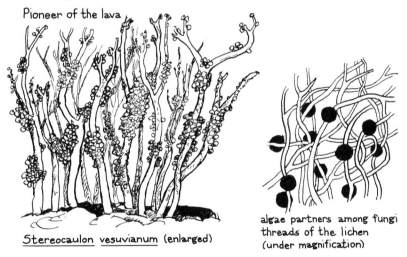

Pioneer of the lava

Stereocaulon vesuvianum (enlarged)

algae partners among fungi threads of the lichen (under magnification)

A VOLCANO

There is a certain plant, a lichen, hardly an eighth of an inch high, that has Mount Vesuvius in its name. *Stereocaulon vesuvianum* is the pioneer of pioneers, leading the stampede of life that surges forth after each eruption of the volcano.

A writhing skein of lava may hardly have cooled before a minuscule fragment of this lichen arrives on the wind. The fragment soon spreads its yellow-green incrustation on the black, scorched surface. If the lichen arrives too soon, while the lava is still hot enough to set fire to oak woods and vineyards and orchards that lie in its way, then the lichen, too, is cooked. But a later wind is sure to bring more of this living dust, with perhaps a pinch of volcanic ash that will make the first step of the pioneer that much easier.

On the slight foothold furnished by the lichen, moss spores find lodging and mosses start to carpet parts of the lava. Then follow annuals and perennials and woody plants. Before long, some hillsides glow yellow with the pea-blossom flowers of *Genista,* broom, or shine green with its spiky twigs. In time the oak trees arrive, both deciduous and evergreen oaks. Presently every rock face is draped with vines of wild grape. Then the farmers hurry back, and their vineyards and orchards start climbing the slopes once more.

These changes, of course, follow each other with varying speeds, according to whether the volcanic deposit is lava or fine-blown ash or porous tufa or clinkerlike scoria. The lava of Mount Vesuvius is recorded as being especially rapid in its decomposition. An early geologist reported that the lavas of nearby Ischia, emitted in the year 1302, were still quite barren of vegetation when the lavas of Vesuvius, from the eruption of 1631, were already covered with rich garden soil.

Looking up at those green slopes, one can have no doubt about the fertility of the lava. J. Logan Lobley, in *Mount Vesuvius,* tells that the productiveness of volcanic soils is due to the "decomposition of volcanic materials which, containing silica, alumina, magnesia, lime, potash, and iron, give the soil formed from them, with the carbon and nitrogen derived from the atmosphere, abundant materials for plant growth." He explains that granite mountains are not so quickly covered with vegetation, because granitic rock disintegrates into clay and quartz materials separately, thus producing a mass of clay from the feldspar, while "in volcanic rocks the associated materials are intimately mingled and themselves decomposable." He wrote this in 1889.

Lobley's book was preceded by many others, and succeeded by many more. Vesuvius has proven a fertile producer of books as well as of grapes, almonds, figs, olives, and peaches.

I can give here only a sampling of what men have told up through the years.

Diodorus Siculus, historian in the first century, speculated about the origin of this mountain: "The entire district . . . from the culminating point which is now called Vesuvius, [bears] many indications of having given forth fires in ancient times." And the geographer Strabo read volcanic origin in the rocks around the crater. Seneca told of an earthquake in A.D. 63 that destroyed part of Pompeii and Herculaneum.

In A.D. 79 came the great eruption that buried Pompeii and Herculaneum. For that eruption we can read an eye-witness account, written by Pliny the Younger, in an account requested by Tacitus. He recorded the death of his uncle:

On the 24th of August, about one in the afternoon, my mother desired him to observe a cloud which appeared of a very unusual size and shape. . . . he immediately arose and went out upon a rising ground from which he might get a better sight of this very uncommon appearance. A cloud, from which mountain was uncertain, at this distance (but it was found afterwards to come from Mount Vesuvius), was ascending, the appearance of which I cannot give you a more exact description than by likening it to that of a pine tree. . . . it appeared sometimes bright and sometimes dark and spotted, according as it was either more or less impregnated with earth and cinders. This phenomenon seemed to a man of such learning and research as my uncle extraordinary and worth further looking into. . . . He ordered the galleys to be put to sea, and went himself on board with an intention of assisting . . . towns which lay thickly strewn along that beautiful coast. Hastening then to the place from whence others fled with the utmost terror, he steered his course direct to the point of danger, and with so much calmness and presence of mind as to be able to make and dictate his observations. . . . He was now so close to the mountain that the cinders, which grew thicker and hotter the nearer he approached, fell into the ships, together with pumice stones, and black pieces of burning rocks: they were in danger too . . . from the vast fragments which rolled down the mountain, and obstructed all the shore. . . . the wind . . . was favourable . . . for carrying my uncle to Pomponianus, whom he found in the greatest consternation. . . . to soothe his fears by seeming unconcerned himself, he . . . sat down to supper with great cheerfulness, or at least (what is just as heroic) with every appearance of it. Meanwhile broad flames shot out in several places from Mount Vesuvius, which the darkness of the night contributed to render still brighter and clearer. . . . he retired to rest. . . . [but] he was awoke and got up. . . . They went out then, having pillows tied upon their heads with napkins; and this was their whole defence against the storm of stones which fell around them. They thought proper to go down upon the shore. . . . There my uncle, laying himself upon a sailcloth . . . called twice for water, which he drank, when immediately the flames, preceded by a strong whiff of sulphur . . . obliged him to rise. He raised himself up with the assistance of two of his servants, and instantly fell down dead; suffocated, as I conjecture, by some gross and noxious vapour.*

We can go to Pompeii and see how it sat on a rise of ground that was lava of a prehistoric eruption, and walk the streets with their chariot ruts, and see evidences of the pleasures and interests and weaknesses and courage of an active town, all abruptly ended in a morning. The vitreous, pumiceous lapilli that covered Pompeii has preserved the rich colors and the details of life and has been easy to excavate, far easier than the water-consolidated covering of Herculaneum.

In 512 Procopius recorded an eruption. He wrote: "But when the mountain bellows like an ox, soon after it casts away a large quantity of cynders, which catching a man upon the way, he hath no means to save his life."

For a long period previous to the great eruption of 1631, the crater of Vesuvius was recorded to contain so much vegetation that it became the resort of wild boars.

In 1767, according to Sir William Hamilton, a British archaeologist and diplomat:

The concussion of the air was so violent, that in the king's palace many windows and doors flew open. . . . The mob also set fire to the Cardinal Archbishop's gate, because he refused to bring out the relics of Saint Januarius. . . . In the midst of these horrors, the mob, growing tumultuous and impatient, obliged the cardinal to bring out the head of St. Januarius, and go with it . . . towards Vesuvius; and it is well attested here, that the eruption ceased the moment the saint came within sight of the mountain.

In 1906 came another great eruption, of which Professor Giuseppe de Lorenze gave an exact account of each day's disasters,

* From *Letters of Pliny*, translated by William Melmth, revised by F. C. T. Bosanquet.

from April 4 to April 10. He told how the flowing lava would sometimes singe the tree trunks in an orchard, while leaving unburned
leaves and blossoms—a "gay canopy over streams of smoking lava."

There were many other eruptions besides these recorded ones.
There will, no doubt, be many more. But fertility will be the recom-
pense. In 1869 Giuseppe Antonio Pasquale demonstrated the effects
of soil on vegetation by drawing up a list of the flora of Vesuvius to
compare with a list of the flora of Capri—volcanic versus calcareous. He found that Vesuvius had twenty-five genera unknown in
Capri.

When the volcano erupts again, and again covers the life with
lava, we can be certain that *Stereocaulon vesuvianum*, the little
yellow-green lichen, will head the recovery, and that other life will
follow.

The Valleys of Italy

≥ 2

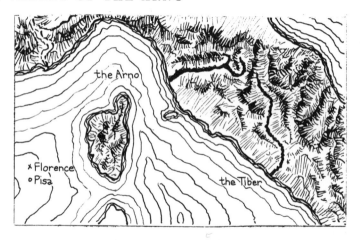

DANTE CALLED the Arno *la maledetta e sventurate fossa,* "the cursed and unlucky ditch." There are many people who would agree.

The trouble with the Arno is simply that it is a born sculptor in a land of born sculptors. The Italian landscape naturally tends to raise sculptors, major and minor. How could it not? There is all that cooperative marble inviting someone to shape it into nymphs and giants, fountains, columns, balustrades, pavements. There are all those steep hills waiting to be terraced, and mountains of stone available for the job. There are all those springs to be honored by the raising of temples. There is all that water coming down the mountains to be guided through pipes and squirted from the mouths

106

of fish and the breasts of mammals. There are growing things, too, amenable to tonsoring: grape vines, olive trees, ilex. And there are trees shaped so formally by nature that they are acceptable among the artifacts: the cypress, the umbrella pine.

The Arno has not cooperated with such shaping. It is a shaper. From its handsomely fashioned stone coffin it rises alive, wielding a spirited chisel to sculpt the land. All the rivers making the steep swift run from the mountains of Italy's boot down to the sea are full of spirit, especially those that flow down the rainy, west-facing side of the country; the streams on the east, the "rain-shadow side," are somewhat less vigorous. But of all the rivers, on either side of the boot, the Arno has produced the most spectacular effects on the landscape.

It certainly didn't look capable of anything when we saw it first near Pisa barely seven miles from its mouth on the Ligurian Sea. In that city we had seen a famous lamp hanging like a pendulum from a cathedral ceiling; it still swings as dependably as if Galileo had never recanted. We saw, too, the font where Enrico Fermi had been baptized. The Arno there is a sluggish river, experiencing old age. It has done one thing, though. On its trip down to the sea it has brought along over the years enough sediment to push its navigable entry further and further away from the town. Pisa, once a great seaport, lost its harbor long ago.

As we set out upstream from Pisa to follow the wide gorge between the hills, we hardly looked at the river itself, because its valley was such a good vantage point for seeing hillsides of olives and grapes and for seeing how the old towns had clung to the hilltops, while the younger ones and the additions to the old ones had come downhill, often choosing spots right on the river. The time for walling out the enemy had passed, and the danger of malaria from the marshes along the river could now be faced without running uphill. (It is recorded that Dante died of marsh fever.) We watched a family picking a few last clusters of grapes in the low afternoon light, laying the perfect bunches carefully on trays and carrying the trays to their cart. The farmer, seeing us down there on the roadside, selected one great bunch and held it high, turning it so that it looked red-gold in the sunset.

From that perfection of form we turned to look down at the Arno. Its shores at that place between Pisa and Florence were covered with an expanse of wading plants, most of which were the reed *Phragmites communis.* At the edge of one wide stretch of marsh, we followed the path down toward the river that some animal had used. The mud was caked and cracked under our feet, almost to the edge of the water. The seed heads brushed our faces as we pushed aside the closely ranked stems.

The reed
<u>Phragmites communis</u>

Wading plants? These where we stood dry-shod? But we had come before the end of the summer drought. Had we been standing there after the winter rains started, we should have been deep in mud. And when the summer drought came again, we should have been plastered with mud as far up as the reeds around us were plastered with the mud of the previous winter's rains.

We were walking on the edge of the flood plain. This is the natural safety valve of any river, especially necessary to a young one, not yet far from its mountain origins. Call it what you will, elbow room, an extra notch in the belt, it is an important element in the way a river comes to terms with its route from the mountains to the sea.

And certainly the massed community of reeds was a functional part of the flood plain. Whenever the flood waters boil up around these stems their violence is somewhat subdued; and when the slowed-down waters retreat the reeds strain out some of their burden.

We stood at the edge of the river and eavesdropped on the community gossip, remembering a legend. King Midas, the story goes, had offended Apollo by declaring that the reed pipes of Pan made better music than Apollo's lyre. As punishment Apollo changed King Midas's ears into those of an ass. Although the king strove to keep his deformity a secret, his barber discovered it. Needing to tell someone but fearing the king's wrath, he dug a hole in a marsh, whispered into it, "King Midas has ass's ears," and filled in the hole. However, some reeds grew in that spot. When the wind stirred them they whispered the buried words, and the rumor has spread from there up and down the riversides of the world. In America I eavesdropped on one community of *Phragmites,* which the Army Corps of Engineers, despite the advice of the ecologists, was approaching with its bulldozers, ready to wipe out flood plains and straighten and corset the river. The gossip that the American reeds were whispering seemed to be, "Engineers have ass's ears," but folklorists and other gatherers of voice-borne legends know how likely such stories are to undergo changes from place to place, and over the passing years.

We also saw *Phragmites* when we got to Florence, but we heard no whispers there. The reed must once have been a prominent member of the native community fringing the lake basin now occupied by the city. This basin had furnished a safety valve for the Arno. Now it was filled with the sounds of Vespas, Lambrettas, Fiats, Fords, Volkswagens, and the river was straight-jacketed in the hard-paved Lungarno, which seemed far out of proportion to the puny stream that it bounded.

We found a small table at a sidewalk cafe on the edge of the Piazza della Signoria, but we could not even see across the Piazza to the David and the Neptune fountain on the other side. We saw instead a thousand parked cars. A pair of white banners was borne past, bearing the painted image of the red lily of Florence. We followed the flags to the end of the Piazza—and there we saw the reeds. They looked as reeds have always looked, with their hollow stems and stony joints. But now no wind could bend those reeds in unison, because they had been brought to the city from elsewhere and had been woven into wide mats; because they had been fastened firmly in place to cover the facade of a building where construction was in progress. The reeds, now rootless and dry, were being used because the building faced the assembled perfections of form which surrounded the Piazza della Signoria at the heart of the city. They protected passersby from ugliness and from dropping tools and stones.

It was interesting to see *Phragmites* back at its old stand. But it was all quite different now in the ancient lake basin. No bitterns boomed there; no moor hens cackled; no marsh hawks flew, gliding low and pouncing; no wild boars, plump on the chestnuts and beech nuts of nearby forests, made narrow paths in the mud. There were only cars.

The Florence safety valve is only one of many. As one goes upstream he encounters other flood plains and still other lake basins. The basin just above forms a flat rich plain now, where cereals and vineyards thrive at the foot of the terraces rising to Arezzo, and above that is the highest basin, Casentino, where the Arno is still reed-fringed for long stretches. The origin of the river is on Mt. Falterona, high in the Apennines, where it rises not far from the source of the Tiber. Along the ridge separating the two rivers, Saint Francis, Dante records, received the stigmata:

> There he received from Christ, upon the bare ridge
> between the Tiber and the Arno, that last seal,
> which two years long his body lived to wear.
> —*The Divine Comedy*

The plain of Florence, as this flat area is sometimes called, has witnessed many changes, some made by nature and some by man. Were we to reconstruct the succession of changes, basing our assumptions on the natural succession evident in the present lakes of northern Italy, and, of course, on historical records, we should read the story as follows:

The first plant life in the waters of the lake was microscopic— minute, free-floating plankton, no doubt.

Soon there came colonies of pondweeds (*Potamogeton* of various kinds), and eel grass (*Vallisneria*), all submerged plants, attached to the floor of the lake.

As the accumulated dead plant parts and the mud deposited

around their bases built up the margin of the lake, the pondweed association retreated to deeper water, and its place was taken by water lilies. These plants were rooted on the bottom and floated their leaves on the surface of the lake at the end of flexible hauser-like stems.

Then, as the water lilies moved out onto the corpses of the pondweed society, and the pondweeds invaded deeper water, there came behind the water lilies the community of wading plants, bullrushes first, and then reeds. On the drier side of the reeds there grew sedges and grass. Sometimes willow and alders crowded forward, or the forest from the surrounding hills took over new areas as soon as they were built up high and dry enough.

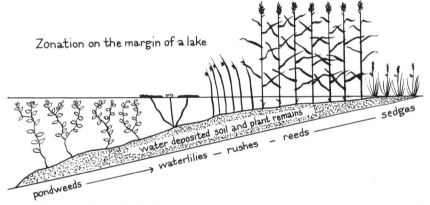

Zonation on the margin of a lake

water deposited soil and plant remains

pondweeds

waterlilies — rushes — reeds — sedges

And up in those hills the Etruscans, as they built their tombs and their towns, looked down on this placid wide lake, which alternately grew and shrank with the changing seasons; today a tourist may look down from the town of Fiesole, once an Etruscan city, for a famous view of the city of Florence.

By the time Julius Caesar's veteran centurions arrived to colonize the area, which had been awarded them, much of the former lake basin had become a plain, across which, in the summer droughts, the Arno divided into several wandering streams. When the winter rains came, however, the swollen river spread across as much of the plain as it needed. In the first century A.D. the Romans built a bridge across the Arnus, as they called the river, at a point close to its emergence from the mountains. Their city, Florentia, was set square with the points of the compass and surrounded with a stout brick wall. A network of straight roads divided it into forty-eight rectangles. Because of danger from floods Florentia was set back some distance from the river.

In the second century, according to Tacitus, the Arnus became the subject for discussion in the Roman Senate. The constant flooding of the Tiber was a menace to Rome, and because the sources of the two rivers were so close to each other in the Apennines, it was suggested that one tributary to the Tiber, the River Clanis, be diverted into the Arno. The Arno, opponents argued, was already subject to flooding.

It was true that the floods of the Arno, as well as those of the Tiber, were gradually increasing. The problem was partly the sheep; more and more of them were being grazed on the slopes, stripping them bare. And people were cutting down the forests. Rain could no longer be intercepted by the trees of the forest canopy. No longer could it drip gradually from layer to layer of undergrowth until it sank softly into the humus, to be held in its spongy mass and released slowly. Rain now meant rapid runoff.

After the Romans left the buildings of the city, the baths, temples, aqueducts, and theaters gradually crumbled, and, in time, crops were being grown where marble pavement had once lain. The reeds probably found some places to reestablish themselves where Roman baths had been, and the Arno passed through its annual rhythm of contraction and growth without causing much of a stir.

The site could not long lie fallow. Its position on the way to Rome, near several mountain passes, and its flatness and ample water supply invited development. The city reemerged with a new government, strong ruling classes, and artisans to furbish their grandeur. The population grew too. In about 1172 a new wall was built, enclosing an area three times that of the Roman Florentia. The Arno lay within that second wall.

Since the river was now urbanized, it began to receive a rich assortment of man-made debris. The butchers, who occupied the shops on the great ancient bridge across the river, the Ponte Vecchio, before they were ousted in favor of the silversmiths, discarded their offal into it. The Arno also carried away the city's sewage and garbage, although rarely fast enough to keep down the stench in the summer heat. Some wealthy citizens actually built private canals to empty into the river. Those people, of course, escaped the smell by taking their families to the higher areas, where they built impressive villas and looked down upon the growing glories of Florence. Eventually the villas advanced far up into the hills, their rows of lemon and orange and olive trees and their vineyards finally replacing more and more of the surrounding forests.

As the acreage of roofs and marble stairs and domes and pavements was increased and the acreage of the forest shrank, there were fewer and fewer places where raindrops could enter the soil. The run-off that followed a rainstorm became more and more rapid.

In 1304 the river received a bridge packed with people. Crowds had gathered to watch scenes from Hell presented on floats that passed under the bridge. It had been advertised that the entertainment would include suffering souls and hellfire and punishments of the damned. Many were drowned.

In 1327 a third wall was completed around the city. It was 40 feet high, 6 feet thick, and 5 miles long. It had to be stout to withstand attack. That was a time of constant warfare. It was about then that Dante made his unhappy observation about the Arno. (Having now been confined in a ditch, the river was having occasional tantrums.)

In the great flood of 1333 the rain-swollen Arno carried away the Ponte Vecchio itself, as well as all the other bridges of Florence. (The German bombardments of 1944 also brought down the bridges of the Arno—except for the Ponte Vecchio, which held this time.)

In the hills above the villas there was still good hunting with falcons, and wild boars still throve. But down in the town the stench prevailed, garbage floated in the river, piled high in the streets and public piazzas, and rats abounded. In 1342, the plague took two-thirds of the population of the city.

Floods began to be chronic. Dams were built upstream, and river channels were deepened. It did no substantial good. In the fifteenth century Leonardo da Vinci wrote in one of his notebooks, "Among irremediable and destructive terrors the inundations caused by impetuous rivers ought to be set before every other terrifying source of injury."

In 1557 came one of the worst floods up to that time. Others followed at intervals. There was an especially bad one in 1844. Waters roared through the streets, carrying away many treasures, and leaving behind a thick deposit of mud on marble and stone and canvas.

On November 4, 1966, the Arno advanced again on Florence. The wall of water struck at dawn; and this time the river carried not only mud and debris, but a modern contribution. The floods had flushed out the city's oil tanks. As the black greasy mixture churned along, it bore uprooted trees, sewage, and carcasses. Unfortunately, the Ponte Vecchio held firm, and the river heaped up its freight behind the famous bridge until it became a dam. Before long the blocked-up river ran over and into the streets of the city.

The old lake basin had waves once more.

When the waters finally receded people from all over the world cooperated in trying to restore Florence's blackened glories. As they worked in the greasy mud they argued about the reason for the disaster. Everyone knew that the rainfall had been excessive; on November third and fourth, nineteen inches of rain had fallen. Various suggestions were made. The channel was not deep enough; there were too few dams in the river above Florence; some dam had been opened too soon—or too late. Some said that the trouble was caused when the Sieve River, higher up in the hills, had poured its water into the Arno. They repeated an old couplet,

> L'Arno non cresce,
> Se la Sieve non mesce.
>
> (The Arno does not rise up,
> Unless the Sieve fills its cup.)

Actually the Arno had not done anything foreign to its nature, and its past, nothing that it cannot still do in its uncaged youth higher up in the Apennines; nothing that it cannot still do in its old age, between Florence and Pisa; nothing that it will not do again and again in the former lake basin which is now a city.

Many suggestions have been made to tame the river. Most of them call for better and more numerous dams, and deeper channels.

Here is one suggestion for a program that would furnish safety valves, and might perhaps yield some additional benefits. That piazza that lay before us when we sat at a table at an outdoor eating place, that famous piazza that had become a jammed parking place, might be scooped out into an amphitheatre, in good Roman tradition, and paved with marble in concentric tiers, to form a place for performances, exhibits, market stalls. All through the tourist season it would serve, and then, when the winter rains were due, its broad gate towards the Arno would be opened. The river could use the amphitheatre for a flood plain, creating an interesting pool to reflect domes and towers and statues. There would be other amphitheatres in the city, with different shapes and uses, scalloping the four miles of river within the city. One of them might be reminiscent of the catacombs instead of the amphitheatres. That one would hold automobiles and motorbikes during the dry season, river during the wet. Florence would undoubtedly smell and sound better. And there would be new work for the new generation of sculptors. They might even carve a frieze of *Phragmites* on the uppermost riser of the Piazza della Signoria.

Not a workable plan? If so, it can simply take its place with all the other plans that have not worked. At least it has the virtue of being an understanding gesture towards a river that has always refused to be an artifact.

THE VALLEY OF THE PO

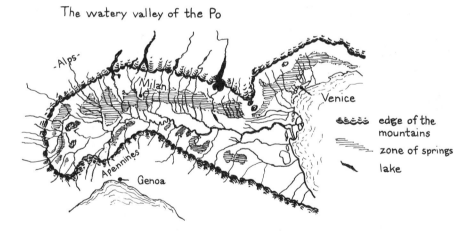

The watery valley of the Po

Americans on vacation seldom choose to visit the breadbasket landscapes. We rush through or fly over Iowa on our way to the Rocky Mountains; we pass over the Po valley on our way to Switzerland. We bypass the wide reaches of the floodplain of the Mississippi to reach the charm of old New Orleans at the end of its delta; and we hurry through the wide floodplain of the Po and other streams to reach the edge of the delta where Venice wades.

Were we to tarry for a longer look, whether in the Mississippi valley or the Po valley, we could hardly help noticing in passing that the flat scene is dominated by two kinds of trees, willows and poplars, poplars, poplars. These are the quick-growing trees that tolerate water around their roots, and do not tolerate shade.

The Po valley is a place of poplars. Three kinds are there. First, there is the black poplar, *Populus nigra* (*il pioppo nero*), the one that most resembles the American native cottonwood. Then there is the white poplar, or silver-leaved poplar, *Populus alba* (*il pioppo bianco*), which has naturalized so vigorously that its sprouts fill many an American vacant lot, often threatening to hide the messages on the billboards. The third poplar, perhaps the one best

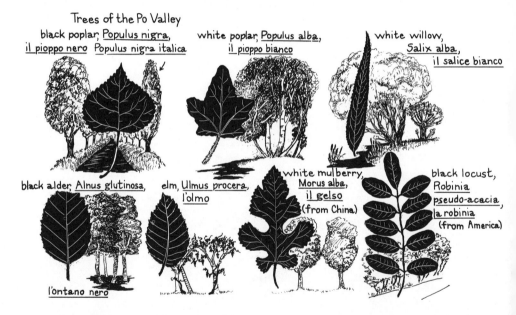

Trees of the Po Valley

black poplar, Populus nigra, il pioppo nero Populus nigra italica

white poplar, Populus alba, il pioppo bianco

white willow, Salix alba, il salice bianco

black alder, Alnus glutinosa, l'ontano nero

elm, Ulmus procera, l'olmo

white mulberry, Morus alba, il gelso (from China)

black locust, Robinia pseudo-acacia, la robinia (from America)

known in American suburbs, is the Lombardy poplar. It is mutation of the black poplar, with a narrow form and short, uplifted branches.

The willows are chiefly the white willow, *Salix alba* (*il salice bianco*), and the black willow, *Salix nigra* (*il salice nero*). Of less prominence are the elms, *Ulmus procera* (*l'olmo*), and European alder, *Alnus glutinosa* (*l'ontano nero*). And there are many rows of mulberry trees, *Morus alba* (*il gelso*), a native of China, raised as pasture for silkworms. A thorny introduction from America, the black locust, *Robinia pseudoacacia* (*la robinia*), has become thoroughly naturalized.

The trees of the Po valley are often uniquely garlanded. They are used as living arbors for grape vines. Virgil wrote of "the marriage" of the elm and the vine.

The two leading trees of the valley, of course, have their origins explained by legend. Of the black poplar the story is told that the Heliades, sisters of Phaëton, wild driver of the chariot of the Sun, mourned at his grave beside the river Po. For days they kept disconsolate, exhausting vigil, and when they decided to lie down and rest, found that they were rooted to the ground. The gods, pitying their grief, it is said, had changed them into poplar trees. Ovid wrote,

> Each nymph in wild affliction, as she grieves,
> Would rend her hair, but fills her hands with leaves. . . .
>
> And now their legs, and breasts, and bodies stood
> Crusted with bark and hardening into wood. . . .
>
> The new-made trees in tears of amber run,
> Which hardened into value by the sun. . . .

We unsympathetically examined the amber tears on one of the trees.

The white poplar was dedicated to Hercules, who often wore a crown of poplar leaves. As he returned from Hades one day, he found that the outer side of the leaves was blackened by the smoke of the infernal regions and the inner side was blanched white by sweat from his brow. We inspected a leaf, dark green and shining above, and white and feltlike beneath, and compared the mythological explanation to the botanical. Botanists say that the smooth upper surface of the leaf furnishes an impervious transparent coating for the dark green chlorophyll, allowing the sun's rays to be absorbed but providing no exits for moisture. The exits and entrances, for moisture and gases, are sunk in the white flannel beneath. (Perhaps the two stories are not so basically different after all—fire above and sweat beneath in both of them.)

The Po valley is a water-built landscape. Water laid it down, and is laying down more every day. It is said to be advancing into the

Adriatic at the rate of about thirty feet a year. The valley started as a deep downfold between two steep upfolds of the Alps and the Apennines. Rivers hurtling down the mountainsides brought a lot of mountain with them, and dropped it into the downfold.

During the great ice ages glaciers crept down the face of the Alps. As the glaciers retreated, they left at the foot of the mountains a belt of moraines, and a broad belt of loose, gravelly outwash plain. The moraines held back water flowing down the Alps, and formed lakes along the northern margin of the valley. The outwash plains let water seep so rapidly down through the gravel that this part of the Po valley became dry. But the water emerged at the lower edge of the gravel in the form of many springs, and flowed to join the many streams tributary to the Po on its soggy delta.

Cross section of the Po Valley (not drawn to scale)

Alps

moraine

springs

Apennines

outwash
plain

lake

levees

dry

wet

Po

We traveled for a while on the floodplain, occasionally turning up onto the levees of the Po, where we sometimes found ourselves above the level of the houses. We saw rice fields on the most watery stretches; and maize, wheat, alfalfa, and hay, and, on the less watery stretches, cattle. Always there was the network of canals, and of poplar trees.

Not far from the rice paddies we ate the gruel-like dish called *polenta,* which is characteristic of the Po valley. Actually it wasn't quite as good as the ripe wheat grains that we had tasted from the edge of a field, but we ate it in the charm of the arcaded square of Vigevano. This town is at the edge of the outwash plain, where the springs emerge. One of the most famous of the springs emerges near Lake Como. It was described by Pliny the Younger during the reign of the Emperor Trajan, and it still ebbs and flows as he described it then, and it still gives the cold mountain water that he extolled.

We came to Lake Maggiore, and crossed it. Many tongues were being spoken on the boat, and many, many more were being spoken by the plants of the estates along the shore. Eucalyptus was there, and palms, magnolias, purple beech, flowering dogwood, yuccas, cactus, rhododendron, azaleas, redwood, and many more. Instead of landscape we were looking at landscaping, done expensively—and that is to say, in any country, done with plants from other countries.

The Structure of the Landscape
  il monte—mountain, or hill
  la valle—valley
  la pianura—plain
  le rupi—rocks
    le rupi calcaree—calcareous rocks
    le rupi silicee—siliceous rocks
    il marmo—marble
  il lago—lake
    le rive dei laghi—the shores of the lakes
  le torbiere—bogs
  i fontanili—springs

The Natural Vegetation
  la vegetazione palustre e acquatica—the vegetation of swamp and water
  la vegetazione lavica e vulcanica—the vegetation of lava and volcano
  le foreste—the forests, woods
  i boschi—the forests, the woods
    le foreste caducifoglie—deciduous forests
      lo querceto—oak forest
      il castagneto—chestnut forest
      la faggeta—beech forest
    la foresta sempreverde—evergreen forest
    la pineta—pine forest
      le pinete litoranee—pine forests of the coast
    il sottobosco—forest floor

The Man-Made Landscape
  la macchia—thicket, resulting from overgrazing
  la gariga—thorn-scrub, resulting from overgrazing
  le praterie—meadows
  i pascoli—pastures

la vigna—vineyard
i cereali—grain
i parchi e i giardini—parks and gardens
il muro—wall

TO READ BEFORE READING THE LANDSCAPE

OF ITALY

Geography of the Mediterranean Region by Ellen Churchill Semple (Henry Holt & Co., New York, 1931). Requires chewing, but it is prepared by a master cook and is well-savored with assorted herbs and spices of legend, custom, history. It can be found in most college libraries, and is worth the hunt.

Environment and Nation by Griffith Taylor (University of Chicago Press, Chicago, 1936). If you have time, read it all, but at least inspect the "mantle maps" and their explanations.

La Flora, Conosci L'Italia, Vol. II (Touring Club Italiano, Milano, 1958). This book is a real surprise. I have never seen anything produced at such a high level of intelligence and literacy for the tourists of any country. The material is chiefly ecological, with exquisite cross sections of vegetation, showing zonation, succession, distribution, and associations. These are done in line drawings. In addition there are many pages of photographs, both black-and-white and colored. The book is in Italian, but clear drawings and Latin names make it usable.

The Love of Nature Among the Romans by Sir Archibald Geikie (John Murray, London, 1912). From their own writings, the author builds a warm picture of the Romans.

The Outdoor Life of Greek and Roman Poets by Countess Evelyn Martinengo-Cesaresco (Macmillan, London, 1911). "This book grew out of my own life south of the Alps. I have walked with Virgil in his fields and listened with Theocritus to Sicilian folk-songs." This book makes a friendly preparation for Italy.

Poets in a Landscape by Gilbert Highet (Knopf, New York, 1957). Highet says, "The translations are my own. They are all, as nearly as possible, in the exact metre of the original."

The Path to Rome by Hilaire Belloc (Putnam, New York, 1936). Belloc made his own sketches. Under the first one he writes, ". . . as to what may be in this book, do not feel timid or hesitate to enter. There are more mountains than mole-hills. . . ."

Arbres by Walter Rytz, one of the colorful small books published by Petits Atlas Payot (Lausanne, n.d.). An excellent help to identification, with a cross section of tree zones, from Norway down to Corsica, crossing Alps and Apennines, in French.

Man in the Landscape by Paul Shepard (Knopf, New York, 1967). The author delights in pursuing the effects of pastorality on man and his landscape. Read especially "A Sense of Place," pp. 49 to 54; and "The Image of the Garden," pp. 71–80.

Great Rivers of Europe by several authors (Weidenfeld and Nicolson, London, 1966). The chapter entitled "The Po" by H. V. Morton deals with man's uses of the river in the past and suggests changes in the future because of new hydroelectric systems and the discovery of deposits of methane gas in the area.

Switzerland

The Shaping of the Swiss Alps

≫ 1

N ow IT is a peaceful sanctuary, but the beginning of its story is violence.

The period of violence started slowly and gently enough, with a sort of ruffling of the layers of bedrock, chiefly limestone. It was as if the earth's fabric were being firmly pushed from the south by a giant hand. The ruffling increased until the rock was pushed into folds that were deep and high. The folds leaned toward the north and became overfolds. Then a pause. And then the thrust started again, pushing a second series of overfolding layers over the first. During all this time there was inevitable violence within the folds of rock: fracturing, compression, the grinding of one rock face against another, displacement that sometimes left older strata above younger ones, and crumbling. Finally the Alpine Storm, or Alpine Upheaval, as all this activity is called, had raised the Alps to their greatest height.

What caused the upheaval? A geography teacher I remember explained mountains by holding up two apples, a fresh one in one hand and a baked one in the other. The baked one, which had cooled inside so that its skin no longer fitted, represented the Earth; the wrinkles were its mountains. But that baked apple was long ago consigned to the garbage pail. Men got other theories.

A German geologist, Hans Cloos, wrote: "What appears to be the pride of mountains actually is the result of weakness and flight. The mountain's majesty is mere facade, a quality borrowed from the unjustly despised but actually stronger lowlands before and be-

The Alpine upheaval
Cross section showing schematically the overfolds of rock

North ←——→ South

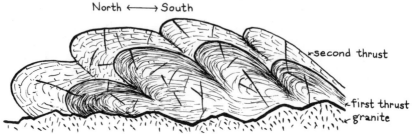

hind." He pointed to where the true strength lies, in those heavy compact masses of basaltic rock at the bottom of the ocean troughs. As evidence of weakness of fiber, he used the long mountain ranges marking the western margin of North and South America. They had been pinched up, he said, like a layer of fat between a strong forefinger and thumb.

Another German geologist, Alfred Wegener, asked us to look farther back to a time when, he maintained, there was only a single land mass, which he called Gondwanaland. It occupied about a third of the surface of the globe. Gradually it split into smaller land masses, which slowly separated and drifted apart and became the continents. As one of his many pieces of evidence Wegener pointed to the neat way in which the outline of the east coast of South America fits the outline of the west coast of Africa. According to Wegener's theory the continent of Africa drifting toward the continent of Europe furnished the thrust that caused the folding of the Alps.

Geologists listened; many were convinced for a time, then doubts set in, and now the doubters themselves are not so sure.

Geologists have turned toward new procedures and new tools for investigation. They go out to explore the bottom of the sea; they plot the evident changes in direction of geomagnetic fields and check the gravity pull of certain mountain masses as compared with sea-bottom pull; they take seismographic records of earthquake waves and use sonic equipment to provide new pictures of the ocean floor. It seems that Wegener's theory of continental drift has been retrieved, and is being strengthened, amended, improved.

Now we may visualize Europe drifting toward Africa, which ocean-bottom investigation shows to have remained more stable. In imagination we may see how the rocks rose like the waves before the prow of an advancing vessel, rose high until they curved over each other. But it is well to listen to the geologists who say that there is still more to be learned about sea-floor spreading and the earth's changing magnetic field. We may be on the brink of yet another theory.

Eroding tops and filling valleys

As soon as the upheaval stopped, the downgrading began. Erosion worked on the upfolds, and the eroded material was deposited in the downfolds, which the main rivers follow and where the Swiss people make their homes. At some points erosion removed layers of younger sea-floor rocks, exposing the older, harder granite and leaving such jagged, crystalline peaks as Mont Blanc.

Younger and softer rocks have been eroded away exposing the granite peaks of Mont Blanc

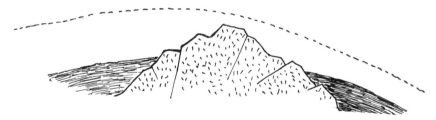

The ice ages brought glaciers, which filled the river valleys and gouged out older V-shaped valleys until they became broader, deeper, U-shaped valleys, such as the Lauterbrunnen valley. Mountain tributaries now tumble over the high precipitous edges of the valleys and form waterfalls, which provide light and power. At certain points the ice cut more deeply or left deposits, moraines that dammed the drainage. These places are the sites for Swiss lakes. The well-known shape of the Matterhorn was sculptured by mountain-side glaciers.

and carved out
the Matterhorn.

Glaciers
gouged out the
straight-walled
Lauterbrunnen valley

The shaping of the Alps, by both upheaval and downgrading, has left a tall landscape fortuitously situated where the Germanic world, the Latin world, the Greek world, and the Slavic world can reach out to touch—but not to mix. This landscape of pockets and shelves and sheltered slits and constricted entrances has furnished refuges for the ideas of such men as Erasmus, Calvin, Voltaire, Nietzsche; for such unique plants as the soldanella and the hirsute rhododendron; for such creatures as the citril finch and the alpine marmot; for the preservation of that last living shred of the Roman language, called Romansch; for numbered bank accounts; for the International Red Cross and the Geneva Accord.

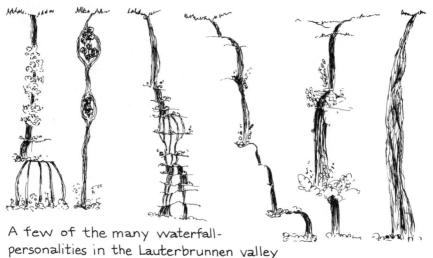

A few of the many waterfall-
personalities in the Lauterbrunnen valley

An Alpine Descent

2

WE BOARDED the funicular at the top of the Gornergrat for its return trip down the mountain to Zermatt, and, we agreed, just as soon as we saw the first patches of open ground, we would get off and continue the descent by foot.

I, for one, had had enough of the boundless, lifeless white, gashed by brittle blue.

"This can't be what men climb mountains for," said an earnest stranger, unique because he was neither using a camera nor posing for one.

"Maybe it would be different if we had come up straining, with crampons and pitons and ropes, instead of sitting," said another fellow, squinting at a light meter.

Everyone talked about mountain climbers there, where the Matterhorn climbs so much of the sky. Every day down in Zermatt we passed the big house marked with the names of the Taugwalders, guides, father and son, who went with the British mountaineer Edward Whymper on his eighth attempt to climb the Matterhorn. A party of seven able men left Zermatt to make that attempt. Throughout the day the excited crowds waited. A flapping shirt hoisted on a tent pole was seen up on the summit, catching the afternoon sun. But at evening there were only three returning conquerors of the Matterhorn—Whymper and the Taugwalders—who brought with them a tragic story of a stumble, a broken rope, and the loss of four lives on the way down after the victory.

Why do men climb mountains? A good question, but I was

equally interested in another kind of mountain climber. Why do plants climb mountains?

Once men accomplish their feat they come down from the heights. But plants stay. Unlike men, they cannot unwrap their high memories when they are old, or when they sit by the fire, or as they fall asleep. They stay there on the cold heights—that they have chosen? that only they can tolerate? that alone give them a chance? Which?

There were, however, no plants at all to be seen at the top of the Gornergrat, not on that June eighteenth at any rate. Nor were there any to be detected at the first stop on the way down, as we squinted out into the white glare.

But by the second stop we had seen promising brown patches and were ready at the door of the funicular. We stepped out on a little meadow with bent brown grasses, too lifeless to rise, even now that the icy weight had at last been lifted. It was much too soon to look for flowers here. The ground was not yet out from under the ice long enough for the sun to warm it. We agreed to start down, watching for the first sign of bloom as we went. (We could see the footpath, over away from the railroad, but close enough so that we could easily find our way back to a station whenever daylight or energy failed. This is one of the welcome provisions for hikers that the Alps so pleasantly offer.)

I hesitated for a moment and turned to inspect the meadow again. My eyes raked the inert brown, back and forth, for any sign of life. Nothing. Unless . . . possibly that snow-filled hollow up there below the slope had a faint warmth at its edge. I crossed the meadow and knelt.

I recognized the flower from pictures in Swiss books. Soldanella! Soldanella of the snow pockets!

A stem—blood-red, translucent (it looked as if one's fingers might be able to feel a pulse beat there)—raised a bell-shaped flower with deeply cleft petals of warm ice, an icicle in sunset.

Another soldanella was just emerging from under the snowbank, wearing a topknot of snow attached to a train of snow, which widened to join the snow around. In form it looked like a bridal train, but not in whiteness. It was dingy, and that was important. When the snow melted the dinginess would add its bit to whatever slight deposit of soil had been left in the snow pocket by the tiny streamlets of meltwater.

I brushed away the cap and train to see the soldanella straighten itself. Then I noticed the two more soldanellas there, under the snow. It seemed as though they had been waiting for someone to come and free them. The odds were against that. Certainly the single hiker who passed us on the trail that day would never have spied them; he had hardly broken the rhythm of his stout boots, impressive calves, and swinging cane to bid us "Grüs Gott!"

The leaves at the base of each stalk were surprisingly dark green. Even through the snow they had been collecting enough sun energy to give the flowers a boost. And the snow itself was being softened because the darker color of the soil that had collected in the snow pocket absorbed the spring sunshine.

But why such a hurry? Why not wait until the snow melts off? True, the days of high summer are few and short, but it doesn't take long to bloom, especially as the flower buds are already finished packages, needing only to be unwrapped and unfurled.

No, it doesn't take long for buds to bloom. But last summer's leaves had used last summer's sun to package the flower buds, and this summer's plants will need every bit of available sunlight for next year's flowers. So speed is essential. Plants that took too much time were eliminated long ago. The survivors are the progeny of the hurriers.

Already the flower that I had seen first was in full costume for its brief role in this capsule drama of summer. Its red-tipped stigma extended far out beyond the bell of its petals, in working position to receive pollen from the hairy body of an incoming insect. Perhaps it would wait unvisited until it withered. Or perhaps a windless, sunny hour might bring an insect bearing pollen grains from another soldanella. In that event the plant would have to work quickly, to package seeds as well as next year's flowers and to build a power reserve in roots and stems and leaves—all this in a few summer days that, even now, would probably hold hints of winter within them.

It is not surprising that the soldanella should be the flower chosen for the colorful wrappers of Swiss chocolate bars. It belongs to the Alps, and to no place else.

In the Tertiary Period there were no Alps, and no soldanellas like this one. Then the tenure of the warm, ferny forest was disturbed by a slow heaving, shifting, folding of the earth's crust. As the Alps rose and shrugged under them, many ancestors of the soldanella must have been eliminated by the new conditions of exposure and cold.

But this one—perhaps a chance variation that would have suffered swift extinction in the blue-green shade of the Tertiary forest—this one survived. The cold, the altitude, and the brief duration of summer actually made its survival possible, because they eliminated competitors for sunlight and soil. It could tolerate the mountain conditions, but it could not tolerate shade and crowding. So here it rears its head against the snow, every spring, on the mountains that tried its relatives and found them wanting.

Soldanella of the snow pockets

I stood up from a last inspection of soldanella, took a few steps, and knelt again above a swirl of deep-blue flowers. An inch or two high they were, and half an inch across. All the blue of the deepest crevasses was in them, and their centers were hoarfrost crystals.

Blue flowers are one of the reasons for coming to the Alps, and I was glad to have met the first one at the very edge of the ice, cold beside the blood-warm soldanella, and glad that it was a gentian. When a traveler reports, "There were gentians there," the listener may not know exactly where the speaker has been, but he knows where he has *not* been: not on a city street, not in a pasture, not along a highway, not in a crowd, not in a tight little suburb, not beside a factory, not in the haunts of a bulldozer. Where men and their machines come the gentian departs. I knew a drift of fringed gentians once, in Indiana, where Gary now makes steel; and I know a forgotten cemetery where prairie gentians bloom around the toppled headstones of the prairie pioneers; and I have found green gentians on the Rocky Mountain tundra. The most memorable, though, was the swirl of inch-high, dark-blue spring gentians, *Gentiana verna* (*gentiana printanière, Frühling's Enzian, gentianella di primavera*), blooming there at the edge of the snow.

I noticed a glossy carpeting of small leaves, deep green and leathery, and knelt once more. I was kneeling in the interlaced twigs of a treetop. *Minima inter omnes arbores*, Linneaus called it, the smallest tree in the world—but also the highest. Its branches and its trunk were set deep in the humus of the snow pocket. Only its twigs were uplifted. Each twig bore two, occasionally three, shiny, small leaves and a tight catkin. This willow, *Salix herbacea* (*saule herbacé, Krautige Gletscherweide, salice erbacea*), the least willow, was keeping under cover up to its neck. I have stood above a carpet of the same tooled-leather leaves in the Rockies.

We turned away from the snow pocket flora and once again found the path leading down the mountain toward Zermatt. It is always difficult to leave the lonely mountain climbers behind. You wonder if you will ever see them again. You wonder if they will survive the next ten months under the ice. They look lonely and vulnerable, but since they refuse to tolerate crowding and shading, they must dwell in their high, humus-rich, isolated snow pockets. They have found their niche.

For a time our path skirted a scree, one of those treacherous accumulations of loose mountainside rubble. Here there were other kinds of plant specialists. These were the scree-sprawlers, their twigs forming a compact latticework over the surface of the rocky debris, their roots making a binding latticework within it. They steadied the unstable mass.

Two of the scree-sprawlers were willows. One had leathery leaves, slightly notched at the tip, and was a native of European mountains. The other had hairy leaves with a network of veins, which were set into deep grooves on the uppersurface and surrounded by a coating of wax on the undersurface; that willow was a migrant, left behind when its relatives went back north.

During the last glacial period, the great ice sheet pushed the veiny-leafed willow—reticulate willow, *Salix reticulata* (*saule réticulé, Netzadrige Gletschwerweide, salice ermellino*)—down from the north. At the same time the growing glaciers of the Alps pushed the leathery-leafed one—the blunt-leafed willow, *Salix retusa* (*saule émoussé, Stumpfblättrige Gletscherweide, salice reticolato*)—down the mountain. The two refugees met at the northern foot of the Alps, mingling across the meadows where stone-tool-using hunters pursued the reindeer and the now long-gone aurochs.

When the climate grew warmer, the blunt-leafed willow moved back up the mountains as fast as the ice retreated. Actually it was driven up, by the taller, crowding, shading plants returning to the foot of the Alps. Most of the reticulate willows retreated to the north, as did the reindeer hunters. But some retreated up the Alps. There the two willows are entangled on the scree, just as they were once before entangled under the feet of the reindeer hunters. I saw another community of reticulate willows in the tundra of the Rocky Mountains.

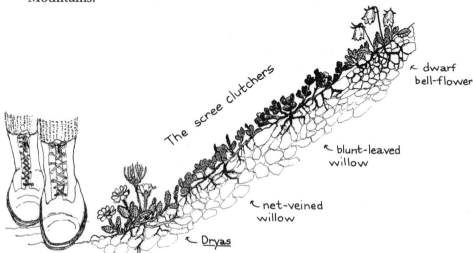

The scree clutchers

← dwarf bell-flower

← blunt-leaved willow

← net-veined willow

← Dryas

Growing beside these two flat, sprawling trees was a shrub that was also lying down. This was the mountain dryad, *Dryas octopetala* (*dryade à huit pétales*, *Silberwurz Dryade*, *driade*). The reticulate willow is not without company from its ancestral homeland. The dryad, too, is an immigrant from the Arctic, left behind on the mountaintops of both hemispheres. It wears a bright crown of numerous stamens, and its seedhead is a feather duster. Its leaf looks as though it must have been selected by the same hardships that selected the willow leaves of the mountains. They are short-stemmed, thick, deep-veined, silvery beneath, with scalloped edges rolled under. The dryad is another trellis plant, binding the scree into a modicum of stability.

This is the plant often depended upon by ecologists to unravel the story of the past, for its presence says, "There was tundra here." We find its pollen or its leaves at the bottom of a bog and are sure that the place once knew Arctic cold. On a plant list *"Dryad* vegetation" or *"Dryad*-willow vegetation" indicates a time of bitter cold, when trees and shrubs were lying down, with only their twigs uplifted.

The scree-clutcher community has its blue flower, too: the dwarf harebell. Its rhizomes—rootlike stems—form an efficient network just beneath the surface; they are always ready to put forth a flowering branch at a new point should the scree shift and cover an old branch too deeply. The harebell looks like a flower that needs shelter and pampering, but anyone who has seen harebells clinging to bare canyon walls knows that shelter is not for them. All that they demand is full sun, limestone rock, and no crowding.

Suddenly we were among the cushion plants. These are in the shape of an old-fashioned hard pincushion, the little flowers forming as a French flower book says, *"des touffes très compactes, de forme hémisphérique."* They huddle into themselves, pulling in their necks, as do the fur- and feather-bearing creatures of the mountaintop. The flowers are closely spaced—so closely that snow cannot get in—and are all flush with the surface of the compact hemisphere. The less heavily filtered ultraviolet light of high altitudes favors short stems, and the leaves are so minute that the plants are often taken to be mosses. Arranged in this way, flowers can pool their resources to attract insects to fertilize them, meanwhile offering a minimum of surface to the wind. In this compact formation, the old leaves cannot blow away, but are gathered into the mass of the plant, making a rich humus-sponge.

This cushion form is designated by German botanists as *Polsterbildende Nivalpflanzen.* The Italians call it *cuscinetto.* Americans say "alpine cushion formation." The highest-known cushion plant has been photographed at 20,130 feet, on a slope of the Himalayas.

One massive bolster that I saw was the moss campion, *Silene acaulis* (*silène à courte tige, Stengelloses Leimkraut, silene acaule*). It was covered with flat-faced pink flowers. The throats of the flowers were wide enough to fit an insect's tongue but not wide enough for snow or hail to enter. This is the flower form most characteristic of cushion plants. In the mountain tundra of both hemispheres moss campion is probably the commonest of all cushion plants.

Growing beside this circumpolar traveler was a more provincial cushion plant, one that grows only in the Alps. This was the Swiss androsace, *Androsace helvetica* (*androsace helvétique, Schweizer Mannsschild, androsace elvetica*), with a form so compact that it resembles one of those millefleurs glass paperweights. How a low-land gardener would love to carry these cushions home to use as a flowery edging for a rose bed! But it will not work. Gardeners have tried. The plants brought down the mountain become scraggly and unkempt, and die.

One elongated cushion looked as though it had been stuffed in, to fill a long vertical fissure in the rock. The wine-red flowers rested on a bluish-green cushion. This was a saxifrage, and *saxifrage* means "rock breaker," the purple saxifrage—*Saxifraga oppositifolia* (*saxifraga à feuilles opposées, Gegenblättriger Steinbrech, sassifraga rossa*).

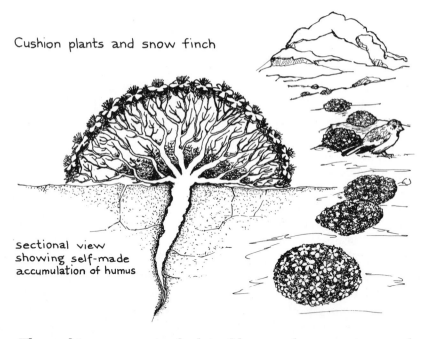

Cushion plants and snow finch

sectional view showing self-made accumulation of humus

The cushion community had its blue member, too, just as the snow-pocket community had its spring gentian and the scree-sprawling community its harebell. The whole plant was the size of a winter-coat button. Its compact gray-blue was enameled with close-set flowers of sky blue. I have never yet seen anyone look at an alpine forget-me-not without kneeling. I knelt and felt that I should bring the plant greetings from far-flung relatives whom I had met on the tundra above Trail Ridge Road in the Rockies.

That day I could find only a single plant of alpine forget-me-not, *Eritrichium nanum* (*eritriche nainé, Himmelsherold, miostidenana*). It was enough.

Now the path was leading down out of the tundra. The grass was no longer brown but spring-green, with purple and yellow violets in it. There were long-spurred violets, purple, with narrow leaves, in the sun; and there were broad-leaved, two-flowered violets, yellow, in shady places beside a rock.

Soon we were down to the altitude where shrubs and trees no longer hugged the ground but ventured to stand up. There were low masses of the circumpolar shrub bearberry, *Arctostaphylos uva-ursi* (*raisin d'ours, Immergrüne Barentraube, uva d'orso*). There was some shrubby juniper, and there were rather sparse forests of pines.

On the bare rock at the edge of one thin, open stand of pines grew the alpine rose, one of the most famous flowers of the Alps. Called *Alpenrose* by the Germans, *rose des Alpes* by the French, and *rosa delle Alpi* by the Italians, this flower, with its leathery foliage and clustered pink tubular flowers, was obviously not a rose at all but a rhododendron. (The name "rhododendron," however, translates literally as "rose tree"!)

This was a dwarf rhododendron. We looked at it, remembering the treelike tangle of those under which we had walked on a slope of the Great Smoky Mountains and pictures we had seen of their heavy treelike growth on the Himalayas. These giant shrubs are relatives, but the Alps, rising into the cold, long ago lopped off the tall branches of all the plant families. In the trial-by-cold some little runt, which would have been denied a toehold in more lush domains, had found its chance.

Actually, this particular runt doesn't face up to wind and exposure—it hides from winter under a complete snow cover and grows only in places where such cover is dependable. Up here above the snow level no twig could possibly survive the winter. So the buds are all packaged and ready before the snow comes. When winter is over the twiggy branches practically seem to spring out, tossing the snow off and finding the sun.

The most unexpected thing about this dwarf, however, is not that it accepts cold and evaporation, since it really hides from these, but that it accepts calcareous rock. Anyone who has attempted to grow rhododendrons in limy soils knows that acid is better. It takes a variety of freaks, sports, mutations, and geniuses to fill all the niches of this world.

The alpenrose that we found was the hairy one, *Rhododendron hirsutum*. We identified it by the fringe of hairs on its leaves, and by the scattered brown dots on the undersurface of the leaves. There is another alpenrose, too, the edges of whose darker green leaves are rolled over on the undersides, which are thickly covered with rusty scales. That one, the "rusty-leaved alpenrose," *Rhododendron ferrugineum*, grows on granite and other acid rocks.

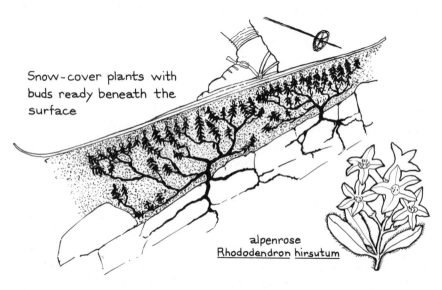

Snow-cover plants with buds ready beneath the surface

alpenrose
Rhododendron hirsutum

The shadows on the mountain were growing longer and cooler when we finally made our way to the funicular.

Naturally we talked about the one flower that we had not seen.

We had seen snow-pocket flowers, scree-sprawling flowers, cushion-plant flowers, and flowers of the snow-cover plants, but we had missed the one flower that means Switzerland to most people, the flower that is carved on music boxes and cuckoo clocks. We had missed the edelweiss.

Probably its very popularity was the reason we did not see it. Those that grow in accessible places have all been picked. There are some left, we were told, but only on steep, inaccessible mountainsides, where only a mountain climber might pass and he would probably be much too busy to pick flowers. I did see a woman in Interlaken take a bunch out of her great patent-leather handbag while she felt for her car keys. "I bought them," she answered defensively, though I hadn't asked.

The edelweiss looks like a native, all dressed in wool. The star-shaped form, which appears to be the flower, is actually a circle of white, woolly leaves framing a cluster of rather inconspicuous flowers. Here the leaves have taken over the advertising usually managed by the petals. (Red leaves perform the same function in poinsettia and bougainvillaea.)

This much publicized plant with its bundled head of flowers may look like a native, but, in fact, it is not one. It emigrated from Siberia during the glacial period and, after the retreat of the ice, some stayed behind. The ones that went back to the steppes of Siberia do not need to cling to the walls of precipices, but grow in pastures where cows graze. As yet, few flower lovers come to those pastures.

We rode the rest of the way down to Zermatt, talking about the mountain climbers we had seen that day, and we speculated that the mountaintops were not a goal but an escape. The mountain climbers were escaping from crowding, and shading, and competition. The price was cold and wind and snow, the reward, survival. Many must have been eliminated for the few that succeeded. There seemed to be some points in common between these plants and the men who climb mountains.

Along the streets of Zermatt we met many who wore alpenroses in their hats; and that evening we found bunches of alpenroses on the restaurant tables, with the fondue. In the shop next door a music box carved with edelweiss was yodeling and an American was buying earrings and a necklace made of spring gentians enameled in deep blue. There were chocolate bars with soldanella on the wrappers, and there were silk scarves printed with harebells.

Next day we walked out from Zermatt, past the Taugwalder house, and up the river path. It was the most flowery walk I have ever taken, that walk through alpine meadows in full bloom. I have walked through the flowery wheatfields of France, and the tall-grass prairie of the midwestern United States in late summer, the Arizona

desert in a spring that followed winter rains, and the Great Smokies
in dogwood season. The American prairie came closest to this mountain meadow in variety, but the prairie has the texture of calico and
denim. This meadow was embroidered in silk.

There were blooms of many heights, from the tall globe flowers
down to the bright pansies. There was a variety of forms, from the
disks of the geums, the bells of the harebells, the spikes of plantain
and lousewort, the loose, small-flowered clusters of forget-me-nots,
mustards, euphorbia, and the compact ball of globe-headed
rampion, to the many ragged hemispheres of the hawkweeds and
dandelions.

We did not find the big blue gentian of the travel posters in that
meadow, although some days later we encountered it high above
Mürren. This is the most famous blue of the Alps, this great blue
funnel growing close to the earth—the stemless gentian, *gentiana
acaulis* (*gentiane à tige courte, Stengelloser Enzian, genziana di
clusio*). Near it we saw another famous plant, one with a special

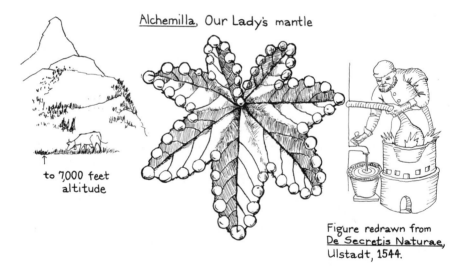

Alchemilla, Our Lady's mantle

to 7,000 feet
altitude

Figure redrawn from
De Secretis Naturae,
Ulstadt, 1544.

adjustment to the dripping atmosphere. Each leaflet was ringed
with droplets, evenly spaced. But these were not dewdrops. They
had been squeezed out by the plant. Thus the root could drink
again, even though the saturated air did not evaporate water from
the leaves. The many names of this plant indicate that it is the

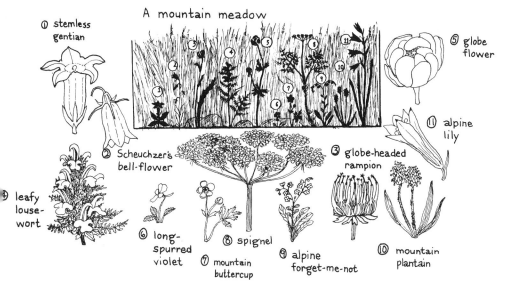

A mountain meadow

① stemless gentian
⑤ globe flower
② Scheuchzer's bell-flower
③ globe-headed rampion
④ leafy louse-wort
⑪ alpine lily
⑥ long-spurred violet
⑧ spignel
⑦ mountain buttercup
⑨ alpine forget-me-not
⑩ mountain plantain

familiar of the peasant: Our Lady's mantle, lady's smock, dew mantle. Its scientific name, *Alchemilla vulgaris*, indicates that it was important to the learned men of the Middle Ages. *Alchemilla* means "plant of the alchemists." Its "dew" was collected and used, hopefully, for producing the philosophers' stone, employed in the making of gold.

On the way down to Mürren that same day (this was another place where we rode the funicular up the mountain, and walked down) we saw dandelions practicing, with cowbell accompaniment, a few steps toward conquering the trodden places around Chicago, and Pittsburgh, and St. Louis, and Kalamazoo. We were walking beside a flowery field in which the dandelion was only a minor character, not belligerent, not tough, just one of the merry peasants. But then we saw wagon tracks through the field. The wagons had evidently packed the wet soil firmly, and no merry peasants danced there—except for dandelions. Two long lines of them stepped out from the mixed chorus and filled those tracks full, right across the meadow. I looked at the parallel bands of triumphant gold, and thought, Well, I guess you already had it in you to conquer America. All you needed was transportation.

But this is digression. The gentians, the our lady's mantle, and the dandelion-filled ruts, were in the meadows above Mürren. We saw them later (after we had seen the marsh marigolds wading among myriads of tadpoles at the foot of the Rhone glacier, and after we had seen inch-high primroses in cracks in the rock above Grimsel Pass, and after we had met tall monkshood and fat slugs in the Lauterbrunnen valley, and before we saw all the red geraniums of Berne, and much more). Let us complete our second day's walk out from Zermatt.

Near the top of that walk, in the very midst of the most flowery of meadows, a red-cheeked woman had set out two tables in front of her brown barn. She served us tea. We continued our conversation with her after she had climbed upstairs into the loft and was forking down hay to the cows.

"Why aren't your cows outdoors?" we asked.

"One never turns them out into the meadows until the first hay has been cut," she explained. No wonder, then, that it is possible to meet travelers who show no enthusiasm for mountain meadows. They must have seen them *after* the cutting of that first, flowery hay. We had been lucky. But one could plan it so.

We followed the path back down to Zermatt.

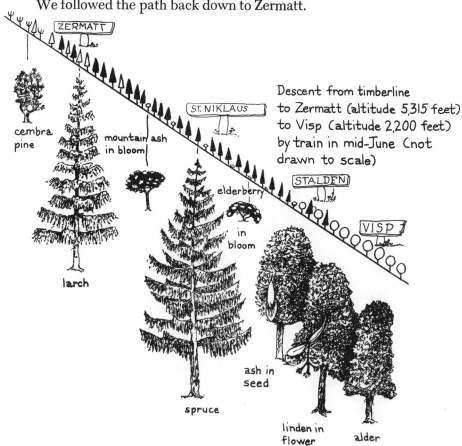

ZERMATT

cembra pine

mountain ash in bloom

ST. NIKLAUS

larch

elderberry in bloom

spruce

ash in seed

linden in flower

alder

STALDEN

VISP

Descent from timberline to Zermatt (altitude 5,315 feet) to Visp (altitude 2,200 feet) by train in mid-June (not drawn to scale)

Next morning we took the train even farther down the mountain, below Zermatt. We passed larches, and mountain ashes in bloom. Hay was being made above Saint Niklaus. Then we passed Norway spruce forests. The dog rose was in bloom, and the elderberry bushes. The ash trees were already hung with clusters of seeds, and cherries were ripening. At Stalden the hay was all made. Then we passed poplars, and stretches of fireweed, and linden trees in bloom. Along the river, which had stopped its tumbling, there were alders.

At the bottom, at Visp, twenty-two hundred feet, we found our automobile, and before long were driving between apple blossoms and blooming lilacs.

A BRIEF GLOSSARY OF THE LANDSCAPE
OF SWITZERLAND

English	French	German	Italian
forest	forêt	Wald	foresta
glacier	glacier	Gletscher	ghiacciaio
lake	lac	See	lago
meadow	prairie	Wiese	prato
snow pockets	combes à niege	Schneetälchen	tasche sotto la neve
scree, calcareous	éboulis calcaires	Kalkschutt	detrito calcareo
valley	vallée	Tal	valle

Zonation of the vegetation from top to bottom:

ice cap	zone nivale	Schnee-und-Eisregion	orizzonte nivale
alpine zone	zone alpestre	alpine Region	orizzonte alpino

tree line	limite superiore de forêt	Baumgrenze	limite superiore della vegetazione arborea

subalpine zone	zone subalpine	Nadelwaldregion	orizzonte subalpino

upper limit of beech	limite superiore de la hêtre	Buchengrenze	limite del faggio

montane zone	zone montagnarde	Laubwaldregion	orizzonte montano
foothills zone	zone des collines	Hügelregion	orizzonte submontano

Principal forest trees from top to bottom:

English	French	German	Italian
cembra pine	arole	Arve	cirmo
larch	mélèze	Lärche	larice
spruce	epicéa	Rottanne	peccio
fir, white	sabin blanc	Tanne	abete bianco
beech	hêtre	Buche	faggio
linden	tilleul	Linde	tiglio
ash	frêne	Esche	frassino
maple	érable	Platane	acero
oak	chêne	Eiche	quercia

TO READ BEFORE READING THE LANDSCAPE
OF SWITZERLAND

About the Shaping of the Alps

A lively account of the riddles of the Alps, and of various theories concerning them, can be read in *Conversation with the Earth,* by Hans Cloos, a translation from German (Knopf, New York, 1953).

For an account of recent research on Continental Drift, read "Sea-Floor Spreading," by J. R. Hiertzler, in the *Scientific American,* December 1968, pp. 60–70.

About the Flora of the Alps

Best of all is *Mountains in Flower* by Volkmar Vareschi and Ernst Krause (Macmillan, New York, 1940). You will have to hunt for it, since it is unfortunately out of print. The flowers are photographed in rich detail against a background of mountain peaks, the text is also outstanding.

A small book that describes the flora with clarity is *The Alps in Bloom,* by Dr. Elfune Wendelberger (Pinguin-Verlag, Innsbruch, 1958).

For Carrying with You

The best is probably *Alpen-Flora,* by Dr. C. Schröter (Albert Raustein, Zurich, n.d.). This book is widely sold in Switzerland. The text is in German, English, and French.

Almost as usable, and also easily available, are two pocket-size books, *Fleurs des Alpes I* and *Fleurs des Alpes II,* by Walter Rytz, published by Petits Atlas Payot (Lausanne, n.d.). They are in French, but the pictures and the scientific names are universal.

Germany

A Rhine Journey

1

THERE ARE five ways of making the Rhine journey.

One way is by boat. That way is best for seeing the tilted layers of slate topped with bulky castles and connected by hammocks of terraced vineyards, and best for feeling the pulse of the busy river.

A second way is by road along the shore. That way is best for enjoying wide streets lined with lindens, sycamores, horse chestnuts; narrow streets bulging with half-timbered houses; town fountains; edifices of red sandstone; red geraniums; wine-tasting; *Kuchen*-sampling.

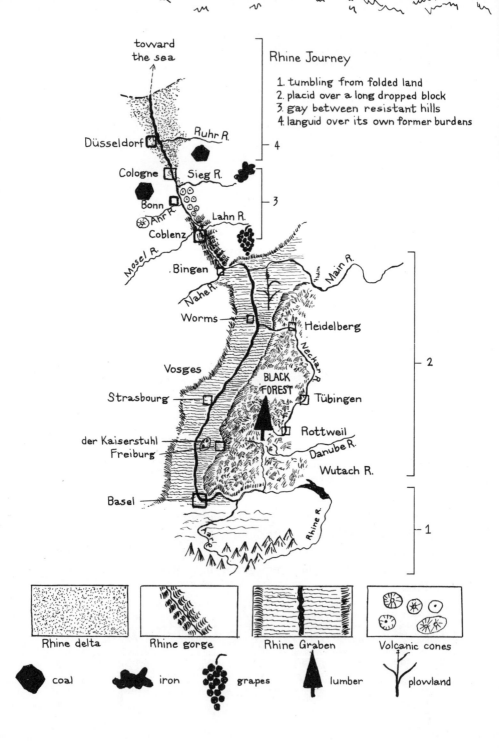

toward
the sea

Rhine Journey

1. tumbling from folded land
2. placid over a long dropped block
3. gay between resistant hills
4. languid over its own former burdens

Düsseldorf

Ruhr R.

Cologne   Sieg R.

Bonn
Ahr R.
Coblenz   Lahn R.

Mosel R.

Bingen

Nahe R.   Main R.

Worms   Heidelberg

Vosges

Neckar R.

Strasbourg   BLACK
FOREST   Tübingen

der Kaiserstuhl   Rottweil
Freiburg   Danube R.

Wutach R.

Basel   Rhine R.

Rhine delta	Rhine gorge	Rhine Graben	Volcanic cones

coal   iron   grapes   lumber   plowland

A third way is by small road above the slopes. That is best for seeing the extent of the beech forest, the darkness of the stands of Norway spruce, and the gaiety of the clearings edged with mountain ash, elderberry, and hawthorn.

A fourth way is by one of the long footpaths that follow the hilltops, with an overnight stop, perhaps, in a castle that has been converted into a youth hostel. This way is best for smelling lily of the valley or grape blossoms in the spring, or ripe grapes in the fall; and best for watching potato-diggers and vine-pruners, and best for feeling the smoothness of beech trunks and hearing the song of a cuckoo.

The fifth way is by train. This is best for seeing the orchards and wheatfields, the precise rows of cabbage, tomatoes, roses; and best for seeing the war damage that was done to the towns that lie atop the old carboniferous coal trough; and best for seeing pioneer plants in the bomb sites. We looked in all five of these ways on our Rhine journey, and found them all satisfying.

The Rhine must surely be the most-storied river in the world, and

some of its stories are true ones. One particular true story, which shaped all the others, is written in the rocks. The Rhine valley displays the record in plain view, ready for reading, *but* the traveler should be warned that some of the pages have been shifted out of historical sequence. Had they not been shifted, the main events of the story could be read as follows, starting (like rock strata) at the bottom and reading upward.

8 The glacial periods brought wind-blown dust.
7 Sea and land alternated.
6 Volcanoes left basalt, ash, tufa.
5 The basin bulged again and became a hot, extensive, rust-colored desert, which was to form a glistening, easily cut stone called *Buntsandstein* (colorful sandstone) and to be raised into castles, cathedrals, forts.
4 Again a shallow sea covered the land, leaving slate, shale, salt, and limestone.
3 The basin of the sea rose, and its sand and mud became a desert.
2 A succession of shallow seas left layers of sandstone, shale, and slate.
1 Ancient molten rock cooled to form crystalline masses.

This outline account of the layers of the Rhineland is true enough, but it omits all evidence of the violence that befell them— all the cracking, heaving, folding, shifting. It is as true as a history of the German nation would be if it omitted all its wars. A Rhine journey reveals a great deal of violence.

We approached the Rhine as its waters approach it, downhill, precipitately.

In Switzerland we had left the headwaters of the Rhone River behind, at the foot of the Rhone glacier, and had climbed the pass to the top of the Rhine drainage. We then followed the Aar River, most important headwater of the Rhine, past lush spruce forests carpeted with ferns, down and down, until sycamores had replaced spruce. Many details of the scenery gave evidence of abundant water: hay hung up to dry, wide roofs overhanging geraniumed balconies in Brienz, a covered bridge in Thun, arcaded shops in Berne. At the foot of the folded mountains the Aar poured itself into the Rhine, and we followed the Rhine to Basel.

There we continued past bridges and warehouses, to the place where the Rhine turned north. We followed to the "Three Corners," where a marker points with three swirling rims to the three countries—Switzerland, Germany, France—that touch each other at that point.

We watched the barges waiting their turns to dock, and read their names: *Nordzee, Destin, Fram, All Right, Rotterdam;* and listened to their shouted languages, and their thumps as they hit against the solid quay.

That quay was made of tightly cemented granite blocks, and there seemed to be hardly a crack where a pioneer plant might pry in. Yet a few dandelions had found an entry; plantain, too. If there were to be any plants on that improbable surface, the first-comers had to be those two European-trained pioneers. But there was also American goldenrod, thriving in a place where only the wind could have planted it; fireweed, too, and a few small black locust trees from the American Southwest. One section of the quay was draped in the American fall color of woodbine, as deep a red as if it were garlanding a stone wall around a New England field. Some bird must have planted that seed, having sampled a foreign taste in some nearby garden in France or Germany or Switzerland.

As we looked northward down the river where more and more barges were approaching, I thought how long ago this setting had been shaped.

In the early Tertiary Period, more than seventy million years ago, even before the birth of the Alps, a great, hard island began to bulge out of the sea. As it bulged upward its strained surface cracked in two long, parallel, north-south cracks. In time the long, narrow block left between the fissures slipped down, and a long, shallow trough was formed. The sea slipped into this trough, bringing some

salt and sediments, then receded, to come back no more. The two
sides of the trough rose higher and higher and became mountains.
The mass lying between the two long fracture zones dropped lower
and lower. Today this Rhine valley measures about seven thousand
feet deep, but actually it is twice that, since much of it is filled in
with alluvial soil, glacial loess, and gravel. At first, the rivers with
their deposits came from the two masses of mountains on the east
and west of the valley. After the Alps were uplifted, deposits came
at an accelerated rate down the Alpine slopes by which we had
approached the Rhine.

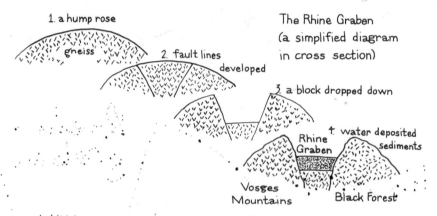

1. a hump rose

The Rhine Graben
(a simplified diagram
in cross section)

2. fault lines
developed

3. a block dropped down

4. water deposited
sediments

Rhine
Graben

Vosges
Mountains

Black Forest

This half-filled Rhine trough, or Rhine Graben, is 180 miles long.
The river enters it near Basel, 800 feet above sea level, and leaves it
at 253 feet above sea level, at Bingen. The Rhine itself uses only a
small part of this valley, which is 25 miles wide. Farmers mine the
soft riches of the rest.

We set out for Freiburg, following a flat road on the flat surface of
the Rhine Graben. On our right rose the dark mountains bearing the
Black Forest on their ancient basement rock. Across the Rhine,
mirroring the Black Forest formation, were the Vosges Mountains of
France.

In Freiburg one might do well to look at the landscape through
the eyes of the geologist Hans Cloos, who, in 1947, wrote a fine book
called *Gespräch mit der Erde*, "Conversation with the Earth." Here
in Freiburg, as he tells us, he sat many years before and mused,
under a linden tree, about the mysteries of the Rhine Valley: the
long trough with its youthful sediment and the ancient basement

rocks, which formed the mountainous sides of the trough. Cloos sat and wondered, and wished for a mine shaft or a series of excavations. He wanted, particularly, to see the inside of the Lorettoberg, a mountain made of the ancient gneiss on its Black Forest side, and of sedimentary layers on its Rhine side. The secret of one hundred eighty miles of the Rhine Valley had to be inside that hill, covered with the streets and buildings of a city.

Then Cloos heard good news. A railroad had a contract to dig a tunnel clear through the Lorettoberg—1,696 feet. In on the west through soft sandstone, and out on the east through the hard, ancient gneiss.

In 1910 the contract was made and the geologists started waiting.

In 1916 came the letting of subcontracts, and the excavation was actually begun—in an old quarry at the west side of the Lorettoberg.

War intervened, and postwar poverty, and inflation.

Finally, in April 1929, the mountain was cut through. Hans Cloos reports in his book the excitement of the final cut. He tells how bitter-cold air suddenly flowed through the tunnel from the mountaintop down to the warm plain; and how he was able at last to see the actual fault line. No man had ever seen that sight before. Realizing, however, that the surface was soon to be sheathed, and only a small window left open for future geologists, he looked, collected, and sketched.

Using a lamp and a magnifying glass, he found the scratched lines, evidence of the valley block's sliding down across the mountain block. He was, he tells us, reading "the earth's own script."

Later he constructed clay models and caused small-scale grabens to develop in the clay. In one experiment the clay was pulled steadily in opposite directions. In another the clay was not pulled, but simply arched upward, thus stretching the upper side. Both experiments repeated the dropping of the center block and the uplifting of the blocks representing the Black Forest and the Vosges. As a result of such experiments as these, a modern guidebook can, with assurance, desiccate this fine landscape into a single sentence: "The Rhine Graben is a rift valley filled with hundreds of feet of alluvial sediments."

It is interesting that Hans Cloos did his musing about the Graben while under a linden tree. In a Rhine town, it would, of course, have to be a linden—that or a sycamore maple, a sycamore, or a horse chestnut. These four trees, which march well in formation and prune well into uniformity, keep step along the busy river front. When unpruned, they all tend to a heavy rotundity.

The linden, *Tilia europaea* (in German *Linde* or *Lindenbaum*), is loud with bees when it is in flower. Its flowers are made into a tea, to induce sleep, and into an oil for a fragrant, sleep-inducing bath.

The sycamore maple, *Acer pseudoplatanus* (called *Bergahorn* in German), glowers darkly over its own black shade, and has no charm of texture or gesture, but it endures to the limit. The bleakest of weather and winds, and even salt spray, usually fail to mar its bulky symmetry. The leaves are used medicinally to cure complaints of the liver and the spleen.

The sycamore, or Oriental plane tree, *Platanus orientalis* (called in German *asiatische Platane*), is probably the most often-planted tree of European cities. Its leaves are boiled in a tea and used as a cure for rheumatism.

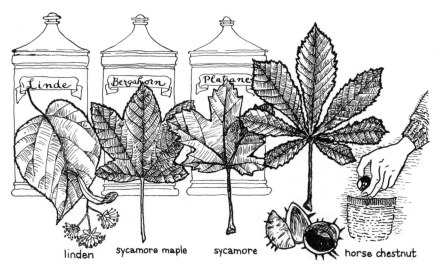

linden   sycamore maple   sycamore   horse chestnut

The horse chestnut is also used. This street tree, *Aesculus hippocastanum* (*Rosskastanie* in German), drops its bristly fruits all along the streets, and the husks burst, revealing the nuts, which look like pieces of polished mahogany with a staring eye. The plumpest and shiniest ones tend to be used as boy-missiles, but when the boys grow older they carry them in their pockets as a protection from rheumatism.

In the shade of these trees we walked through Freiburg. The pavement contained neat patterns of Rhine pebbles, smooth, water worn, the kind that we had seen being polished in the white water of the Alps.

We crossed the Rhine Graben, to climb past vineyards to the top of an old volcanic cone, the Kaiserstuhl. Whenever there is enough force and tension to fault the rocks and displace a great block like the Graben, there are usually other evidences of pressure. We remembered America's Yellowstone Park, with the dramatic geysers and hot springs along its fault lines, and were not surprised to find the word, or the suffix, *baden,* indicating medicinal springs, scattered about the fault lines of the Graben.

Throughout our Rhine journey we were confronted by one kind of ancient rock, from a time that knew no rivers, no trees, no shady pebbled walks, no comfort. *Buntsandstein,* the rock is called, meaning "colorful sandstone," and its dark warmth continually colored our days and accented the landscape. Just as the limestone of France binds that country together with a ribbon of gray or creamy white, this ribbon of rusty red ties together a Rhine journey. We seldom went many minutes without seeing it—knotted into bulky castles, fashioned into bows for cathedrals, looped into walls, snipped into windowsills, hollowed into the basins of town fountains. It was formed at a time when this part of the earth was just desert, with rivers bringing down sandy alluvium and spreading it on the plain, where the iron between the quartz grains rusted in the air. The desert was treeless, but not lifeless. In a book called *Exotic Zoology,* Willy Ley tells the story of the identification and interpretation of some "Footprints in Red Sandstone." The footprints, found in a quarry on Hess Mountain near Hildburghausen, were made by an armored crocodile-like creature with a thick, long tail.

The first *Buntsandstein* we saw in Germany was at the Freiburg cathedral, with its single graceful, perforated spire.

We next confronted it farther north on the Graben, at Strassburg, or Strasbourg (as it should be called now, since it is French again). Whatever we call this city of canals, carved facades, and forts, its red sandstone cathedral links it firmly to the Rhine country, as do the statues of Gutenberg and Goethe in the town square. It is the town where one of the most stirring of all national anthems had its birth. The song was first called "Chant de guerre pour l'armée du Rhin," but it is now known as "The Marseillaise."

At Heidelberg the *Buntsandstein* was not drawn out gracefully, as in the cathedrals of Freiburg and Strasbourg, but heaped into a hulking, formidable, thick-walled mass. We saw the castle first at a distance, as we walked along one of the world's most famous footpaths, Philosophen Weg, the Philosopher's Way. Then, from the castle tower, with its thick walls long split by lightning and gunpowder, we looked at the Neckar River, bringing offerings from the Black Forest to deposit in the Rhine. We thought about the Heidelberg man who lived in this valley in a warm period between glacial advances. And we remembered two later men, with thinner jaws and larger braincases, two scientists, Bunsen and Kirchhoff, who discovered the facts of spectrum analysis and thereby taught us to read a rainbow. Many other problems have been wrestled with at Heidelberg; not a few were settled by dueling.

We descended to the Graben again, to another red sandstone edifice. It, too, was riven by violence and has been the site of historic wrestlings. The Cathedral of Worms raises its frowning round towers on the spot where Caesar stood, where the gloomy Attila drove his hordes across the Rhine, where wars have stamped, and where Martin Luther said simply, "Here I stand, I cannot do otherwise, God help me! Amen!"

We walked around unlovely Worms. It smelled of cabbage cooking. We looked into a kitchen garden at the rows of cabbages, recalling that sauerkraut was a German invention, and that to the American soldier of World War I the name for a German was "Kraut." We talked about the winter of 1917/18, a winter of hunger in Germany that had been called "the cabbage winter." How strange that an inconspicuous little plant of sun-baked sea cliffs, *Brassica oleracea*, should have exploded into such a variety of mutants, to dominate the meals and flavor the homes of the common people. One of *Brassica*'s sports pulled in its neck and wrapped itself in fat, overlapping leaves of the same gray-green color that served it well on ancestral sun-baked cliffs and became cabbage. Another swelled the bases of its leaves into kohlrabi; another formed the compact flower-bud bunches called broccoli; another kept its flower bunches low, pale, in cauliflower; another produced many small cabbages on a stalk and is called brussels sprouts.

As we looked into one garden a housewife in an apron came out and cut a big red cabbage. I knew what she was going to do with that one, fry it with bacon and onions and vinegar and chopped apples. As she tore off the big outside leaves I reached, *"Bitte,"* across the fence for one of them. When she saw me showing and admiring its markings, she invited me into her kitchen to see the inside of the head.

"*'S ist schön,*" she said, and cut down through the head with a carving knife, laying it open in four crisp quarters. Its compact roundness and efficient packaging were reminiscent of the German landscape. It was all webbed and veined and clotted, too, with the color of the red sandstone, and exuded a smell incompatible with French wines, but belonging with rye bread, beer, and wurst.

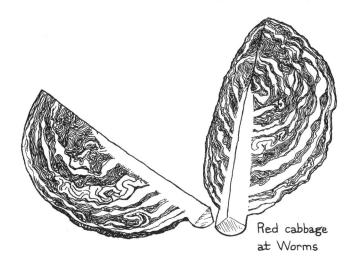

Red cabbage
at Worms

Several countries have legends evidencing a belief that the vine and the cabbage are not compatible. A Greek legend tells that the first cabbage sprang from the tears of Lycurgus, prince of Thrace, who was bound to a vine-stock by Dionysus in punishment for having destroyed some vines. Roger Bacon wrote that the cabbage is unfriendly to all plants, not the vine only, because "it draweth strongly the fattest juice of the earth." The Greeks and the Egyptians are said to have made use of the antipathy between vines and cabbage as a cure, because, wrote John Gerard in his English *Herball* published in 1597, cabbage "driveth away drunkennesse." According to a German legend, the man in the moon sits holding a basket of cabbages, stolen by a hungry peasant from his neighbor's garden on Christmas Eve, and discovered by the Christ Child, who was riding past on his white horse.

Punishment looms large in German tales, but rewards loom even larger. We have all been brought up on the stories that the Brothers Grimm gathered carefully from the mouths of German peasants, recording them in the simple language of the tellers. Among them are Hansel and Gretel, Cinderella, Snow White, Rumpelstiltskin.

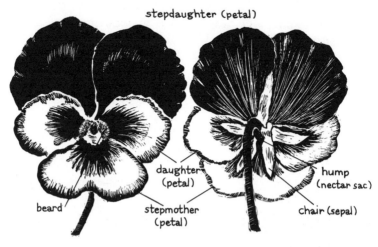

stepdaughter (petal)

daughter (petal)

hump (nectar sac)

beard

stepmother (petal)

chair (sepal)

Stiefmütterchen (pansy)

I thought of punishment and reward themes as I looked down another trim garden path. It was bordered with pansies, not the delicately colored wild pansies found in so many European meadows, but rotund ones with velvet texture and wide-open faces, richly colored. "Pansy" is the American name; the English call it love-in-idleness, three-faces-under-a-hood, or heartsease, and dedicate it to St. Valentine; the French call it *pensée* and use it in their language of flowers to say "I think of you." The Germans call it *Stiefmütterchen,* and tell this tale:

This broadest fattest petal is the stepmother, and the two side petals, one on each side of the stepmother, are her daughters. You can easily observe the family resemblance, though they are not as fat as she is, not yet, and that is to be expected. The two stepdaughters are up in back, a bit crowded, and that is the fault of the stepmother. Because in that household there were five chairs. If you turn the flower over, you can see them. They are those five green sepals supporting the backs of the petals. The stepmother sat on two of the chairs, as you can see. Each of her daughters took one chair. And the two stepdaughters had to crowd on to one chair. But in the old days wrongs like that never went unpunished. A little elf came along. He punished the stepmother by making her ever after to wear a hump. It is the purplish nectar sac there on the back of the flower, between the sepals. Her two daughters were made to wear mustaches. You can plainly see them on their faces. The two stepdaughters were left without any blemish, and clad in the richest velvets. The moral is not to sit on two chairs.

North of Worms we continued on the level surface of the Graben, with its wheat fields, fruit, hops, and sugar beets, all thriving on the layers of alluvium and loess. But ahead loomed a barrier, the Taunus Mountains. The Rhine continued north to the base of the high mass, and then, when the Main River entered from the east, it turned abruptly west.

This is the part of the Rhine that the traveler knows best, and with everyone else, we boarded a white steamer. With everyone else, too, we purchased a colorful strip map of that section of the Rhine, and unfolded it full length to get a foretaste of the castles, vineyards, and islands we were to watch all that day. Most of the people on deck were holding their maps straight up-and-down. They should, of course, have been holding them sideways, so that from Mainz to Bingen the Rhine might be seen flowing west, slightly southwest. Then, at Bingen, the maps could be held up-and-down again, almost, so that the river would flow northwest. It is important for the Rhine traveler to keep always in mind the direction of the sun. Otherwise he might miss some important points about this stretch of the river, where the warm south-facing slopes that rise on the right are like flouncing petticoats, all stitched and decorated with rock terraces full of vineyards.

Once the great Charlemagne stood on the balcony of his castle (now long gone), at Ingelheim, and saw how warm the sun lay on those slopes, so he sent men to Orleans for grape vines. "Ere the moon had gone round her course" the men were back, and Charlemagne "planted with his royal hand the French vine on German soil," so the tale is told.

It is also told that, when the fragrance of the grape blossoms fills the air, "a tall shadow wanders about the vineyards at night, a purple mantle hanging from his stately shoulders, and a crown on his head. It is Charlemagne . . . and he comes to bless the grapes. . . . At the first crow of the cock he returns to his grave in Aix-la-Chapelle, and sleeps until the scent of the grapes wakens him next spring."

Some days we wandered about on roads and footpaths in the Taunus Mountains, up above the Rhine, and looked down through seemingly endless slopes of beech forest, with their clear forest floors. We looked, too, into the cleared forest floors under thriving stands of spruce. One *clear*, the other *cleared*. We will understand that difference later, in the Black Forest. Wait.

In his chronicle of the Gallic Wars, Julius Caesar records that his men traveled through the forest east of the Rhine for months and still saw no light ahead. Up there, from our vantage point in the mountains, it was easy to visualize the landscape that he had seen. The beech forest must have seemed to extend endlessly into the distance, as it reaches far into the past, continually replacing itself in its own shade, which is too deep for any other tree to tolerate. Perhaps the wild boars did important planting (just as squirrels planted forests of white oaks in America). Rooting around in the forest, they must occasionally have nuzzled a beechnut into an inaccessible position under a root, or a log, or a rock, and then abandoned it. A forest could grow quickly in that moist, shaded, snout-cultivated soil. At a hunting lodge we saw a mounted boar's head.

We followed a footpath above the famous white-wine country, past fields where women were digging potatoes, past vineyards where white rags kept the birds away from glowing, heavy bunches of fruit, through a beech forest, and came at length to the Nieder-wald Denkmal, the tall memorial known also as the Wacht am Rhein. The people gathered before the memorial that autumn week-day were almost all German. As the German guide lectured, the faces of young and old were lifted toward that hopeful memorial to the "unified Germany" of 1871, but when he pointed to the words of the song engraved there, only the older people were singing it softly to themselves. I could tell that some of them knew the words by heart, because they were forming them without looking at the monument. I knew the words, too. We had sung them lustily, in English, back in grammar school; later we proudly sang them in German, in our German class in high school, and then they were silenced:

Lieb Vaterland
Magst ruhig sein,
Fest steht und treu
Die Wacht,
Die Wacht am Rhein.

At Bingen the Rhine becomes a different river. From there to Cologne we found it best to see it all from shipboard. Not only does its direction change toward the northwest (we twisted our maps around), but it becomes narrower, more vigorous, younger-acting. After its middle-aged wandering over the rich deposits of the Graben, the Rhine appears to have regained its youth. One old geology text writes that it was "faced with a solid block of stone and did not despair, but gathered its forces and corkscrewed and sawed its way to the ocean." The dramatic gorge from Bingen to Coblenz actually records a rather straightforward and undramatic story.

The river must once have wandered across the scene here, just as it wanders across the Graben, yielding to the resistance of the harder banks and eating into the softer ones. The curves, once formed, enlarged steadily because of the natural difference in cutting force between the slower inner side of the river and its swifter outer side. Underneath, however, the layers of rock were bulging. The curves deepened and became permanent. Still the rock layers bulged upward, and as fast as the land bulged upward, the river sawed downward. "Entrenched meander" I heard one student on board file it. "Incised meander," proclaimed another. "Petrified wandering," murmured a priest. (And I mused again about some advantages of traveling by common carrier.)

The gorge looked forbidding. The darkness of the slate rocks, the swiftness of the confined current, the concealing curves, and the echoes, all conspired to furnish a landscape out of which grew legends—violent ones.

The violence starts at Bingen, at the narrow gate of the gorge, called "the iron gate of the Rhine." On a quartz island there stands the "Mouse Tower" with its story of the cruel Bishop Hatto, who locked his hungry people into a barn and set it afire, saying, as they screamed, "Listen how the mice are squeaking in the corn." He was punished by mice, who poured from the barn and pursued him to the tower, where they devoured him.

There were robber barons, too. Opposite Bingen, on that same deep curve, the castle of Ehrenfels sits high, in an advantageous position for watching traffic up and down the river, and for exacting booty from hapless travelers.

Many vantage points along the river have such castles, usually built of red sandstone, perched on eminences formed of uplifted layers of slate, with cleared views ahead and forests at their backs.

Strangely, these forests owe their survival to the robber barons. Not, of course, because the barons rested from their looting by walking in the deep shade of the beech trees and listening to the cuckoos. Certainly not because they came out to enjoy the sudden unfolding of the tailored beech leaves in the spring, or to appreciate the russet coloring of the fall, or the long tapered tan buds of the winter. And not because they delighted in listening to the rain soaking into the humus with a promise of clean streams. Not even because they knew the beech bark to be the best of all for receiving carved hearts, and initials, and "*Ich liebe dich's*." It was probably not even that they were not somewhat sympathetic with the peasants, who were set on clearing the forests for crops and pastures or lumber or fuel, and who longed to have cabbages and wheat instead of forests.

No, the barons in their castles simply wanted good hunting. They had horses and dogs and weapons and hunting horns. So, the forests stayed.

Ahead of us lay a bend in the river that is familiar to most people whether they have traveled in Germany or not. This is the curve where the Rhine rushes in a narrow channel, around the base of the dark basaltic mass called the Lorelei. In the moonlight, according to legend, the enchantress sits on the summit, combing her golden hair with a golden comb and singing her song, knowing that "everyone must expire who looks into her eyes." Fishermen who could not resist were dashed against the rocks by the swift current.

Today no fisherman would even have a reason to be there. The number of fish was gradually reduced by pollution; then suddenly, in 1969, all the fish were dead in this part of the river, perhaps through an accident with insecticides. A news story calls the old Rhine "the world's longest sewer." At one time there were salmon here in such abundance that the servants at Saint Goar, it is recorded, stipulated that they not be required to eat salmon more than three times a week.

At Saint Goar, the less-forbidding bank of the river has produced a more tender tale than that of the Lorelei. In the year 611, Saint Goar, converter of heathens, produced miracles so great that he was summoned by his bishop and called to account. In answer, the gentle monk simply took off his cloak and hung it on a sunbeam.

Another miracle of the curve of the river is the echo. We tested it for ourselves and heard four replies. Others report hearing more.

As we made our way down the river, the slate mountains continued to hump along beside us. The houses above which they towered were roofed with slate, and many had slate siding as well. These ancient layers revealed in the mountains were deposited as mud under the waters of a shallow sea, so long ago that plants had not yet come ashore. Hans Cloos once found here a complete crinoid, an upright creature that looks so much like a plant that it is commonly called the "sea lily." The animal, he wrote, was "preserved entire and exactly as it had been when, dying, it laid its head on the down-soft pillow of the still waters' muddy bottom." But this crinoid was standing straight up on a layer of slate, just as it had once grown on the floor of that Devonian sea; clearly it had been gradually raised again to an upright position as the rock layers folded.

We continued along the base of the slate folds to Boppard, where the Rhine makes such a deep curve that the vineyards cross over to the opposite shore to be able to bask in the sun.

The busiest curve of all lies at Coblenz, where the Mosel River enters from the left, and the largest castle of all, the Ehrenbreitstein, commands the river bank. Beleaguered Coblenz showed us many stumps of buildings and many bomb sites. One bomb site beside the Rhine was covered with the yellow of two hardy flowers. One was American goldenrod; the other was the butter-and-eggs, or toadflax (*Frauenflachs* or *Leinkraut* in German), a pioneer of disturbed places in America. It is one of the stowaways that crossed the ocean to congregate on roadsides with many other hardy immigrants.

Back on the Rhine again there spread before us a slower and older river, but still one with plenty of violence recorded along its route. Here volcanoes broke through the old upfolded layers, topping the mountains with volcanic rock. The dramatic Siebengebirge, Seven Mountains, on the right, and the great Eifel on the left, revealed the column formation of gray basalt in many steep cliffs.

The towns began to show us some new building materials, volcanic instead of sea bottom. At Niedermendig the houses looked gray and solid. They were built of the gray basalt, fine-grained because it cooled rapidly, forming only small crystals. At Andernach the church has four towers all built of tuff, a water-cemented, tan-gray volcanic ash.

At the next curve the mass of the Erpeler Ley, a towering gray cliff, shows the columned structure of basalt in its quarries.

The next curve rounds the slope of Rolandseck, Roland's castle. The unhappy knight fought bravely, but by mischance slew the master of the castle Drachenfels, who was the father of the maiden he loved. All his remaining years he sat looking down to the island-convent to which she retired, and across to the Drachenfels on its columned basaltic height.

There is a cave in the side of that height in which lived a dragon, who came out from time to time to swallow peasants. Nearby, the young Siegfried worked for an armorer, as apprentice in the smithy. But the smith became so alarmed at his strength that he sent him out to burn charcoal near the dragon's lair. The dragon came out roaring, but Siegfried raised an iron bar and cracked its head. The black blood flowed, and Siegfried, on the advice of a little bird singing in a linden tree, threw off his clothes and bathed his body in the blood to make himself invulnerable. A linden leaf fluttered down on to his back. The spot was not protected by the dragon's blood, and Siegfried later received his death wound there.

As we left the Drachenfels, we left behind the most northerly of the vineyards as well.

It is a very old and slow-moving Rhine that arrives at Bonn, but its history has been far from placid. The river moves out onto sandy sea floor, accumulated through recent times. At the same time it is moving over an ancient trough, the carboniferous trough, where once throve the lush vegetation of a warm, humid fern forest, and now lie the riches of coalfields. This is the same trough that underlies the coal towns of Britain. That the ancient ferny forests should have laid the groundwork for factories, and thereby for bombings, does not seem any more incredible than that . . . —, the opening phrase of the Fifth Symphony of one of Bonn's great citizens, should have become a war cry.

Finally came the last wide curve. In it was mirrored Cologne Cathedral.

We were lucky. It was Saturday night, and suddenly, over a chorus of all the bells of Cologne, the deep Emperor Bell of the cathedral spilled its black ink into the Rhine.

That should have been the end. It would have been right that the Rhine now pour itself, with whatever freight it still carried from the Alps, the Graben, the gorge, the Seven Mountains, the bomb sites, into the ocean. But the ocean long ago moved away.

We folded our scenic strip maps and continued by train, past the clustered chimneys, ruined factories, new factories, homes sliced in half, new apartment buildings, and the flowers that bloomed in bomb sites. We looked at such things in Düsseldorf and Essen. But when the river became pathetically senile, futilely dividing itself between channels, we turned our faces away, and left it to the Low Countries to witness the feeble end to the long Rhine journey.

The Black Forest

I STOOD in oozing shoes, ankle deep in black-green mosses. Rain dripped from the tip of my nose, and I felt like a spruce tree. Like just another of that uniformed company of pendant-twigged, dripping stalwarts that marched before me, and behind me, and beside me, as far as my eyes could see. And that was fairly far, even in the drizzle, because the forest floor had been cleaned of upright growth between those spaced, rain-blackened trunks, which had all been stripped house high of side branches.

From where I stood the Black Forest seemed to have a single idea: spruce trees, and Norway spruce at that. This is the name attached to the tree in every nursery catalogue, every botany book in the English language. (In German it is *die Fichte*, or *Rottanne*.) It seems unfair that this Black Forest of Germany, which is known by name to possibly more people than any other forest in the world, should be dominated by a tree called "Norway" spruce. Justice is served, however, by the "spruce" part of the name, which is the older part. Originally "Pruce" meant the country of Prussia, and was applied to articles obtained from there. As early as 1500, "spruce beer" meant a beer from Prussia. (The "s" could have become attached from a lagging *das*, as [*da*]*s Preusse Bier*, perhaps.)

I had stepped into the deep moss there among those "Norwegian Prussians" when I left the path for a moment to sit (I thought) on a boulder. But it proved to be already occupied by oozing layers of liverworts and mosses, and by seven seedling spruce trees, each about three inches high.

The boulder seemed to repeat the succession in the Black Forest

It looked like a miniature representation of the forest. The boulder itself was, like the bedrock, gneiss. And on the bare gneiss, liverwort, chief pioneer of wet rocks around the world, had unrolled its carpet. Then the mosses had come, raising a carpet of deeper nap and catching the windborne seeds of the spruce trees. And now, finally, there stood the seven little spruce trees in the rain.

The boulder seemed to be telling a condensed version of the whole story of the Black Forest, but it was not, in truth, the whole story.

Foresters don't want the rest of the story to happen. They can't afford to let it happen. So they keep the forest clear of upstart seedlings. They know that, in the natural succession, spruce can only be a pioneer because it cannot successfully rear its own seedlings in the deep shade of its own horizontal branches. They know, too, that the most shade-tolerant trees of all are beeches, that they can thrive in the shade of spruces and can presently overtop them. With their wide-spreading stout branches beeches can easily elbow out spruces and eventually establish for themselves a permanent hereditary dynasty in the forest. So the woodsmen keep the forest floor clean. History has shown many similar cases of resistance to a destined succession: Herod's slaughter of the innocents; the murder of the two princes in the Tower of London. It happens in other forests, too. In America, vast areas of the Pacific Northwest are carefully controlled in order to keep the Douglas fir dominant, even though it is a pioneer tree like the Norway spruce.

Twenty-eight percent of Germany, we read, is still covered with forest, and 70 percent of that forest is evergreen, predominantly spruce. The spruce is a most efficient manufacturer of usable lumber. One can watch trees being cut and peeled carefully, so as not to damage those left standing; and one can see the long straight poles of spruce being carried away on Rhine barges.

The hand of the forester is firm on the forest, but not everywhere. There are places where the hold has been relinquished and others in which it has never been applied. It is in these places that one can read other chapters in the forest story, not told by the boulder with the seven seedling spruce trees.

The next chapter was told nearby. As I stood, I detected, through the sound of water dripping, the wilder sound of water rushing. I returned to the path and followed it toward the sound, and came to a stream, tumbling white over great chunks of gneiss. The path dipped to the stream to cross it on stepping-stones of gneiss, then climbed again.

There I found myself in a different kind of forest. It was still canopied by spruce trees, and from an airplane would still have worn the dark blue-green that gave the name to the Black Forest. But I was underneath, looking up—at the light green of beech branches. Only by peering up through openings in the light green could I see that the dark-green spruce tops were still there, above the closely woven shade. The spruces had only small tops left. They would not last long. There were young beeches rising between the middle-aged ones, and there was a scattering of sycamore maples, and a cluster of mountain ashes in a chimney of sunlight.

Evidently here the foresters had released their rigid control, perhaps because of the extreme roughness of the contour of the stream valley, or perhaps they had been forced to leave when this scenic section was converted into a public preserve. The tall, regularly spaced spruces overtopping the forest were the only evidence of their former control.

Another day, at an inn beside another white and noisy stream, I ordered blue trout, *Schwartzwaldforellen,* and waited, looking out through small panes of glass at seemingly endless ranks of blue-green spruces, and listening to the roar of water. The fräulein brought a

The Black Forest - three phases

nature's choice - beech

forester's choice - spruce

return of nature's choice

covered dish and whisked off the cover. There they lay, deep blue, two of them, just the right color for threading the deep-blue shade; and long and tapered in just the right shape for swimming against mountain currents.

Next day on the steep slopes above the deep lake called Titisee, I found the concluding chapter of the forest story, the conclusion that German foresters prevent wherever they are in control. Here the ranks of smooth gray beech trunks extended up and down and over the hills. Layers of gray branches spread horizontally, holding their thin tailored leaves flat. No blue-green of spruce was here, only beech, above in the canopy and below in the saplings and seedlings, of which there were few. Horizontal, wide-spreading roots laced the light-tan forest floor, which wore fallen beech leaves and nothing else. Such was the forest that once covered Germany, and would cover it again if men were to abandon cabbage plots and wheatfields and vineyards and factories and plots of spruce.

After exploring the Black Forest near the Rhine, from south of Freiburg to north of Heidelberg, we turned westward, and soon found that we had left the old basement rocks, the gneiss and granite, and were on the sandstone that we had seen used for the castles along the Rhine. Town after town glowed with its redness. Most delightful of these was the turreted, red-walled, aptly named town of Rottweil. Most impressive was the dark-red gloom of the Hohenzollern Castle, glowering from the divide between the Rhine and the Danube. This castle has been the setting for many tales of power politics and other machinations. But these are nothing compared with the story of usurped lands, of piracy and decapitation, recorded by the rivers and valleys at its feet.

The Wutach River, in its gorge, was once only a small tributary of the Rhine, but it was a swift one, chewing steadily farther back into the mountain. Then one day it bit away a final piece, and suddenly it had arrived at the valley of the Danube. The headwaters of the great river abandoned their course and deserted a future that included the gaiety of Vienna, and the mosques and minarets of the Black Sea; instead, they accepted a swift ride with the Wutach to the Rhine and, from there, an eventful trip to the Atlantic. This is called river piracy. As evidence of the event, the beheaded Danube now lies in a valley that is oversize for its diminished waters; and it still rolls along on its floor some pebbles of gneiss and granite col-

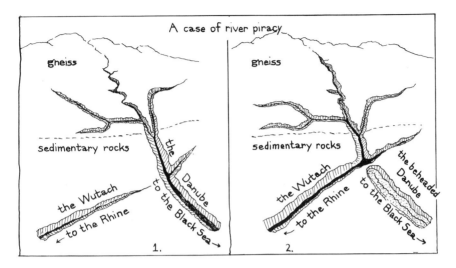

A case of river piracy

gneiss

sedimentary rocks

the Wutach

← to the Rhine

the

to the Black Sea →

Danube

to the

1.

gneiss

sedimentary rocks

the Wutach

← to the Rhine

the beheaded

Danube

to the Black Sea →

to the

2.

lected by its former headwaters, though it no longer extends far enough to reach the source of those rocks.

When one has looked long enough at forests and mountains and torn streams, it is often a relief to emerge into a man-made clearing. The Black Forest has many of these. The buildings, especially the barns with their excessively long, sloping roofs, and the drooping haystacks hung up to dry, record in their shapes, as does the Norway spruce, perfect designs for letting the rain run off.

Between the forest and the clearing there is always the forest edge, a ruffled skirt, with bird nests, abundant blossoming, and brilliant fruits. Always, that is, unless the forester is too efficient to permit a frothy edge; then the forest ends in a neat fence.

At the natural edge of one forest, in June, I found a wild geranium, *Geranium sylvaticum* (called in Germany, *Waldstorchschnabel*, "forest storkbill"; in storkless America the wild geranium is called "cranesbill"). I got out my hand lens and looked eagerly into the center of the flower to see the jutting hairs that had started one preacher-botanist on a train of thought that led to an important discovery.

One day, in 1787, at a time when the pollination of flowers was still not understood, Pastor Kristian Konrad Sprengel of Spandau happened to look into a *Waldstorchschnabel*. Later he wrote a book and recounted his inspection of that flower. He told about noticing hairs jutting out from the bases of the five petals, and about wondering what they were for, and about thinking that they stuck out like his own eyebrows, and then considering what his eyebrows were for. To keep sweat from running into his eyes, he decided, but what did those hairs keep from running into the flower? Obviously, rain. But why?

Pastor Sprengel pondered. He pondered so much about flowers that his congregation complained about his poorly prepared sermons. Probably he failed as well to make all the required inquiries into the state of his people's rheumatism and other afflictions. The next summer he looked into a forget-me-not, *Myosotis palustris* (*Vergismeinnicht*), and noted the yellow ring around the center. He noticed that many other flowers had a yellow mark at the throat. Why?

He observed that the center held a juice, and that the juice was protected against rain by hairs. He tasted the juice and found it sweet, though he knew that someone had written that it was poisonous and that bees benefited the flowers by drawing it off. Rain would certainly dilute this sweet juice, and bees might not come to drink it. Would it matter if they did not come?

The answers came gradually. The yellow mark, the hairs, the sweet nectar, began to reveal their functions. The pastor observed that a yellow mark seemed to indicate the place where a bee would drink. The jutting hairs seemed not to impede his probing tongue, but only to ensure that the sweetness would not be diluted by rain. And the benefit to the flower did not depend on what the bee carried away, as had been supposed, but on what he unknowingly left behind—pollen dust, which adhered to his hairy body as he moved from flower to flower. Some of the pollen grains were caught on a sticky surface in the flower, positioned to receive them; the presence of the grains triggered seed production.

When he had the answers to these questions, Pastor Sprengel began to ask others and to understand something about the importance of color, odor, structure, and other characters of flowers.

He wrote a book about his observations, but his publisher never bothered to send him a copy. He was shunned by men of science on account of his eccentricities. He lost his church at Spandau and went to Berlin, where he lived in straitened circumstances, and conducted botanical field trips on Saturdays and taught language.

One can inspect an original edition of his handsome, beautifully illustrated book at a few fortunate libraries, including the Library of Congress in Washington.

He begins:

Als ich in Sommer 1787 der Waldstorchschnabel (*Geranium sylvaticum*) aufmerksam betrachte, so fand ich . . .

As I, in the summer of 1787, considered the *Waldstorchschnabel*, I noticed . . .

And after the geranium story he tells about the forget-me-not:

Im folgenem Sommer undersichte ich das Vergismein-nicht (*Myosotis palustris*). Ich fand nicht nur, dass diese Blume Saft hat, sondern auch, dass dieser Saft gegen Regen völlig gesichert ist.

In the following summer I investigated the forget-me-not. I found not only that the flower has juice, but also that this juice is completely protected against rain.

Pastor Sprengel sees jutting hairs that remind him of his own eyebrows

Waldstorchschnabel

Ever since the day when the pastor with the bushy eyebrows looked into the wild geranium, botanists have been building upon what he learned. They have constructed much that would have made those grand eyebrows lift in amazement.

In a trim garden in Tübingen I saw an edging of Sprengel's *Vergismeinnicht*, "forget-me-not," and also *Stiefmütterchen*, "pansy," those familiar associates of gardens, valentines, and language-of-flowers nosegays.

At the back of the garden were spikes of *Digitalis*, known for sending another sort of message to the heart. These were not the colorful, towering hybrid foxgloves of show gardens, but the original wild form, native to European forests and marked with the color of dried blood. These markings, according to the Doctrine of Signatures (a medieval belief that the Creator of herbs had marked each one with a sign indicating its use), warned of the poisonous properties of the plant. Perhaps the color was responsible for some of the plant's country names in England: dead man's bell, bloody finger, witches' thimble. The German name is *Fingerhut*, meaning "thimble." But the botanical name *Digitalis* was the important one there in the garden at Tübingen, because that name was given to the plant by Leonhard Fuchs, who was professor of medicine at the university for the last thirty-one years of his life. Fuchs came to the new Protestant University at Tübingen in 1535 after becoming a Lutheran. In *De Historia Stirpium* published in 1542, he named *Digitalis*, taking pride in his naming, since, as he wrote in his Latin description, the Greek and Roman herbalists had left it *"destituta."* He described, for the most part, plants from the landscape about Tübingen, but he also included a few of the plants from newly discovered America, among them maize and marigold. His book, with five hundred outstanding woodcuts, was printed at Strassburg in the Rhine Valley, where also was printed, in 1530, another botanical milestone, the three-volume herbal of Otto Brunfels, a Carthusian monk turned Lutheran preacher.

Leonhard Fuchs had, apparently, received reports about America and her Indians, but he could hardly have comprehended that more than four hundred years after the publication of *De Historia Stirpium,* a copy of it would be flown (*flown?*) across the ocean to be placed in the library of the Morton Arboretum. Keeping it company are Otto Brunfels's *Herbarium vivae eicones* and Christian Konrad Sprengel's *Das entdeckte Geheimniss der Natur.*

It should be noted, incidentally, that at the time Fuchs was bestowing its lasting name on the *Digitalis,* the place where these great books now reside was under six-foot-tall prairie grass, and wild Indians were pursuing great herds of buffaloes.

Tübingen has a story in its name. In that part of the Black Forest there are many towns bearing names ending in -*ingen*. Those are old names, applied by the early Germanic people to their defended, nucleated settlements. That these settlements were made in heavily forested land is evidenced by the frequency of names containing *Wald*, "forest." That those forests were composed largely of beech is evidenced by the appearance of *Buch*, "beech," in many place names, and by the scarcity of any word indicating spruce.

Some names record the wildlife of the forests by including *Hirsh*, "deer"; and *Schwein*, "boar"; and *Biber*, "beaver." Some names tell of clearings in the forest by including *Heide*, "heather"; and -*au*, meadow. And some names record the method used in making those clearings, by ending in -*bran* or -*schwand*, "burning"; or -*hau*, "hewing"; or -*rode*, "rooting up." And some place names record the forest's return to a disturbed area, by including that pioneer, *Birche*, "birch tree."

But the place names do fail to record the most ubiquitous wildlife of heavily forested countries, the little old people. Everyone seems to know about them, and everyone in America seemed to understand when a certain small imported car wore a sign, "Made by elves in the Black Forest."

A BRIEF GLOSSARY OF THE LANDSCAPE
OF GERMANY

There are many names on maps of the Rhine and the Black Forest containing words or syllables that tell a lot about the landscape.

Names Indicating High Places
   Berg—mountain (often crowned by a castle, *Schloss*)
      as: Schlossberg
   Hohe—high
      as: Hohenzollern
   Hoch—high
      as: Höchst (highest)
   ober—upper
      as: Oberkirch
   nieder—lower
      as: Nieder Ingelheim
   kopf—head
      as: Totenkopf

Names in Which Rock Crops Out
   Stein—rock
      as: Neuenstein
   Fels—rock
      as: Drachenfels
   Ley (Lei)—rock
      as: Lorelei

The redness of Bundsandstein, "colorful sandstone," is suggested by:
   rot—red
      as: Rottweil
   Röte—redness
      as: Röthenbach

Names Indicating that Volcanic Activity Resulted in Springs, Which
Resulted, in Turn, in Resorts
    Bad—bath
      as: Wiesbaden, Baden Baden

Names Referring to Forests
    Wald—forest
      as: Schönwald
    Buch—beech tree
      as: Buchenwald
    schwartz—refers to the blackness of spruce woods
      as: Schwartzwald
    Hirsch—stag, *Schwein*—wild boar, and *Biber*—beaver were seen around
      Hirschhorn, Schweinfurt, and Biberach

Names Indicating Human Settlement
    -ingen—indicates an ancient nucleated settlement
      as: Tübingen
    -dorf—indicates a more recent settlement
      as: Düsseldorf
    -au—meadow, which is one kind of clearing
      as: Oberammergau
    -feld—field, a second kind of clearing
      as: Blumenfeld
    Heide—heather, a third kind of clearing
      as: Heidenheim
    -schwand—indicates that a clearing was made by burning
      as: Höchenschwand
    Brand—also indicates burning
      as: Brandenburg
    -bach—brook (indicates that a favorite site for settlement was beside a
      stream)
      as: Eberbach
    Mühl—mill (often used with *Bach*)
      as: Mühlenbach
    -kirche—church (often built in the forest)
      as: Waldkirche
    -tal—valley (a good site for settlement)
      as: Wuppertal
    -heim—home
      as: Mannheim
    Roth—indicates clearing by rooting out the forest
      as: Rothenburg

TO READ BEFORE READING THE LANDSCAPE
OF GERMANY

The Rhine, From Its Source to the Sea by Karl Stieler, H. Wachenhusen, and F. W. Häcklander (Lippincott, Philadelphia, 1878). Translated from the German by G. C. T. Bartley and has 425 illustrations. This grand edifice of a book, nobly and lovingly constructed by many able Germans, is long out of print but will amply reward a search through libraries. You cannot afford to miss its illustrations, its history, its legends, its descriptions—but most of all its illustrations. Color would insult them.

Conversation with the Earth by Hans Cloos (Knopf, New York, 1953). Translated by E. B. Garside. Chapters 17, 18, 19, 20 deal with the geology of the Rhine and the Black Forest. You will probably read all the other chapters as well.

The Background of Plant Ecology by Anton Kerner (Iowa State College Press, Ames, 1951). A translation, by Heny S. Conrad, of the German book *The Plant Life of the Danube Basin*, 1863. The translator says that this book "is the immediate and direct parent of all later works on Plant Ecology." This pioneering book treats lands lying close to the Black Forest.

Exotic Zoology, by Willy Ley (Viking, New York, 1959). Read chapter 7, "Footprints in Red Sandstone."

The Finest Legends of the Rhine by Wilhelm Ruland (Verlag von Hoursch and Bechstedt, Köln-Ehrenfeld, Germany, 1930). The English edition is a small book, often available where the Panoramic Maps of the Rhine are sold. Sample: ". . . every human feeling has its place in the hero's biography, great joy, deep sorrow, passionate love, glowing hatred, heroism and perfidy, cowardice and high courage, until at last the legend of Siegfried ends in a pitiful wail of grief."

Unsere Waldbäume, Sträucher und Zwerfholzgewächse by Ludwig von Klein (Carl Winter's Universitätsbuchhandlung, Heidelberg, 1924). An excellent small book of identification for trees and shrubs, with colored illustrations, in German.

Sommerblumen by Fritz Fischer and Karl Mahler (Verlag Erich Hoffmann, Heidenheim, Germany, 1959). The colored drawings of wild flowers, and a few ferns and fruited shrubs, are spirited. The text is in German.

Denmark

The Bogs of Denmark

≫ 1

Denmark is young land—soft, spineless, soggy, and immature, lacking mountains, canyons, caves, waterfalls, and other such dramatic evidences of past turmoil. Nor does it display even such minor evidences as trees with thick bark or aromatic foliage, or evergreens. Its insignificant mass has been haphazardly arranged by the most gigantic of bulldozers, the great ice sheet, and its outline has been the much-handled plaything of a fumbling sea.

Admirers may protest, of course, that the land claiming the most ancient kingdom in the world, and the oldest flag, is not all *that* young. And they can point to the island of Bornholm far out in the Baltic, which is composed of solid granite, the "basement rock," the oldest granite in Europe; to a brief stretch of old limestone cliffs just south of Copenhagen; to the dazzling chalk cliffs of the island of Møn; and to the flotsam of the sea, bits of amber, the fossilized resin of an extinct and ancient pine.

True enough, but excepting such small exhibits, Denmark belongs, geologically, to only the very latest hours of yesterday. Its main constituent is boulder clay brought down from Norway and Sweden in the polar ice sheets and dumped unevenly when the ice melted.

The unevenness resulted in many depressions among the clay hills, in which glacial meltwater, increased by snow and then by rain, collected. From most of these depressions the water eventually found exit toward the sea, and those hollows gave rise to Denmark's many pleasant lakes and streams. But, from some, water found no such exit, and it was these that were destined to be important because they gave rise to Denmark's famous bogs.

Of course the undrained bodies of water did not become bogs overnight. They were open lakes at first, with the usual fringes of water lilies, cattails, bull-rushes, and with good fishing. But gradually their unstirred, unaerated water became brown and acid and unfit for the bacteria of decay. Whatever was received on the surface of these great open bowls sank quietly to the bottom, intact, preserved from decay, to rest upon earlier arrivals and to be pressed down and compacted by still later ones.

First to arrive on the bare clay hills around the bogs was a small plant with tiny scalloped leaves and white flowers, the mountain dryad, *Dryas*. It was soon joined by a miniature shrub, the Arctic willow. We met those two earlier on top of the Alps. Leaves and stems of *Dryas* and pollen grains of Arctic willow floated down on the open water, and settled quietly on the clean boulder-clay bottom. Soon, roughly shaped arrowheads fell to rest on the clay, too. The reindeer hunters were following their prey northward as the tundra retreated.

Each spring brought more and more kinds of pollen grains to the bogs. The trees moving north into Denmark were birch, hazel, and aspen. All bore their pollen in long, dangling catkins, shaken by the wind. Sometimes, the surfaces of the bogs were yellow with it.

On the surface of one bog a paddle carved from hazel wood floated, and then sank down among the pollens and other plant parts. It had been skillfully shaped with a thin knife of flint.

The cool, moist climate that had followed the retreat of the glacier was slowly changing. As it became drier and drier birch trees appeared, not in a forest formation but widely spaced across the hills. A few pine trees appeared, too, but they were only stunted, thick-barked individuals. As birch and pine pollens collected at the bottoms of the bogs, some flint pieces, many showing fine craftsmanship, joined them.

Across that sparsely covered landscape, one day there came a great aurochs with splendid, widely curving horns. Hunters pursued him. One arrow found the aurochs, and then another. Still he fled, plunging at last into a bog. The placid surface of the water, reflecting pine and birch and hazel, was stirred and reddened. The aurochs sank, the water cleared, the reflections straightened. The tragedy of the beast left no mark on the surface, but was recorded only at the bottom of the bog. Artifacts fashioned from the bones of other aurochs also found their way there, some carved with fine patterns, some made into harpoon heads.

By about 6000 B.C. the pines were taking over the landscape. No longer were they dwarfed and widely separated; now they stood tall in the close formation of pine forests. In the clearings and at the edges of the lakes, birch trees grew. Beneath the trees men sat and chipped flint to make axes and arrowheads. They had learned to barb their arrows, too, using two small chips of flint. The bogs have given up an arrow from this period. It still has one flake of flint embedded in resin on one side of the shaft and the resin on the other side shows the mark of another chip. The climate then was still dry, but it was gradually growing warmer.

Here and there among the pines an occasional oak seedling was finding life possible. Presently the upright unity of the endless pine forests was broken by rounded forms that were bare and leafless in the winter. The oaks were taking over. By about 5000 B.C. they were dominating the landscape.

The pine society faded out gradually, and by 4000 B.C. the pines were gone from Denmark. The climate, which had been warming up for the last thousand years, grew moist once again.

Shade had now come to the land: deep shade to the uplands with their layered canopies of oak branches, and filtered shade to the lowlands with their mixed assemblages of ash, elm, linden, and alder. From these dense forests the aurochs, a creature of thin woods and open lands, was gone. But there was still good hunting for bear, wild boar, red deer, and beaver. In one bog a fisherman left a fishhook carved out of bone, and some man or woman lost, or deposited, an amber necklace.

A new way of life was coming to the land. Men who planted seeds and cared for the plants were arriving from further east. They brought with them animals, which they fed and cared for, animals such as the native hunters and fishermen had never seen before: oxen, pigs, and sheep. And they brought pouches filled with seeds of barley, and wheat, plants never known in this land.

Some other seeds came in by accident, mixed with the cereals or riding along in fur or clothing. In the wake of the newcomers sprang up two kinds of plantain: the broad-leaved one, *Plantago major;* and the narrow-leaved one, *Plantago lanceolata*. Hundreds of years later when plantain arrived in America, it would be called "white man's foot" by the American Indians, who noticed that it became established across America wherever the white man went. Plantain pollen began to settle down into the bogs, among the pollens of oak, ash, linden, elm, and alder.

In addition to the new plants and new animals, these "new stone"—Neolithic—farmers brought new sounds to the forests, chopping, followed by a loud crashing of trees, and then by the sound of rushing fire, as the slashed-down forests were burned to make cultivated land. Many axes with polished flint heads dropped into the bogs, where the brown acid water was turning even darker as rains washed the charcoal from the burned forests into the hollows. A thin black layer was deposited on top of the tree pollens.

The sphagnum moss envelops a bone-comb offering

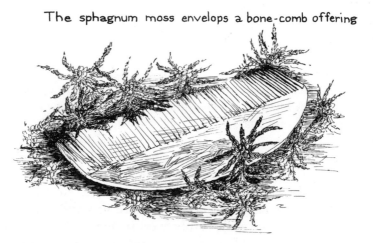

By about 2000 B.C., however, a new assortment of pollens was drifting down and covering the charcoal layer. Where the forest had been cut and burned, the soil used for a time and then abandoned in favor of new clearings, there the birch and hazel had taken possession and shaken out their pollen. Where the new clearings were producing crops of barley and wheat, there cereal pollen was launched on the wind. The remaining oaks added their bit.

Slowly the bogs were filling up, not only with light wind-borne stuffs, with fallen leaves and twigs and branches, and with objects thrown in, but also with plant life that grew naturally in the bog water. The dominant inhabitant of acid bogs, in both North America and Europe, the sphagnum moss, also called "peat moss," formed the bed into which all arrivals were received and enmeshed.

Sphagnum moss has a sort of everlasting life, as its living green stems rise in dense masses from the dead brown stems of former growth, which in turn are piling up on yet older parts and compacting them into peat. Hollow cells, with pores in their walls, enable the sphagnum, alive or dead, to hold much water.

As the sphagnum and all that was entangled in its mass filled up the bogs and reduced the expanse of open water, men were learning that a good supply of fuel was available there. In the solid parts they began to dig up bricks of peat, heaping them up to dry. And new sphagnum grew where the old had been cut out.

One day a precious thing was brought to rest in a less solid section of the bog, gleaming gold and contrasting with the dull brown of the place. It had taken a long time for the craftsmen of these

Trundholm bog envelops the Sun chariot

northern lands to achieve the skill to shape such a delicate horse, modeled in the round, to trace his mane in fine lines and shape a star around each eye, to make a wagon for him to draw and a disc to be carried on edge on the wagon, and then finally to cover the disc with gold and to decorate the gold with fine lines. It had taken a long time for the copper and tin for bronze-making to arrive from the south.

But there it was, a fine expression of man's concept of the sun as a disc being drawn across the sky by a horse. The people who brought the image went away and left it. It was gradually engulfed. No matter how many folk knew about its presence in the bog, there were none who would remove it and risk offending the god to whom it had been offered.

Another product of the bronze-makers' skill was a wind instrument with a long twisted tube, flaring gradually to a decorated disc. It is tempting to believe that the horn, which the Danes call a *lur,* was blown in a salute, or petition, before being consigned to the acid waters. More than thirty *lurer* were left in the bog.

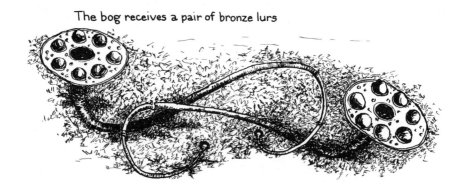

The bog receives a pair of bronze lurs

These Bronze Age deposits had long ago been received into the bogs, but whatever gods may have been propitiated by them were still being worshiped and feared when a different sort of offering was brought one day, in winter or late spring.

The men who brought the offering came not to dig peat but to use a former peat-digging place. Into the grave-shaped place they lowered the body of a man. He was dressed in a cloak and a pointed skin cap. The men did not remove the noose of plaited skin drawn tight around his throat. And even as they turned away the brown waters and a fresh growth of moss started to enfold the body. The man with the noose has come to be known as the "Tollund man," because of the place where the bog lay.

In another bog a woman's body was deposited, and precautions were taken to make sure she would not rise again. Her executioners broke her right arm off, and fastened the left one tightly across her chest with a strap. Across her breast they laid a stout willow stake.

The woman was not dressed as if she were going to her execution, but wore a plaid wool skirt and a lambskin cape. She had fastened her head kerchief with a pin made from a bird bone and carried in her pocket a comb, carved from bone and well designed and decorated. It is possible that the bog woman was considered a sort of evil fairy or witch, for the bog in which she was found is called Huldremose, and a *huldre* was a sorceress, who enchanted young men with singing and dancing.

There were many, beside the Tollund man and the Huldre woman, who were consigned to the bogs during this period, which is known as the Pre-Roman Iron Age.

In time, simple tools of iron began finding their way into the bogs, and then silver appeared, in the form of a great cauldron twenty-seven inches in diameter. It was made up of plates bearing figures of animals and gods that were beyond the experience, even beyond the imagining, of local peasants. There were scenes from a bullfight, for example, and elephants. It is certain that the god who was being honored, or propitiated, was powerful indeed to merit such a shining and interesting offering. But it is equally certain that his days of power were reaching their end, for the Christian era was almost at hand.

After the Year One, several changes came to the bogs. A new tree pollen began to mingle with that of the oak. The cooler, moister climate had brought the beech tree. Now Roman helmets were deposited in the bogs, and handsome swords, drinking horns, and two elegant, decorated carts. Some of the new objects may have been acquired by travelers, some by traders dealing with peoples to the south, some may have been booty. The sphagnum mosses enveloped them all.

In about A.D. 400 a man was brought to a bog where peat-cutters had been at work for centuries. This man was naked, and his throat had been slit from ear to ear. Over the deep cutting where his body lay, the bog waters and the sphagnum moss closed, and the acids of the bog started tanning his skin. He was, much later, to be called the "Grauballe man," after the name of the bog.

As the cool, moist climate continued and the deep shade of forests of beech trees covered the hills between the bogs and the farms, offerings of a different nature began to appear in the bogs: thank offerings for victories in battle; bribe offerings for whatever acts were thought to have irritated the gods into helping the other side. Many swords and shields were given, and horses were sacrificed (two were poleaxed and stabbed, and their eyes were gouged out). The edge of one sword was made jagged and saw-toothed so that it could never be used again. A handful of Roman coins was deposited. Perhaps these had once been received in payment for Danish amber.

Among great deposits of war gear, war canoes appear. In one deposit of the early centuries A.D., men sank three boats. Another deposit, slightly earlier, was a great canoe, fifty-three feet long, rising to two high ramlike ends, a forerunner of the seagoing long-boats of the Viking era. Into the bog with it went 8 swords; 138 spears with shafts made from the branches of ash, hazel, willow, and mountain ash; coats of iron chain mail; and many wooden shields. The bog enveloped all.

As time went on many bogs filled up entirely, so that it was possible to walk right across the place where open water had once reflected the sky. But Denmark was gradually getting new interests, new ways of life, and new gods, who made different demands. Soon even the bogs that still remained open were receiving no offerings.

But the peat-diggers were still busy. And that is how we first began to learn the history of the bogs. On June 4, 1773, a peat-digger brought up a human foot in his spade. He and his co-workers carefully removed the three feet of peat that covered the rest of the body. It lay naked, except for a skin cap. Its arms were crossed behind its back, and its throat was cut. The judge of the district where the find was made put a notice in the local paper in an appeal for information about the man, although he himself suspected that the body belonged to a more distant past than any reader of the notice could have heard about in reminiscences of even the oldest settlers.

In 1797 peat-cutters uncovered another man. This one had curly red hair and was dressed in clothes made of skin. Beside his body lay three hazel rods, known by the peat-diggers themselves to be potent against sorcery. They made a coffin for the body and buried it in the churchyard.

More and more bodies were found, and many of them were re-buried in local churchyards. But people were becoming aware of the preservative qualities of bog waters, and of the antiquity of the bodies.

Meanwhile scientists were beginning to use the compound microscope, and acquiring new skills at identifying tree pollens that were found in the bogs along with the other organic remains. In 1916 Lennart Von Post of Stockholm reported to the Geological Congress in Oslo his findings about pollen. He had found out a great deal about the lasting qualities of the outer skin of pollen grains; also that the shapes of pollen grains from different species of trees were distinctive and identifiable; and that the successive horizontal layers of tree pollens recorded the changes in forest types.

The scientific study of bogs is now highly developed. Researchers use a special boring device, which brings up from a known depth a core sample with its layers undisturbed, and they are equipped with techniques for centrifuging pollen grains from the peat moss. At the Geodetisk Institut in Copenhagen, one Danish botanist kindly prepared a pollen slide for me to place under the microscope, so that I might see how it was done. He also permitted me to examine other slides from the files. It was exciting to look at the minute specks of what had been potent living dust thousands of years ago, and to realize that those grains had kept the record at the bottom of the bog through all those centuries before men had even learned to read the stars.

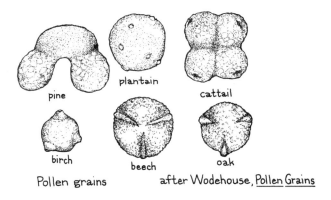

Pollen grains   after Wodehouse, <u>Pollen Grains</u>

And then came yet another tool. At the University of Chicago, Willard F. Libby discovered that the amount of radioactive carbon (carbon 14) that every living thing contains begins to decrease at a fixed rate the moment it dies. By comparing the amount of radioactivity in a living plant or animal with the amount in a dead one, it is possible to know how long ago it died. The measurement of radioactivity is done with a Geiger counter, an instrument that gives off clicking sounds at a rate corresponding to the amount of radioactivity present. This kind of carbon 14 dating, or radiocarbon dating, was applied to the bog pollen, to the bodies of the bog people, to their clothing, to the wood of their boat offerings; and their antiquity was confirmed.

By now the public was fully alerted. When two brothers digging peat in the Tollund bog one spring day in 1950 found a body, the same one I described a few pages ago, they did not make a coffin for it, nor did they send for the local sexton. They sent instead for the police, who brought along representatives from the local museum, who telephoned the well-known archaeologist Peter Glob at the university in Aarhus. With the museum staff and others, he investigated the body. From the coloring of the sphagnum below and above, it was learned that the man had been deposited in an old peat-cutting; from the pollens and a certain reddish peat layer common in bogs at a known date, it was established that he had been deposited there about two thousand years ago. From the fact that his wisdom teeth had developed, it was found that he was over twenty years old; from the contents of his stomach and intestines it was established that his last meal had consisted of the seeds of native plants; it was also noted that his execution had taken place in winter or early spring, since there were no seeds of summer fruits such as raspberry, strawberry, or whortleberry; and that he had lived for twelve to twenty-four hours after eating.

Eleven miles away from the Tollund bog, peat-cutters uncovered another body, in the Grauballe bog. These peat-cutters summoned the local antiquarian, who sent word to Peter Glob. A crew of museum experts made a long investigation. X-rays, made at the Aarhus hospital, showed that the man had been about thirty years old and had suffered a skull wound made with a blunt instrument. A fingerprint expert found that he had been unaccustomed to hard labor. Pollen analysis revealed rye pollen among the other cereal pollens; and indicated that the burial had taken place somewhere between the Year One and A.D. 400. Carbon 14 dating placed the date at A.D. 310, plus or minus one hundred years.

At the small Silkeborg Museum we gazed at the gentle resigned-looking face of the man from Tollund bog. Then we read the list, which hung on the wall, naming the plants from which had come the seeds that formed the gruel of the man's last meal. Knotweed was there, and bindweed, chickweed, mustard, pigweed, shepherd's purse, plantain, and others. They were almost the same weeds that might be gathered along many an American roadside today. Certainly they included some of the chief adversaries in our own garden. Those plants, however, did not cross the Atlantic until more than a thousand years after the Tollund man had died.

At the Aarhus Museum, where the Grauballe man is exhibited, we had the privilege of a talk with Peter Glob himself, who told us where we could see a bog exploration in progress. The site was at the end of a lake. We watched three students at work in their deep, straight-sided excavation. They were removing bits of the dark bog with small flat trowels, investigating each trowelful carefully and then evidently depositing it in some appointed order. Digging was going on at that point, they explained, because workmen who were putting through a ditch there had come upon a wooden shield. The students showed us their finds thus far: two broken jars, a spearhead, a knife, a skull, some bones.

The Danes had been exploring and interpreting their bogs for years when an ecologist, Johannes Iversen, decided to test the suppositions scientists had made about Neolithic agriculture. Iversen had been first to notice the charcoal layer, and the change in pollens that was associated with it. The scene was set as nearly as possible as it had been when the Neolithic farmer arrived in Denmark. Iversen chose a plot of mixed forest, without beech (which did not become important until later). He then took stone axes found in bogs and fitted them with new hafts, and he and coworkers chopped down a section of forest. They soon learned not to take long swinging blows, but only quick short ones. A tree of medium size, about a foot thick, could be cut with a stone ax in about an hour's work. Then they burned the plot and sowed seeds of primitive grains in the ashes.

The seeds throve in the ashes, and produced a good crop; similar seeds sown in a control area, which was only hoed and kept free from weeds, failed to produce a crop. After the crop in the burned plot was harvested, the plot was not cultivated further, but it is being closely observed.

The experiment was begun in 1953. We saw the test acre, in Draved Woods near Løgumkloster, on a summer day in 1958.

The bog story, a composite account, with evidence from many Danish bogs

		The changing scene around the bog, as recorded by pollen deposits in bog	Bog finds (not drawn to scale)
cool	moist	1000 A.D. beech forest — beech	boat (restored), Roman coins
cool	moist	0 oak forest, beech increasing — oak	iron sword with silver hilt
warm	dry	1000 B.C. oak forest and rye, buckwheat — oak	bog man, lurs in pairs
warm	dry	2000 B.C. hazel, birch, plantain — birch, hazel, plantain	flint ax heads (a few shafts)
		The coming of the Neolithic farmer	thin layer of charcoal
warm	moist	4000 B.C. oak and mixed forest, no pine — oak, linden, ash, elm, alder	amber beads, bone fishhook
warm	dry	5000 B.C. oak forest, some pine — oak, pine	weapon of reindeer antler
warm	dry	6000 B.C. pine forest — pine	ornamental bone of aurochs, bone harpoon head
cool	dry	7000 B.C. sparse growth; birch, pine — birch, pine	finely worked flint
cool	dry	8000 B.C. sparse low growth; birch, pine — birch, dwarfed pine	flint ax
cool	moist	9000 B.C. birch, hazel, aspen — hazel, birch, aspen	paddle of hazelwood
cool	moist	10 000 B.C. tundra Dryas, dwarf birch	arrowhead flint scraper

Doctor Iversen put into my hands one of the stone axes with which the trees had been felled. The stump at my feet was still black and charred. But around the stump the first woody plants were beginning to make their return. They were the pioneers, birch and hazel. Later generations of men will have to check the next arrivals of plants to see if the succession develops as predicted. Thus far, at least, the scenes are being reenacted as written in the bog.

The Seacoast

Wᴇʀᴇ ɪᴛ ironed out straight, the salt-encrusted ribbon that is Denmark's coast could wrap up some great, severe, uncomplicated hulk of land fully ten times as large. But all ruffled and knotted as it is, it serves instead to gift-wrap a small, merry, and highly complicated land. And much of its length is in mere snippets, surrounding four hundred-odd islands, which well deserve gift-wrapping.

We decided to follow the ribbon of seacoast around Denmark and back to our starting point, Copenhagen naturally.

One is always aware of the sea in Copenhagen, if for no other reason than the omnipresent sea gulls. We saw a gull perched atop the head of a sturdy statue of a fishwife standing near the harbor. A lot of gulls, in fact, seemed to be awaiting turns at that spot, hovering raucously above the living fishwives who stood near the statue, wrapping living eels in newspaper for their waiting customers. In a nearby park there were actually more gulls than pigeons on the grass, snatching up the grains that a Copenhagen woman was tossing out to them from her bicycle basket. (The swarms of bicycles we saw in the city added a comment on the smallness and flatness of the land.) Both the common gull and the larger herring gull were there, together with the brown immature ones of both kinds. We watched the mature herring gulls slant in on their gray wings, braking with their black wing tips as they extended their yellow legs for a landing on the grass, and we talked about Niko Tinbergen's long watch of the gulls in Holland, recounted in his fine book, *The Herring Gull's World*. The mature ones all looked alike to us, and it

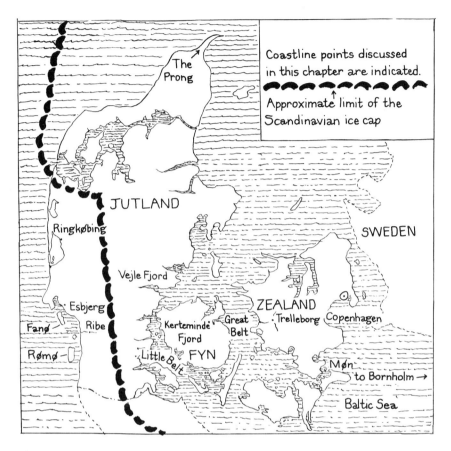

Coastline points discussed in this chapter are indicated.

Approximate limit of the Scandinavian ice cap

was hard to see how they could tell each other apart. But Tinbergen had found that the male herring gull does indeed recognize his mate arriving at the herring colony, picking her out from a white gull web approaching across the sky. He will permit only her to enter the small territory that is theirs. Should a stranger intrude, there is always a great show of ferocity, with wings elevated and legs spread. Instead of pulling each other to bits, however, both gulls lower their heads and start viciously pulling up the dune grass by its roots.

Out along the harbor we stopped for a look at another expression of the close relations between land and sea. The Gefion Fountain showed the giantess Gefion guiding her four stout ocean-splashing, ocean-spouting bulls as they plowed Denmark loose from Sweden.

An old legend tells that the giantess, who was a close friend of the great god Odin, was taken by Odin to his favorite island, Funen, and had longed to have such a gentle green island of her own. She looked at the sound separating Funen from Sweden, and decided that there was room there for her island. Disguised, she appeared in the court of the king of Sweden, made friends with him, and charmed him with her story-telling skill. While he was relaxed and bemused at one of her best stories, she lightly asked him if he would be willing to give her a piece of land around which she could plow in a night and a day. Smiling, he agreed. Gefion rushed away, up into the north, where she picked for her husband a *jotun*, one of the mighty frost giants. She bore him four mighty sons, changed them into bulls, and hitched them to her plow. Then, in one night and one day, she plowed around a piece of Sweden and finished by plowing it loose from the mainland. It floated free, and as the king stood on the new shore and fumed, she made a stout hauser and hitched the new island to a shoal. It is fitting that the island is called Zealand, "sea land."

Actually, Copenhagen's island is not free-floating, though it looks that way, and occasionally seems to feel that way—probably the effect of Tivoli and, perhaps, the fine native beers.

We took a small boat out into the harbor past the statue of Hans Christian Andersen's Little Mermaid. As we approached her another small boat took off from the shore, and the man and young woman on board smiled and waved to us. It happened they were the King of Denmark and the Crown Princess. Denmark, one remembers, is small. The Little Mermaid, partly of the land and partly of the sea, is seated, as is Denmark herself, on firm granite. The gulls seemed to be disputing the site with her.

Denmark's firm foundation is deeply hidden. Recent deep drillings by oil prospectors (which, many are thankful, have failed) found that the ancient basement rock lay three thousand feet deep under Funen, and much deeper under Jutland.

We decided first on a brief trip to what is the oldest and most distant part of the coastline. So a side excursion by boat took us to the island of Bornholm far out in the Baltic. We enjoyed that coastline, first as we looked up from the sea to its dark heather-wrapped granite and then as we looked down from the cliffs and across the sea to Sweden; but most of all we enjoyed it from its many footpaths, especially the long cliff walk. This bulk of dramatic rock scenery did not really seem to belong to Denmark. That is exactly what Sweden and Germany and Russia have also thought at various times, as the island's fortresses, and its round churches built to serve as fortresses, give ample evidence.

Returning to the softer masses of Denmark's Baltic coast, we stopped at another place where the foundation shows, but here a foundation of soft chalk laid down geologic ages later by a quiet sea. This was the island of Møn, and we scrambled and climbed over its high chalk cliffs looking for fossils and flint nodules. Walking along its cliff top, we followed a footpath under beech trees, through masses of lily of the valley, primrose, hepatica, oxalis, and windflower plants. Møn, like Bornholm, seemed just too dramatic and too skeleton-revealing to be part of the Danish landscape, so we turned from the Baltic and from Denmark's bony bed-rock structure and moved on to her better-padded parts.

the forest canopy

the forest margin

the forest floor

From the chalk cliffs of the island of Møn

The canopy tree, *a*, is beech, *Fagus sylvatica (bog* [Danish])
The forest-margin small trees are: *b* high-bush cranberry, *Viburnum opulus (kalkved)*
               c hedge maple, *Acer campestris (navr)*
               d hawthorn, *Crataegus oxyacantha (hvidtjørn)*

The forest-floor herbs are: *e* lily of the valley, *Convallaria majalis (lilien konval)*
           f cowslip, *Primula veris (hulkravet kodriver)*
           g touch-me-not, *Impatiens noli-tangere (spring balsamin)*
           h anemone, *Anemone nemorosa (hvid anemone)*
           i hepatica, *Anemone hepatica (blaa anemone)*
           j oxalis, *Oxalis acetosella (skovsyre)*

We crossed the bridge from the island of Møn and turned northward along the west coast on Zealand to visit some havens of the Vikings. It is interesting that when their booty-laden ships came home from England, the Vikings did not tie up on the nearest parts of the Danish coast—far from it. They sought, instead, the considerably more distant eastern coasts. Why, we were to discover later.

The shaping of the Viking lairs began during the last period of European glaciation, beneath an arm of the great ice sheet called the Scandinavian lobe. For a long time the southern edge of the huge ice mass was stationary over eastern Denmark, melting and depositing its accumulated burden of boulder clay and chalk, while new ice continually pushed down from the north, carrying more and more debris. Under the ice, streams of meltwater were digging dark, tunnel-like channels through the frozen earth. To the west of the ice sheet its meltwaters spread flat, outwash plains of sand and gravel.

When the ice sheet finally withdrew to its northern home, the sea invaded the low places among the glacial deposits, or moraines, creating islands. Long fingers of the sea pried their way into the narrow channels that had been cut by meltwater, creating long inlets, or fjords, or *viks*.

Men came, hunters first, then farmers who slashed down trees, burned them, and planted their crops in the ashy soil. The population grew and grew, and after a while the habitable areas of this submerged section simply became too crowded. The land was rich enough, but it was overpopulated for the simple agricultural economy. A custom was that elder sons might stay home (generally to fight their neighbors), but the younger sons had to leave. Many became sea raiders—Vikings—whose longboats, tough, buoyant, flexible, shallow, narrow, were built to conform to the fjords, as well as the open sea. These were rough people, these Vikings, great bearded men who inspired terror among settled peoples from the Arctic to the Mediterranean. In England (which the Danish Vikings favored because of its resemblance to their home country), a special prayer was inserted in the liturgy:

A Furore Normannorum Libera Nos

But the raids, the pillage, the killing went on for centuries before the fury of the Norsemen was not stopped but at last absorbed.

Along the west coast of Zealand we came to a place where two small streams had joined before flowing out to the arm of the sea called the Great Belt. The sea invaded the Y formed by the two streams, and made the inlet into a good haven. Longboats then (not now, because the inlet no longer opens to the sea) could sail right up to safe harbor. Sven Forkbeard (of a famous line—son of Harald Bluetooth, grandson of Gorm the Old, and father of Canute the Great) selected the site at the top of the Y for building the great Viking fortress, Trelleborg.

We looked across the meadows where fat horses were nibbling grass and imagined high dragon-headed prows moving up the river. It is possible that even then the fields around the fort were being grazed, for we know that the Vikings had horses, but the surrounding hills must have been deep under forest. It is estimated that eight thousand oak trees were used in the construction of Trelleborg. Thick oak planks standing on end formed the walls, which bulged like the sides of a hull. Stout oak logs supported the roofs of outside galleries. Oak shingles covered the long roofs, which had slightly convex ridges. The buildings looked as if they had been constructed by men who were more accustomed to building ships than warrior's dormitories. At least twelve hundred men could have been quartered there. One of the buildings has been reconstructed, but since all the original wood had been rotted away, leaving only dark marks in the clay soil, considerable imagination had to be used.

From Trelleborg we crossed the Great Belt to the east coast of the island of Funen, where the Kerteminde Fjord cuts westward and then turns sharply southward. It may have been this turning that influenced the crew of one particular longboat in about A.D. 950 to choose this inlet for the grave of their ship and its dead chieftain. There they could leave the prow pointing south, where every one of these northern people knew Valhalla quite naturally lay. Perhaps the crew took one long last pull at the oars, and then all leaped over the side to allow the lightened war galley to run aground. Next, it appears, they dug a niche for the prow and forced the ship a bit further ashore, covering it with thick boards, followed by a layer of mud from the fjord, and a final layer of turf. They had left their chief with his horses and dogs, his best garments, his swords, ready for his journey to the halls of Valhalla. They even provided him with an anchor for his arrival there.

Word must have spread through the great forests and the small clearings, rumors of treasure buried in the hill. Inevitably, robbers and vandals came and broke into the ship-grave. They took away the body of the chieftain with its splendid raiment. They took his weapons, but one spur dropped off and remained to tell the story. They took whatever other treasures were in the burial chamber. Then they left, and the slightly rounded, man-made hill, making only an inconspicuous bulge in the flat farmland, waited almost a thousand years for discovery. In 1935 it was found by an Odense apothecary. The National Museum has prepared the site so that all can go down to see the ship (called the "Ladby ship") in place in its grave.

The few steps of the cellar-like entrance took us down to a gallery where we could walk around the ship. It is twenty-two meters long and three meters wide, and we could see that there had originally been seven stout oak planks on each side, overlapping, "clinker-built." The oak was, for the most part, decomposed, but the rivets had been left behind, lying in the lines of their original positions. We looked down at horse bones and dog bones, and the iron ax that had probably been used to kill them. Then we came up into the sun and grass and gull landscape.

From Fyn we crossed another channel, the Little Belt, to the east coast of the peninsula of Jutland. The rivers there had flowed down a long slope and had cut longer channels, which the invading sea had converted into fjords. We followed Vejle Fjord to its head at Vejle, and then took a winding road through a glen to Jelling, ancient seat of the kings. At Jelling, in a neat, flowery churchyard, between two tumuli, we saw two famous rune stones. Because they are so famous, it was a surprise that we were free to walk up to them and to run our fingers over the granite to follow the intricacies of the serpentlike, entwined, flat carved ribbon surrounding the first depiction of Christ in this land where allegiance had long belonged to Thor. The smaller stone had been erected by Gorm the Old, last of the pagan kings, to the memory of his wife, Queen Thyra (or Thyri). The larger stone had been erected by Harald Bluetooth, first of the Christian kings, to the memory of Gorm, his father, and to his mother. It reads:

Harald, the king, commanded this memorial to be made for his father Gorm, and his mother Thyra; that Harald who won over all Denmark to himself, and Norway, and converted the Danes to Christianity.

The inlets north of Vejle Fjord were all deep, and all had long-boats in their past.

Our next stop on Jutland was to be the west coast, which the longboats seem to have passed by when they returned from their raids. As we crossed the peninsula we crossed the line where the edge of the last ice sheet had stood, leaving behind boulder-clay hills and a submergent shore. We entered instead upon flat reaches of outwash gravel and sand and soon were facing the wind off the North Sea, and feeling the sting of the windblown sand of the rest-less, emergent coast.

On the island of Rømø, down near the German border, the foamy sea brought bits of amber to our feet. The wind had built small dunes, which alternated with low, wet corridors that held bog plants, such as sphagnum moss and cotton grass. The strait separat-ing the island from the mainland was, and still is, filling up with sand, and we could walk across at low tide.

From Rømø we moved north along the coast to the old town of Ribe. The coast there has moved away, leaving Ribe on the edge of marshlands. We rented a rowboat, broad enough and stout enough for four of us to walk around in, and rowed down the slow stream, out through the rushes and high grasses of the marshes. We watched a stork there catch a frog and fly back toward town with it, the frog's legs dangling from his long beak. Perhaps he was going to feed it to those four fledglings we had seen that morning in a broad nest built on a wagon wheel fixed to the ridge of a cottage roof. An aproned, pink-cheeked, cigar-smoking woman had emerged to tell us that the storks had been building there for as long as she re-membered—fifty years. "They bring good luck," she said. "No one dies under a roof where the storks are nesting. Certainly no one has died under this roof during my memory."

From this old town we moved north to a new one. Esbjerg has the only good harbor of that entire long west coast, and that one harbor gives shelter to hundreds of fishing boats and to stolid seagoing vessels that plough the same routes as those skimmed by the long-boats. Esbjerg harbor is possible only because of the island of Fanø, which sits in front of it and takes the wind. On the island itself, the women who work in the small fields wrestled from the heath some-times tie black kerchiefs across their faces to keep out the blowing sand. But at other times vacationers come from all over to play in the white sand and to build fantastic sand castles. The coast there shelves off so gradually that many swimmers choose to be drawn far out to the water in horse-drawn carts that carry a dressing room.

Wind-shorn

We turned further north toward Ringkøbing, where a long bar covered with sand dunes cut off the bay from the sea. Standing at the base of the Ringkøbing lighthouse, we looked up, but could not see its top through the gray, stinging mist that was sandblasting our faces. The stout farmhouses seemed to be huddled close to the ground to get out of the wind, and the single tree that seems to come with most farmsteads was invariably bent and dwarfed by the wind. Its long west slope was sheared close, forming such a dense mass that it resembled a thickly thatched roof.

Along the coast one plant appeared to be the chief pioneer of the beaches and dunes. This was the marram grass, *Ammophila arenaria*. Tolerating salt spray, and thriving on the shifting sand, it seemed to be taking hold of what the wind and the sea were giving to Denmark, and making sure that they would not take it back again. Another pioneer, lyme grass, *Elymus arenarius,* was helping. We came to dunes where men were attempting to speed up the services rendered by these two grasses. They were planting them extensively, along with compact ranks of evergreens, in order to protect their efforts at making ploughland out of the wide sweeps of heathland. We shuddered a little at seeing yet another antique cover of the land, ordained by natural forces, being homogenized; and wished the avid, drooling power tools no success.

At the extreme north tip of Jutland the west wind, like a potter shaping a lip on a wheel-turned vessel, gives a final flourish to its sand. The flourish still growing is called *Grenen,* "the twig." This is a restless prong of shifting sand, sparse wind-pruned heath, and wind-beaten grasses, altering shape constantly, according to whether the winds off the Kattegat succeed in pushing it west a bit, or whether the winds off the Skaggerak give it a mightier shove than usual to the east.

As we turned southward and eastward to Copenhagen again, we could easily imagine how glad the Vikings must have been to round this point on their way home to their sheltered havens.

Fairy Tales in a Landscape

≥ 3

Aɴ ᴏʟᴅ notebook of mine says "Denmark . . . platter of open-faced sandwiches . . . condiments and garnishes by H. C. Andersen."

This was scribbled in my lap, surreptitiously, I recall, while my hostess poured the coffee, and we had just a moment to ogle the frilly-edged platter of *smørrebrød*—open-faced sandwiches—that, a moment before, had been ceremoniously set down before us. The platter filled the center of the damask-clothed garden table, so that we could select judiciously from the assorted artifacts, and reach easily.

A platter of open-faced sandwiches

I had walked out from town early that morning, following country lanes, meeting along my way only boys and girls with neatly strapped schoolbooks.

Where a forest extended down to the lane I had followed a cart track, and gone in through its sunny edge. I found myself checking off the blooming crab apple trees, the gleam of white birch trunks, the big elderberry shrubs, and the huddle of huge burdock leaves as if I had been there before and expected to meet them all there in their appointed places. Then I walked through the dignity of a beech forest and checked the forest floor. Yes, the sweet woodruff and the anemone were there, as I seemed to expect. I leaned against a smooth trunk and looked up through the beech branches. This was their moment of the year. The new leaves were unfolding in translucent, tailored perfection of pleats and silver fringe, from fans of flat sprays layered one above the other.

Someone must have described this to me once. Not my professor of Geographic Botany at the university, certainly. He would have described this forest floor with its sweet woodruff as the "vernal aspect of a geophyte community with *Asperula odorata.*" He would have dealt with the shady condition of the forest by stepping to the blackboard to draw "simultaneous light curves made on May 23, in the open, in the forest under *Alnus,* under *Quercus,* under *Fagus,*" while we were scribbling in our notebooks, "shadiest woods—beech." And he would have discussed the soil under "the pH optimum for beech forests," while we wrote "limy." I may have been given my formal introduction to the beech forest and its margins by a professor, but I had lived in them first with my companions, through *The Fairy Tales* of Hans Christian Andersen—early enough so that their essences could be recorded on the fresh pages of a child's memory. Children around the world have learned to know Danish landscapes, because this book is widely translated and is still one of the world's best sellers.

When these forests are the setting, the stories tell:

Around the beautiful rolling meadows where the deer played, grew massive oaks and beeches; and wherever a tree had a crack in its bark, mosses and tendrils grew.

The Bell

. . . a single Spring night is often enough to dress the beech wood, and in the morning it appears in its young bright foliage.

Anne Lisbeth

Then they were standing in the new-leaved beech wood, where fragrant sweet woodruff lay spread at their feet, and the pale pink anemones looked glorious against the vivid green.

The Elder-Tree Mother

According to human calculation, it was now in its fourth century; it was the tallest and mightiest tree in the forest . . . and in the autumn, when its leaves looked like hammered-out copper plates, the birds of passage rested there awhile before flying on across the sea.

The Old Oak Tree's Last Dream

When the sunny edge of the forest is the setting, the "wild crab apple tree that bloomed so beautifully" is there; and so is the birch, "like a flash of white lightning, its slender stem shot up, its boughs waving like green gauze banners" (*The Bell*); and the elder, too, with the dryad who inhabits it and is known as the "elder-tree mother, or Hulda, mother of elves":

Once there was a little boy who went out and got his feet wet and caught cold. . . . His mother had the tea urn brought in so that she could make him a good cup of elder tea, for that keeps one warm. . . . The boy looked toward the tea-pot. He saw the lid slowly raise itself and fresh white elder flowers come forth from it. . . . The branches even stretched to the little boy's bed and thrust the curtains aside—how fragrant the blossoms were! And right in the middle of the tree there sat a sweet-looking old woman in a very strange dress. It was green like elder leaves, and it was trimmed with big white elder blossoms. At first, one couldn't tell whether the dress was cloth or the living green of the elder tree.

The Elder-Tree Mother

Elder tea

I walked along the edge of the woods to where a wide community of burdocks gave evidence that the soil had been disturbed by plough or cow. Had the season been far enough advanced I should no doubt have looked (as I did when a child) beneath their spread to see if Thumbelina's cradle of grass hung there, or whether the snails were having their wedding while "six glowworms lighted up the place as well as they could."

All summer long, poor Thumbelina lived alone in the woods. She wove herself a hammock of grass, and hung it under a big burdock leaf to keep off the rain.

Thumbelina

The biggest leaf we have in this country is certainly the burdock leaf. If you hold it in front of your little stomach, it will be like an apron, and if you lay it on your head, it will do almost as well as an umbrella. Now a burdock never grows alone, no, when you see one, you will always see others around it. . . . "The burdock forest has been planted just for us," said the Mother Snail, "I wonder what lies beyond it!" "There can't be anything beyond," said Father Snail, "that's any better than we have here." . . . the rain beat on the burdock leaves to play the drum for them.

The Happy Family

Returning to the lane, I presently stopped to lean on a fence before a farm. The spring-green grass with buttercups in it stretched up to a pond, where ducks were busy and two swans were sailing, placidly stirring the reflection of the half-timbered, thatched farmhouse. A farm wagon with two fat horses came out of the portal in the hollow square formed by the farm buildings, the *gaard*. A cat moved out of their way, yawning.

It was so beautiful out in the country. It was summertime. Wheatfields were golden, the oats were green, and down among the meadows the hay was stacked. There the stork paraded about on his long red legs, clacking away in Egyptian, which was the language his mother had taught him. Round about the fields and meadowlands rose great forests, in which deep lakes lay hidden. Yes, it was indeed lovely out there in the country.

The Ugly Duckling

I continued along the lane, past the apple orchard and the gay cosmopolitan assemblage of roadside flower gypsies often called "weeds."

All the apple trees in the garden were blooming. They had hastened to cover themselves with blossoms before their green leaves were unfolded. All the ducklings were in the farmyard, and so was the cat; it basked in the sun and tried to lick the sunshine from its own paws.

A Story

The apple branch looked down with especial pity on one kind of flower that grew everywhere in meadows and ditches . . . they could be found among the paving stones. They were dandelions, but people have given them an ugly name, "the devil's milk pails." "Poor miserable outcast" said the apple branch.

There Is a Difference

The lane crossed a bridge, and I turned down along the stream, among willows. In part I was conscious that the zonation of plants was the one that we meet in many lands: the floating-leaved stage, farthest out, then the wading-plant stage; then the pioneer tree; but in part I was listening to try to hear a church bell ringing, as it had rung in the deep part of the river where the merman lived.

Ding-dong! rings out from the Bell Deep in the Odense River. And what kind of a river is that? Why every child knows it well. It flows around the foot of the gardens, from the locks to the water mill, under the wooden bridges. Yellow water-lilies grow in the river, and brown feather-like reeds, and the black, velvety cat-tails, so high and thick. Decayed old willow trees, bent and gnarled, hang far over the water . . .

Ding-dong! rang the bell when it hung in the steeple. But one evening just as the sun was setting and the Bell was in full swing, it tore loose and flew through the air. . . . Ding-dong! Now I'm going to bed, sang the Bell, and it flew to the deepest spot of the Odense River, which is the reason that spot is called the Bell Deep . . . it still rings and clangs.

The Bell Deep

Back on the lane, I walked until I came to a dooryard garden that filled every inch of space between a low half-timbered cottage and the white picket fence—every bit, that is except for a trim walk from the gate to the doorstep. Such welcome-mat gardens are one of the delights of Danish towns, and country.

Now listen to this! . . . Out in the country, close by the side of the road, there stood a country house; you yourself have certainly seen many like it. In front of it was a little flower garden, with a painted fence around it.

The Daisy

That house was my destination, and my hostess was at the door. On the other side of the house a lawn between flower borders stretched down to a meadow, and, on the lawn, friends and a white table awaited the platter of open-faced sandwiches. My first selection was sour rye bread with sliced *frikadeller* (Danish meat balls), sliced pickled beets, a swirl of cucumber, and a sprig of parsley. The whole succulent buttery display on that tray of *smørrebrød* was a miniature of the placid, colorful landscape from which I had been sampling that morning.

But that was on the island of Fyn, called the soft bosom of Denmark. In following days, on Jutland, I sampled other landscapes made on dark pumpernickel with much less butter. There Hans Christian Andersen furnished a sharper mustard, a stouter cheese, and there were even bits of gristle left in the meat.

On both sides of a small road bricks of peat had been stacked, else I should not have realized that the road had been built across a former bog. At the far end of one flat low field a ragged line of trees and a gleam of water showed where the shrunken lake still existed. Hans Christian Andersen showed such a scene in an earlier stage, viewed from a rooftop where a father stork stood telling a story to the mother stork, who was sitting on the nest.

In the middle of the marsh there is a kind of lake, as you know. You can see a bit of it if you raise your head. Well, there is a big alder stump between the bushes and the quagmire. The princess moaned and wept. Her tears trickled down the alder stump, which was the Marsh King himself. It stretched out long miry branches like arms. The poor child was terrified, and she sprang away on the quaking quagmire where it would not bear even my weight, much less hers. . . . Big black bubbles rose, and these were the last trace of her.

The Marsh King's Daughter

Northward through Jutland our road passed two kinds of molded mounds: at first it was lined with long tumuli, molded by ancient man and kept trim by modern cows; further north it was lined with sand dunes, brought by the North Sea and molded and constantly remolded by the west wind, until the new dunes gave the old ones enough peace from the wind so that vegetation could stabilize them. The conformation of the dunes—the long windward run for the sand grains, the ridge where the grains have tumbled over, the steep leeward slope where they land and are soon buried by later arrivals

—all this is familiar to anyone who has watched moving dunes in any land. But these dunes have little of the human dimension. Hans Christian Andersen added this dimension with *A Story from the Sand Dunes,* which tells the peasants' explanation of the Jutland dunes.

Houses and farms were strewn among the shifting sand dunes—it is a wild land where the wind plays constantly in the loose sand, and where the screams of sea gulls, sea swallows, and wild swans, cut sharply through the eardrum. . . . the sand whirled about and buried the houses until the occupants had to creep out of the chimneys. . . . ship after ship was wrecked on those fatal reefs. . . . The heath was like an immense cemetery studded with hundreds of viking grave mounds.

. . . .

Then they talked about the sand dunes, and about how they came to be. . . . The peasants found a corpse on the shore and buried it in the churchyard; then the sand began to fly about, and the sea broke in with violence. A wise man of the parish advised that the grave be opened, for if the stranger was found sucking his thumb, they would then be sure that the one they had buried was a merman, and that the sea would never rest until it had fetched him back to itself. So they opened the grave, and sure enough, the dead man lay with his thumb between his lips. He was quickly laid on a cart drawn by two oxen, and, as though stung by hornets, they rushed with him over the heath and moor to the sea. That stopped the shower of flying sand, but the dunes that had been formed are still there.

Hans Christian Andersen, like many of us, was an inveterate presser of flowers between pages of books (you can see some of them displayed in his home in Odense). But he did better than that, pressing also whole landscapes, and preserving them for the world to know, in the pages of his *Fairy Tales.*

A BRIEF GLOSSARY OF THE LANDSCAPE OF DENMARK

as shown by place names on maps and signs

Words Dealing with Water

aa—stream
  as: *Ribe Aa*
     Aagaard

bro—bridge
  as: *Kongebro*

bugt—bay
  as: *Aalborg Bugt*

faerge—ferry
  as: *Faergelunden*

fjord—inlet of the sea (Danish fjords do not have the same history or
    depth as Norwegian fjords)
  as: *Vejle Fiord*
     Mariager Fiord
     Limfjorden

havn—harbor
  as: *Kjøbenhavn* (anglicized Copenhagen)

mose—bog, or moss
  as: *Vildmose*
     Borremose
     Trundholm Mose

ø—island
  as: *Fanø*
     Rømø
     Laesø
     Praestø
     Mandø

sø—sea
  as: *Arresø*
     Furesø
     Skanderborg Sø

sund—sound or strait
   as: *Guldborg Sund*

Words Dealing with Land
   bakke—hill (*Bakker*—hills)
     as: *Dollerup Bakker*
       Rebild Bakker
   by—town or village
     as: *Nordby*
   gaard—farmstead, yard, enclosure
     as: *Kirkegaard*
       Herregaard
   hede or *lyng*—heath
     as: *Hedeby*
       Lyngby
   skov—forest (often added to the name of the dominant tree)
     as: *Egeskov*—oak forest
       Askov—ash forest
       Lindeskov—linden forest

TO READ BEFORE READING THE LANDSCAPE
OF DENMARK

About the Bogs and Bog-finds

Denmark Before the Vikings (Praeger, New York, 1957). The bog-finds are considered along with other finds from prehistory, by Dr. Ole Klindt-Jensen, chief curator of the National Museum.

The Testimony of the Spade by Geoffrey Bibby (Knopf, New York, 1956). Read especially "The Bodies in the Bogs"; "The Golden Horns"; and "Interludes: Dating the Past."

From the series *Guides to the Danish National Museum* you will want to own and study *The Danish Collections: Antiquity.*

The Bog People: Iron-age Man Preserved, by Peter V. Glob (Cornell University Press, Ithaca, New York, 1969).

Kuml, the yearbook of the Archeological Society of Jutland, 1956, published by the University of Aarhus, Aarhus, Denmark. In Danish, with chapter summaries, and illustration labels in English.

About the Seacoast

The Vikings by Holger Arbman, translated by Alan Binns (Thames and Hudson, London, 1961).

The Vikings by Johannes Brønsted, translated by Kalle Skov (Penguin Books, Baltimore, 1965).

A History of the Vikings by Gwyn Jones (Oxford University Press, New York and London, 1968).

The Long Ships by Frans G. Bengtsson (Knopf, New York, 1954). A novel of Viking life.

Trelleborg, Jelling, The Ladby Viking Ship, three pamphlets published by the National Museum in Copenhagen.

Certain Tales of Hans Christian Andersen That May Well Be Read, or Reread for the Flavor of the Landscape

The Ugly Duckling
The Little Mermaid

The Nightingale
The Marsh King's Daughter
The Swan's Nest
The Elder-Tree Mother
A Story from the Sand Dunes
Thumbelina

For Identification of the Flora

Illustreret Flora, by Baltzer, Lange, and Ursing (Gads Forlag, Køben-havn, 1960). Text in Danish, many illustrations.

Træer og Buske, Skov og Hegn, by Vedel and Lange (Polstikens Forlag, Copenhagen, 1964). Text in Danish, outstanding illustrations.

Norway

Two Thresholds of the Coast

≫ 1

Norway is a land of many thresholds. Life is shaped by them. Shelter lies just behind each one; confrontation waits just beyond.

But this was not the impression that the first sight of the long west coast of Norway made on the passengers of our ship who had come on deck to see the sun rise out of the mountains. To all of us, whether we were seeing it for the first time, or were repeaters who knew better, that dark mass looked only like a land of high, impregnable barriers ranged one behind another in the gray mist, offering no welcome, no shelter after the violence of our North Sea crossing, no sunrise.

Then suddenly we turned north along the coast, among islands of many sizes. We could look down on some of the small ones. Some were quite bare, and some had a white house or two, and some had bent pine trees, and one had a single crooked birch tree. We realized that our deck was horizontal at last, and we were proceeding placidly near the base of steep mountain slopes. We were over one of Norway's most important thresholds.

We could have followed that welcome sheltered passageway north beyond the Arctic circle, as the fishing boats do, but we turned in to the harbor at Bergen.

At the far end of the harbor, past the schools of fishing boats, the fishmarket was already busy. Displayed there with other fish were the two kinds most important to the history of Bergen: the herring and the cod. The stories of herring fishing and of codfishing are linked with the stories of two separate thresholds of the coast, as well as to the history of Bergen.

1. Generalized section of Norway's mass after upthrust

granite and gneiss

The beginning of the codfishing story lies far in the past, before codfish existed. The earth was undergoing a paroxysm of mountain-building, slowly thrusting up, and overthrusting, contorted, interwoven masses of granite and gneiss. The contours of the mass were humped and knobby, without sharp peaks and without horizontal planes. Stresses and strains resulted in many fractures.

This high long mass intercepted the west winds, cooling them. It received abundant precipitation, which had a swift run down the steep slopes. In some places a stream would find and then follow the straight line of an old fracture, to another old fracture. Such a stream's course would have long straight stretches, with angles at points where fractures had crossed. Slowly the heights were mostly eroded down to a level high plain. This plain was later thrust slowly higher, and the cutting power of the rivers was rejuvenated.

While erosion continued, there was a new paroxysm within the earth. The Alps were being upthrust, and the disturbance was affecting a huge area. A long crack developed along the west base of the land mass that is now called Norway. To the west of that crack, a great block slipped down, and down, under what is now called the North Sea.

Then the cold and the snows came. Presently the mass of Norway, with all its contortions and fractures and plains and river valleys, lay deep, as much as two miles deep, under the continental ice sheet. As the limits of the ice sheet made its four major advances and its four major retreats, there came a time when the western edge of the lobe

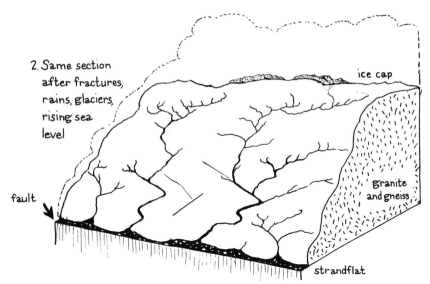

2. Same section after fractures, rains, glaciers, rising sea level

ice cap

granite and gneiss

fault

strandflat

covering Scandinavia lay along the western coast of Norway. It is not hard to imagine how the power and weight of the coastal glaciers could have gouged out channels and leveled obstacles, and how tongues of ice could have separated before some resistant rock masses and joined again beyond them, leaving them standing, isolated.

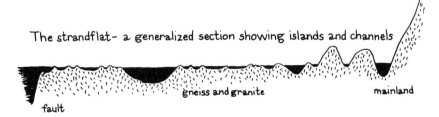

The strandflat– a generalized section showing islands and channels

gneiss and granite

mainland

fault

The next, the final, stage of continental glaciation, which pushed its front far beyond this coast, could have thoroughly ice-scoured and rounded these isolated blocks before it retreated to the mountaintops and high valleys. Then the rising sea level could have completed the threshold we had found so welcome. It seems best, in telling this series of events, to say "could have" rather than "did," because this is only one of several theories of the formation of this *strandflat*, as it is called. The famous explorer-author Fridtjof Nansen, born near Oslo, had his theory. He considered the chief shaping forces of the shelf to have been waves and intense frost.

But without any theories at all about the history of the channels and islands, many kinds of creatures have benefited from them both. A shifting web of wings enfolds them; seals thrive along the northern islands, their dark, glossy humps scarcely discernible against the dark, glossy rock; the red-breasted mergansers nest at the edges and line up in the channels for their cooperative beating of the water to drive small fish together to a good fishing site; codfish and codfishermen thrive on the channels; the long boats of the Norsemen skimmed these channels; and the merchant ships of the Hanseatic League plowed them, on their way to Bergen from their headquarters on the Baltic.

As we docked at Bergen we looked across the harbor through a forest of masts to a solid line of gabled roofs on tall, narrow buildings, the former dwellings and places of business of the Hanseatic League.

Remembering the interest of exploring that district in 1920, I had returned for further exploration in 1965. In the intervening period, fire, an old hazard of those frame buildings, had come again, and destroyed all but a third of the district. City planners have moved in and have made many drastic changes for fire protection, and will make more. And archaeologists, taking advantage of devastated areas, have dug down into the layers of Bergen's past. Walks are provided where one may look down at history neatly exposed between layers of charcoal, and a building where the best of the finds are displayed.

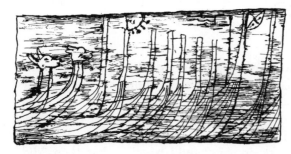

Part of a piece of wood carved in the thirteenth century, found in a dig in Bergen (under Bryggen)

From the lowest, oldest layers, finds include wood and bone with runic inscriptions and other carvings. Three ship finds, of the wide, stoutly built ships probably used as merchant vessels by the Norsemen who followed in the routes of the narrow longboats of the Viking raiders, probably date back to the time when Bergen was named Björgvin, meaning "hill of many pastures," and was the seat of kings. Other finds include some exotic artifacts, some of them recording far-ranging Norsemen, and some recording the taking over of this part of Bergen by the Hanseatic League. This German section became called Bryggen, meaning "the wharf," or Tyskebryggen, meaning "the German wharf."

To Bryggen the German ships brought wheat, which cannot mature in the cold, wet climate of this area; from Bryggen they carried away cod liver oil and whale oil. Bryggen was one of the four chief *Kontore,* or countinghouses, of the league. The others were in London, Novgorod, and Bruges. From the fourteenth century to the sixteenth they throve. In the seventeenth century they left Bergen, and soon disbanded.

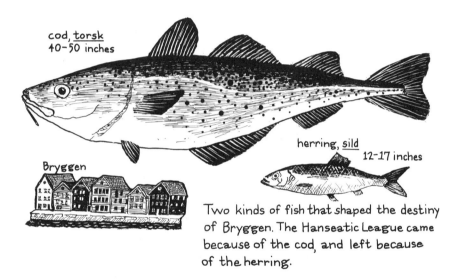

cod, <u>torsk</u>
40–50 inches

herring, <u>sild</u>
12–17 inches

Bryggen

Two kinds of fish that shaped the destiny of Bryggen. The Hanseatic League came because of the cod, and left because of the herring.

To consider the chief cause of the failure it is necessary to consider a second threshold, the narrow, shallow entrance to the Baltic Sea, though it may seem remote from Bergen, as an important part of that town's total environment.

At the point where Denmark almost joins Sweden, and formerly did join it, the narrow and shallow separation between the two countries is called the Sound. The Danish historian Saxo Grammaticus, writing in 1200, told that the Sound was "likely to be so thronged with fish that any boat which strikes on them is with difficulty got off by hard rowing, and the prize is captured . . . by the simple use of hands." A drawing showing the herring fishing off the southernmost tip of Sweden illustrated the history written by Olaus Magnus of Sweden in 1555.

Herring catch

Redrawn from Olaus Magnus, 1555

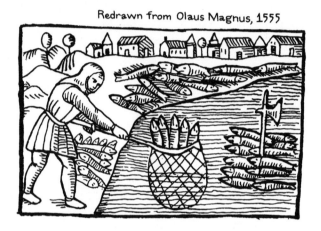

The Hanseatic League, which had originally pried its way into the Baltic area and established its main headquarters at Lübeck, and had gradually made the Baltic into a German sea, was dependent on thriving herring fisheries. And then the herring throngs came no more to the Baltic.

Otto Pettersson, a Swedish oceanographer who lived his long life on a cliff overlooking the Baltic, evolved a theory concerning tides and herrings. Once in every eighteen centuries, he wrote, the sun and moon and earth are so lined up that the strongest possible pull is exerted on the waters of the earth. At a time when the "moon waves," as he called them, are drawn up into "water mountains" almost one hundred feet high, shoals of herring are carried in through the narrow entrance of the Baltic, and fisheries thrive there. When the tides subside, the herring come no more to the Baltic. This is what happened at the end of the Middle Ages.

One comes to Bergen not only for itself, and the thresholds in its story, but also for access to two other kinds of thresholds, the ones that shape fjords and waterfalls.

The Thresholds of the Valleys

⚇ 2

THE HARDANGERFJORD gave us a chilling, frowning greeting when we first entered it. The long barrier of Norway's west coast had scowled at us, too, but that had been on a gray dawn after a wild North Sea crossing. We approached the fjord on a sunny morning, after we had left behind the flower market, the masts, the white houses, the church steeples of Bergen; and had traveled first by a friendly country bus loaded with school children and market baskets and baby buggies; and afterwards by a small boat through sheltered passages among wooded islands. Then suddenly the fjord was there.

The horizontal water and the vertical mountainsides appeared to have no relations with each other. There seemed to be no sign of the confrontation or overture that usually mark the meeting places of land and water: no feuds of smashing waves and pounding surf, no middle ground of sandy beach and wading birds; no truce of reeds or cattails, no trespass of cave or inlet. One simply ended and the other quietly began.

Actually some scars of confrontation are there, but they are too massive to be recognized at first glance, and somewhat blurred by time and the growth of plants. They are scars, not of water, but of ice carrying broken bits of rock embedded in it. The scraped and scratched surface extends along both sides of the long fjord.

The story of the Hardangerfjord begins with rain squeezed out of the west wind by the heights of granite and gneiss, and continued as the work of a river digging a V-shaped trench down the steep west slope.

When the periods of continental glaciation came, ice pushed its broad fist down the valley the slender finger of the river had pried open. The force of the glacier altered the V-shaped river valley, gouging and planing it out into a deeper, broader, vertical-sided U. Ice filled this valley up to the top level of the scars visible on the side of the fjord.

The point at which the glacier attained its greatest power was some distance from the mouth of the valley. As the ice reached the base of the mountains it was warming and weakening, and was no longer able to transport the tremendous load of rock debris it had accumulated. Some of it was dropped along the channel, and then all the rest was dumped at the mouth. In this way the fjords, though they are so deep (Hardangerfjord is over half a mile at its deepest and Sognefjord is almost four-fifths of a mile), all have shallow thresholds, which are narrowed as well. The sea makes its entry over the shallow threshold, and salt water mixes with the mountain rainwater. But the deep-water organisms that make up the rich web of life in the sea do not enter over that shallow barrier. The water of the fjord is poorly oxygenated; life is sparse.

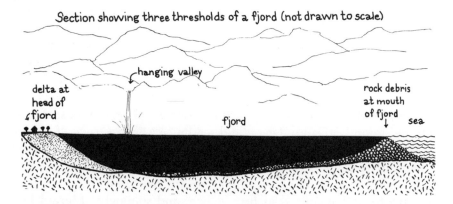

Section showing three thresholds of a fjord (not drawn to scale)

delta at head of fjord — hanging valley — fjord — rock debris at mouth of fjord — sea

Thresholds across the entrances of fjords are of minor importance compared with those high up on their sides. Waterfalls drop from those high thresholds to shape the economy of the country, making it possible for Norwegian ships to carry out cargoes of many electrometallurgical products, in addition to the traditional cargoes of fish and lumber products.

Each waterfall marks a place where a tributary glacier fed into a main one. The tributary, being smaller, did not dig so deep a valley. When the ice melted the river now flowing down the smaller valley came suddenly to the edge of a high threshold, and had to fall the rest of the way down to the water in the main valley. Norway is loud with the roar of her waterfalls and busy with their power. The "hanging valleys," as geologists call them, have made many changes. A housewife in a small frame house showed us her hanging lamp, painted with pink roses and hung with crystals. It had burned whale oil, but her husband had wired it for electricity. She turned it on for us. But her mother said that we should have seen how pretty it was before they spoiled it. It had glowed with a yellow light then, she remembered, and one could pull it down to the table, and besides, she had liked the smell of it.

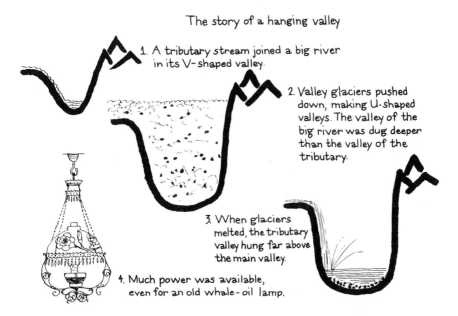

The story of a hanging valley

1. A tributary stream joined a big river in its V-shaped valley.

2. Valley glaciers pushed down, making U-shaped valleys. The valley of the big river was dug deeper than the valley of the tributary.

3. When glaciers melted, the tributary valley hung far above the main valley.

4. Much power was available, even for an old whale-oil lamp.

At the head of the fjord we lingered on another of Norway's most important thresholds. This one was gentle, sheltered, wrapped in a greenhouse atmosphere. The river flowing down the mountain had been slowed down there at the entrance to the fjord, and had dropped its burden to form a broad delta. Such deltas at the heads of fjords and their branches furnish practically the only flat, tillable cropland of the country. Travelers are refreshed by such thresholds;

the glowering masses of the fjord seem to make admirable backgrounds if there is a cow, or a hen, or an apple tree, or a spade, or a
line of washing in the foreground.

We saw two additional kinds of valley thresholds, higher up in
the mountains. One of them was, in fact, not basically different from
a fjord. Finger lakes were made by glaciers, but small ones; they
have the same sort of barriers across their lower ends, but the sea
and its salt could not enter over them; they have the same gently
sloping alluvium at their heads, and cows are pastured on them.
There are especially many finger lakes west of the mountain crest,
and in Sweden, where neither rainfall nor slope was as great.

And finally, hanging high against the skyline crest of Norway, the
crest that they, in fact, are responsible for carving into its sharp
intricacies, are the thresholds that geologists call "cirques."

When snow gathers on the side of a mountain, in a hollow, however slight, a cirque develops. Ice, freezing and thawing, plucks at
the rock of the mountain and carves the original hollow deeper and
broader. As bits of the mountainside give way, the upper parts may
be undermined and weakened so that they tumble into the cirque,
until the top of the mountain is cut into peaks and sharp-edged
crests. Along its lower edge the ice disgorges the chunks it has
bitten out of the mountain, and forms its own threshold, from which
a river, sometimes as a waterfall, continues its way downhill toward
the other valley thresholds.

Should the river reach the end of its downhill trip in Oslofjord it
will arrive at a situation different from that in the other fjords. That
is because the bottom of Oslofjord was not gouged out by a valley
glacier; it dropped out between two long, parallel fractures. That
was at the time when the upthrust of the Alps was having such far-
reaching effects. The sea extends a long arm into the land. Probably
this arm should be called an estuary rather than a fjord. Glaciers
and rivers and the sea have all had a hand in carving, sifting, depositing these gentler shores. Archaeologists must be grateful for the fine-
textured blue clay that was deposited along both sides of the
estuary, because it proved so efficient as packing material around
the Viking ships that were buried on those shores. So were preserved the bodies of royalty, with their horses and dogs and weapons and artifacts, as well as the architecture of the buoyant vessels.

At Oslo's ship museum we visited the great Viking ship finds, as well as the ships of modern Vikings, Fridtjof Nansen and Thor Heyerdahl. Then we left the Oslofjord, the most gentle and most used of Norwegian thresholds, and boarded the Oslo-Bergen railway for the bleak threshold of the taiga.

The Threshold of the Taiga

3

THE TAIGA is the biggest forest in the world. It starts in Norway, and then continues, repeating itself drearily with the ditto marks of its two same trees, right across the sub-arctic of Sweden, Finland, Poland, and Russia, and on into Siberia, where it picks up its name. The same type of forest, called by the same name, continues across North America, too, but with two different evergreens monotonously punctuating the landscape.

For something so huge, a broad, gradual threshold is fitting. Many impressive man-made structures—the Parthenon, the Capitol at Washington, D.C., the Taj Mahal, Versailles—are provided with them. The taiga threshold, the Arctic tundra, outclasses any of these examples, in interest and decoration.

It was necessary for us to enter the taiga, and traverse its gloomy expanse for a time, so that we might enjoy emerging.

When we boarded the train in Oslo for the north, we were already north of the point where beech trees drop out, and from the train we watched the rest of the deciduous trees dropping out. Then the monotony of the Norway spruce–Scots pine duet took over, broken only by a mountain stream, or a bog, or a farmed valley, or an occasional town, or a fresh clearing.

At the edge of one town the train stopped for a few minutes beside a place where an excavation had been made very recently, perhaps during the previous day, since the rain had not yet blurred the sides of it. We could plainly see that the soil was in three distinct layers. The top layer was dark, evidently composed of needles of spruce and pine accumulated for several years. The needles had had little chance to decay; during the short rainy, cool summers, the sunlight could not reach down through the evergreen branches to warm the ground. And earthworms did not thrive on that raw acid humus, else they would have drawn it down, and mingled its darkness with the layer beneath. But the rain washed down through the acidity and became acid enough so that it dissolved the iron in the second layer, leaving the layer ash-colored. Some of the iron was deposited in the third layer, which was brown and looked as if it might be dense and packed enough to delay the rain in its downward course, and help make the forest floor still more acid and boggy.

When the train moved on we found ourselves looking with more understanding at both the trees of the taiga and its impoverished understory shrubs and mosses.

We passed pastured valleys with large barns, and orchards, and log sheds with sod roofs (one with a goat tethered out on it), and long fences for hanging hay out to dry. We passed one newly made clearing where the soil had been turned with a plow and looked ashen and discouraging. It was easy to understand why this taiga soil is called by the Russian name, *podzol,* meaning "ashes beneath."

The stretches of taiga were occasionally enriched by taller shrubs, and even by ferns. Those marked the places where mountain streams rushed through. As we passed one of those streams with its white water I suddenly realized what was missing on this, my second trip on this railway (1965) which had been present on my first (1920). We couldn't hear the water; we couldn't smell the pines and spruces. On the first trip we had poised on the edges of the wooden benches occasionally, but for much of the trip we had stood at the open windows along the corridor side of the train, and only rushed back to the compartment side when we heard a waterfall that could best be seen from there. And we had smelled good smells, too. Of course there was soot, plenty of it, and it was necessary to shut the windows through the tunnels, especially the five-mile-long tunnel. Remembering the open windows, I felt kinship with the Norwegian woman who regretted the wiring of her whale-oil lamp.

After we passed Geilo, gradually the barns were smaller, and the spruces narrower. Flashes of gaiety brightened the taiga where white birches invaded a chimney of sunlight. Soon the birch invasions became more frequent, as the spruces and pines stood further and further apart, and were of diminished height and girth. Then the spruces dropped out; and soon the pines, too, had gone. The taiga lay behind us and its lively threshold stretched ahead.

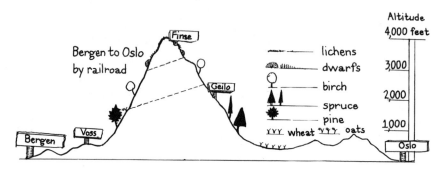

The sunlit groves of birches at the very edge of the taiga were almost as upright and slender as the ones back in the openings; but they soon began to stand further and further apart, and to show signs of a need to be closer to the warmth that is just above the surface of the ground. Taller ones stood in grassy, flower-filled places, but the hunched and diminished ones stood among twiggy, low shrubs.

As the white birches with their slender twigs dropped out, the gray birches took over. These were more densely twigged and stood far apart, stooping and hunching their shoulders more and more, over the twiggy mazes of huddled heaths. These were explosions of color in the fall, and full of bright berries.

This was the last appearance of any tree. It looked as though it was the last appearance of any birches, but woodiness had not yet become impossible on the tundra, though upright woodiness had. Down there, close to the ground among the heaths, dwarf birches were crouched, and would probably soon be under snow cover. We saw one dwarf birch that had espaliered itself against a boulder, flattening and spreading its branches against the sunny side of the granite as a French gardener might flatten and spread a choice pear tree against a garden wall.

Around and under and through the patches of dwarf birch and heaths streamed the gray-green of reindeer lichen. Gradually it took over the ground, more and more completely, as the woody plants of all kinds dropped out, and only scattered and dwarfed flowering

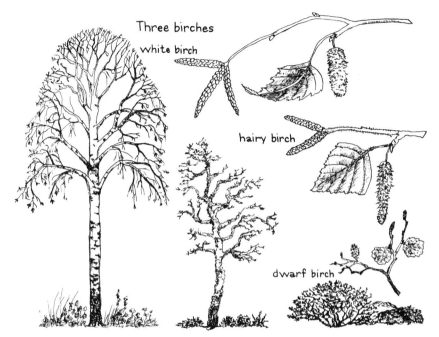

Three birches
white birch
hairy birch
dwarf birch

plants survived. Finally the lichen had achieved a wide expanse in the sun, where neither its permanence nor its dominance was disputed. We remembered the other lichen that had been the pioneer on the lava of Mt. Vesuvius, but its hold was as temporary as that of most pioneers, whether animal or vegetable, on the substance of the earth. That lichen was destined to be crowded out and overwhelmed by a succession of societies, each standing on the last one's neck. Here, at the edge of possibility for life, the lichen filled all niches: pioneer, intermediate, climax (as final a climax as the beech forest is to most of Europe).

The color of the lichen is gray-green: gray from the enveloping fungus, which can stand erect and endure a drying wind; green from the fibers of alga, which cannot stand erect, nor endure drying, but can use the sunlight to make food. This union of two primitives is the chief pasture of reindeer.

There is one other necessary ingredient to this lichen pasture—the wolf. Because the growth of lichens is extremely slow, this pasture cannot endure overgrazing. The reindeer population must never explode. Controlling it is the wolf's niche.

From the gray-green of lichens, our train climbed to the permanent ice cap. At Finse the passengers all got out and threw snow-balls, and then we got back in and soon the train was starting downhill and the reindeer lichen took over again.

At Voss we found a hotel, and stayed our downward progress so that we might feel and taste and smell and hear, and see more closely the ingredients of the landscape, and have time to wonder about some of its features. We explored by foot, and occasionally by whatever friendly lift was offered. We felt the soft pubescence of the hairy birch; and tasted bilberries, bearberries, crowberries, and cranberries, hoping that they tasted better to the bears and the birds. We marveled at the numerous kinds of plants assembled here; and wondered about the routes by which they had returned home after being driven out by the glacial periods. Many of them, we knew, simply worked north as the edge of the ice retreated, leaving behind some colonies on the Alps. But the whole story is not as simple as that, because some plants could not return fast enough to avoid being shaded out by the trees of the taiga, which seem to have followed upon the very heels of the retreating ice; and some of them left no pollen or other remains in the bottoms of the bogs of southern Scandinavia, to record their having passed that way; and some plants are found nowhere else, only in Scandinavia. For explanation many botanists point to Greenland, which is still in an ice age. They point to separate high peaks, entirely surrounded by glaciers, but ice-free. The Eskimos call such isolated peaks *nuna-taks*. There are plants on them. The botanists suggest that there must have been similar nunataks, probably along the coast of Norway, where certain species of plants must have survived the Ice Age. A certain small dandelion is found nowhere else on earth than in Scandinavia. How many generations of that plant may have watched the ice endlessly pushing past its nunatak!

We walked on the expanse of the Hardangervidda, that great plateau which is really the roots of tall mountains worn down by ages of erosion, and then slowly uplifted. We listened to the tumbling streams, wondering how much they were carrying to contribute to the delta that we had seen at the head of the Hardangerfjord.

As we enjoyed the various types of plant communities around Voss, I kept my eyes open for three famous things of Norway I especially hoped to see: a Hardanger violin, a lemming, and a herd of wild reindeer.

We heard a violin playing on one light summer evening when we came out for a walk. We hurried toward the sound. The violinist was seated on a bench under a tree, and a circle of townspeople of all ages was seated on the ground around him, perfectly silent and intently listening (but that again is a memory from 1920). It would be nice to be able to report that the instrument was a gaily colored and handsomely decorated Hardanger violin, and that the music was by Edvard Grieg, and that the playing had a virtuosity reminiscent of Ole Bull, but no part of that report would be true. However, more than thirty years later, all three parts were true about a performance by the first violinist of a touring Norwegian orchestra, performing in a midwestern town in the United States, and I had a chance to see the handiwork on a Hardanger violin. Such work is as typical of the isolation, and long, cold winter evenings in Norway, as cuckoo clocks and music boxes are of similar conditions in Switzerland.

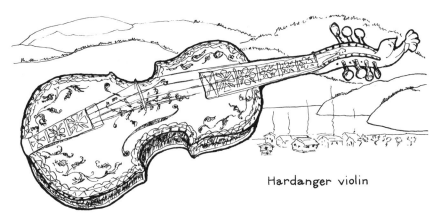

Hardanger violin

About seeing a lemming, I am not sure. Someone said, "Look! lemming!" and I saw a warm-brown something skittering down between the twigs of a dwarf birch. There was a narrow track in a solid bank of reindeer lichen, which could have been one of the lemming runways. But what one really expects of lemmings is a mass migration, flowing down across the landscape like a furry flood.

Today the lemming is being much used as an awful example of the dangers of overpopulation; or as a hint that we already are feeling and responding to the same urge to headlong, precipitate, mindless reduction of the population. In the past the lemming migration has been the subject of many theories. In 1532 a writer in Strasbourg suggested that they fell from the sky. In 1718 another writer warned that these creatures dropping from the sky were poisonous. The Eskimos held with the sky-origin theory, because they gave them a name meaning "creature from space." Many have subscribed to the theory that the blind plunge into the sea results from a subconscious urge to return to the ancestral homeland on the lost continent, Atlantis. Sunspots, and various aspects of the zodiac, have also been offered in explanation.

There is no need for theories about the ordinary years in the life of the lemmings. During the summer they hide from their many predators among the twiggy tangles of the tundra. In the winter they seek higher, drier places, and make tunnels along which they forage for food and nests in which they breed and breed and breed again. When spring comes, if it is one of their ordinary years, they all simply migrate downhill to a moister site near summer food.

But there are extraordinary years. These follow winters of extraordinary population explosions. The migrations become massive downpourings of fabulous numbers, which seem to be undeterred by barriers. It is reported by many that even the sea does not deter them, and they swim till they drown. This is sternly denied, or modified, by others. But there seems to be no doubt at all about there being a decided reduction in lemming population after one of these mass migrations.

No herd of wild reindeer—nor, in fact, a single reindeer—did I see (unless that gray blur that seemed to shift across the gray of the distant tundra really was reindeer, as we wanted to believe). We did not go far enough north to see any of the half-wild, half-domesticated herds.

It was difficult to visualize this tundra as ever having covered the plateau above the Lascaux caves. The reindeer hunters, moving north with their prey, had no way of knowing that the rocks up here would hold no nodules of flint for tools; and that the slanting rays of the low sun would spread light so thinly; and that there would be no caves. But they left their pictures on open rocks; and their encampments for archaeologists to find.

We stopped at a small pool beside a snowbank and decided to try a reindeer meal. We pinched off some lichen (I looked at my inch-long piece and realized that I was about to eat what may have taken anywhere from a fourth of a year up to four years to grow, depending on conditions) and we ate. It needed salt. We looked for flowers of the glacier buttercup, because a Norwegian flower book said "the flowers are eaten by reindeer," but the plants had finished their seed-making, and we settled for nibbles of the fleshy leaves. Then we cupped our hands and drank from the pool.

It was time to take the train down the mountain to the taiga, and to Bergen.

A BRIEF GLOSSARY OF THE LANDSCAPE OF NORWAY

Words Applied to the Long Coastline
  fjord—steep-walled, ice-scoured valleys leading to the sea
    as: *Hardangerfjord, Vestfjord, Oslofjord, Sognefjord* or *Sognefjorden*
      (*-en* added is similar to "the")
  vik—inlet, cove, creek, or fjord
    as: *Narvik, Larvik, Ulvik, Kopervik, Rørvik, Vikna, Viking*
  øy, or *ø*—island
    as: *Bygdøy, Vorøy, Langøy, Arnøy, Sørøy, Magerøy, Florø, Tromsø*
  sund—sound, or strait, a narrow passage
    as: *Farsund, Egersund, Haugesund*
    some straits have islands in them, as: *Godøysund, Brønnøysund*
  os—mouth, outlet
    as: *Os, Oslo*
  havet—harbor
    as: *Lopphavet, Frohavet*
  sand—beach or strand (there is very little of this type of coastline except on the southern tip of Norway)
    as: *Kristiansand, Tvedestrand, Lillesand*

Words Applied to the Mountains
  fjell—mountain
    as: *Fillefjell, Dovrefjell, Lifjell*
  vidda—wide plateau
    as: *Hardangervidda*
  dal—valley (these are many, deep, and long)
    as: *Gudbrandsdalen, Osterdalen, Hallingdal, Viksdalen*
  saetter or *seter*—outfarms above timberline, with small huts for storing cured hay
    as: *Setesdal, Videseter, Elveseter, Dalseter*

TO READ BEFORE READING THE LANDSCAPE
OF NORWAY

Scandinavia Past and Present, from the Viking Age to Absolute Monarchy, 3 volumes, edited by Jørgen Bukdahl and others (Arnkrone, Denmark, 1959). Set available in many libraries. The first volume is a rich compilation of materials on Vikings, runes, sagas, and shipburials.

The Changing World of the Ice Age by Reginald Aldworth Daly (Yale University Press, New Haven, 1934). Chapter 2, "Recession of the Fennoscandian Ice."

Geomorphology, An Introduction to the Study of Landscapes by A. K. Lobeck (McGraw-Hill, New York, 1939). Chapter 8, "Alpine Glaciation," and Chapter 9, "Continental Glaciation."

A History of the Vikings by Gwyn Jones (Oxford University Press, New York, 1968).

The Sea Around Us by Rachel Carson (Oxford University Press, New York, 1951). In Chapter XII, "The Global Thermostat," the theories of the Swedish oceanographer, Otto Pettersson, are discussed.

Farthest North, Being the Record of a Voyage of Exploration of the Ship Fram, 1893–1896, 2 volumes, by Fridtjof Nansen (Harper, New York, 1897).

The Testimony of the Spade by Geoffrey Bibby (Knopf, New York, 1956). Chapter 10, "The Reindeer Hunters."

The Great Migrations of Animals by Georges Blond, translated by Francis Frenaye (Macmillan, New York, 1956). An unusual account of the lemming migration, in Chapter 5, "The Race to Destruction."

Europe, A Natural History by Kai Curry-Lindahl (Random House, New York, 1964). Chapter 16, "Birch Forests, Eagles, and Lemmings," gives a quite different account of lemming migration from that in the reference above.

Mountain Flowers of Scandinavia by Olav Gjaerevoll and Reinar Jørgensen (Trondhjems Turistforening, Trondhjem, 1950). For carrying in the pocket. Outstanding text and illustrations in color.

Britain

The Two Sides of Britain

⤳ 1

A STRAIGHT LINE drawn from the mouth of the river Tees to the mouth of the river Exe will divide the map of Britain, very roughly, into two kinds of landscape.

⤳⤴ --

The Northwest Side   The Southeast Side

highland Britain

lowland Britain

the down-tilted side

the uptilted side

young Britain (the
"elder Britain"
of historians)

old Britain

the rocks are young,
soft, often deeply
covered with
fertile soil

the rocks are old,
hard, often thinly
covered with poor
soil

rainfall is less than
30 inches a year

more wheat grown
than oats

the rocks weather
easily, forming low
rounded hills

rainfall is more
than 30 inches
a year (often
much more)

most of the land
is farmed

human occupation is
almost continuous,
favoring societies,
pubs, bingo; and
long words, short
sermons, padded
pews; and many
fences, hedgerows,
and laws

more oats
grown than wheat

much of the land
is in a wild state

the rocks resist
weathering,
forming high,
rugged hills

the long, slow
rivers invited, from
a similar landscape,
Danish invaders
who left behind
many town names
ending in -by, from
the Danish word
for "town"

human occupation is
discontinuous, favoring solitude,
silence, blunt, short words,
clans, bloodshed, bagpipes,
stern religion, and long sermons

swift, rock-walled rivers and
bays attracted, from a similar
landscape, Norwegian invaders,
who left behind the word "firth"
(same as fjord)

Map Key:
M = Moor
H = Heath
GM = Grouse Moor
G = Glen
VN = Volcanic Neck
D = Downs

C&P = Coppice and Pollard
BC = Bomb Crater
F = Fen
S = Shingle
HR = Hedge-row
PF = Public Footpath

A Vocabulary
of the British Landscape

$\gtrsim$ 2

MOOR

We walked at Dartmoor for the first time through a heavy fog which exuded a fine cold rain. Moving cautiously, our shoes squirting among the grass hummocks, we suddenly saw the black faces of many sheep—and then, just as suddenly, their white tails. A few steps beyond, our shoes were grating on granite; three dark ponies started away so abruptly that I almost collided with a lonely, fog-shrouded hawthorn tree.

It is good to see a landscape for the first time in the kind of weather that molded it. Dartmoor, according to the records, has about one hundred days with fog each year.

That is to be expected, for this high old granite mass in southwest England intercepts the warm, moist south winds and cools them suddenly, squeezing out fog and rain.

We squelched our way to the base of an abrupt bulk, which rose high over our heads. This, we told ourselves, must be one of the famous tors, which punctuate the dark tales of the moors. This is where the murderer hides.

The rock that formed the tor was molten when it bulged up under a fold of the surface rock. When it cooled it became much harder than the folds above it. Later the softer rock was slowly worn away, leaving the hard core to bulk like an island out of the moor.

As we stood at the base of the tor we felt like soggy hummocks. We were saturated, in air so sodden that it would not let our wetness evaporate. That is the very essence of a moor.

Dead plants make a lasting soggy blanket. And when their sogginess becomes too acid for the bacteria that cause decay, the layer of undecayed vegetation becomes peat. Plenty of water is present, but it is too acid to be available to the roots of plants. This condition is called "physically wet but physiologically dry."

Tors on Dartmoor

There are, however, some plants that can survive in the acid sogginess of peat, and these show some of the same characteristics seen in plants that tolerate drought. Reduced leaf surfaces, for example, help reduce the outgo of water; this is made necessary by the limited intake of the roots. Two of the narrow-leaved plants growing in the humpy, hummocky places where the sheep were feeding were purple moor grass, *Molinia caoerulea,* and matgrass, *Nardus stricta.*

As we explored the moor, we came to some places where our feet sank in too deeply for comfort on that cold day. Mosses were underfoot, chiefly sphagnum moss. These places were bogs. There are, basically, three kinds of bogs: valley bogs, raised bogs, and blanket bogs. In each of these three the bog condition results from inefficient waste disposal; in each of them the orderly process of decay is inhibited in a different way. In valley bogs it is lack of drainage that causes the dead plants to accumulate and turn sour; in raised bogs (common in Ireland, rare in Britain) tussocks of wading fresh-water plants have grown up above plants that have died, mounting themselves higher and higher, until the surface of the bog is convex, with the center higher than the shoreline; in blanket bogs inadequate evaporation has the same effect as inadequate drainage, and a bog drapes itself over hills and mountains like a huge soggy blanket. This is the bog that is a conspicuous and admired feature of Scotland and southwestern England. It is called "moor," or "heather moor," after its chief resident.

Heather, genus *Calluna*, also called "ling," has small leaves with thick, hardened surfaces that conserve moisture. And there is another aid to survival, not easily visible but deeply hidden within *Calluna*'s tissues. That is a fungus that is able to do what the heather plant cannot: take nourishment directly from the acid, raw humus. The fungus penetrates the roots of the heather and sends its fine fungal threads up through the entire plant, even into the seedcoat. Thus it is already present when the seedling starts its growth.

With the heather grow other plants with similar small, hard, leathery leaves, especially the bilberry, *Vaccinium myrtillis*, and the cowberry, *Vaccinium vitis-idaea*.

These plants of the moors have reduced leaves; the gorse has them modified into spines.

common heather or ling
Calluna vulgaris

common cotton grass
Eriophorum angustifolium

matgrass
Nardus stricta

crowberry
Empetrum nigrum

gorse, or furze, or whin Ulex europaeus

heath bedstraw
Galium saxatile

cranberry
Vaccinium oxycoccus

wavy hair grass
Deschampsia flexuosa

We explored cautiously around the valley bogs, wading deep in sphagnum, until the foundation felt somewhat wobbly and we drew back, remembering *The Hound of the Baskervilles:*

"By George, there is another of those miserable ponies!"
Something brown was rolling and tossing among the green sedges. Then a long, agonized, writhing neck shot upwards and a dreadful cry echoed over the moor. It turned me cold with horror, but my companion's nerves seemed stronger than mine.
"It's gone," he said. "The mire has him."

We saw a thread of a path, edged with gorse, and followed its prickly way to a tor. Probably the path had been made by sheep seeking shelter on the lee side of the granite hulk, but we speculated, too, on its having been made by some fugitive convict from the Dartmoor prison. We were beset by memories of the prisoners we had seen in nearby Princetown, especially the small, flint-faced one that we had happened to see being escorted by two granite men from the railway station to the jail. We recalled the convict who had hidden on the moors in *The Hound of the Baskervilles.*

With feverish haste we had turned the body over, and that dripping beard was pointing to the cold, clear moon. There could be no doubt about the beetling forehead, the sunken animal eyes. It was indeed the same face which had glared upon me in the light of the candle over the rock—the face of Selden, the criminal.

We came back to Dartmoor next day in a steady rain, and on the third day in a fog. On the fourth day we visited Bodmin Moor. During our wanderings we hardly met a soul. Loneliness is one of the assets of the treeless places of the earth.

The few British we met seemed to have various names for that place. They called it "moor," or "heather moor," or "grass moor" (the part where the sheep were), or "heath."

In *Return of the Native* Thomas Hardy used "heath" and "moor" interchangeably, but there is no lack of definiteness in the way he described it:

It was at present a place perfectly accordant with man's nature—neither ghastly, hateful, nor ugly; neither commonplace, unmeaning, nor tame; but, like man, slighted and enduring; and withal singularly colossal and mysterious in its swarthy monotony. . . .
The face of the heath by its mere complexion added a half hour to evening; it could in like manner retard the dawn, sadden noon, anticipate the frowning of storms scarcely generated, and intensify the opacity of a moonless night to a cause of shaking and of dread.

HEATH

Although the plants that dominate the heath are the same as those that dominate a moor, ecologically the term "heath" is usually applied to a place shaped by a different set of circumstances.

We caught sight of a purple hill, south of Guildford, and climbed it. There our shoes did not squirt. They crunched.

The top of the hill, the driest part, was covered with bell heather, *Erica cinerea,* but most of the hill was covered with *Calluna vulgaris,* the same heather that we had seen dominating Dartmoor. There was also a great growth of bracken and of gorse. The plants, for the most part, were the same as those on the moor.

But at Dartmoor we had been on the old side of Britain: it was high, foggy, wet, and acid. Here in Surrey we were on a sunny hill of lowland Britain. How could the same plants thrive, on this dry heath, as on that sodden moor?

The answer, of course, is that *both* were dry. The difference between the two regions lay in the nature of the dryness: Dartmoor had been only physiologically dry, but this Surrey hill was physically dry. We were walking on a rock layer called the greensand. This rock, which is acid and quite porous, permits rain to drain away so rapidly that the plant remains that collect become unrotted peat. The thin peat layer is occupied by small-leaved plants that are equipped for holding their moisture—*Calluna,* first of all.

At the edge of the heath, toward the base of the hill, grew evidence that this was not destined to be a treeless area. There was a grove of small birch trees advancing on the hill.

Seeing them, I turned back to examine the ground that had crunched so dryly under our feet. It was covered with lichens and mosses, but it was blackened. Fire had been there. Repeated fires had probably kept this hill from being covered with forest.

Later, on the flat top of a hill in the downs, we were to see *Calluna* again. Heather on the alkalinity of chalk! It seemed improbable, but there it was, thriving. There was, however, an explanation. The heather we saw was growing only on the flat top of the hill, not on the slopes. What had happened was that over the years the rains percolating through the upper layers had carried calcium deeper and deeper, leaching out the surface chalk, until finally heather could germinate there on the top and grow. On the slopes, however, the rain had simply run off instead of percolating through the chalk.

Evidently heather fills not one but several ecological niches.

Most important is its role on the Scottish moors, often called "grouse moors."

GROUSE MOOR

White heather, "for luck, madam," was being sold at the cross-roads. But we didn't need any. It was good luck enough just to be in Scotland in August, with the common heather in full pink-purple bloom across the mountains.

At the foot of heather-covered mountains south of Inverness, we left the car beside a small road and crossed a fence into a field where black-faced sheep were grazing. We crossed because of the drifts of harebells and buttercups, but we soon forgot them because of the many-patterned wild pansy faces peering up through the grass.

We slowly worked our way across that flowery, grassy moor, stepping over many cold rivulets, until we reached the far fence, higher up the mountain.

At this fence the grass moor ended abruptly. We crossed it into heather moor that stretched away to flow up and over the next mountain, and the next, and the next, and to melt into the gray sky. We were facing humped miles of common heather, *Calluna*, with a mixture of its associates: bell heather, bilberry, heath bedstraw, and much bracken fern.

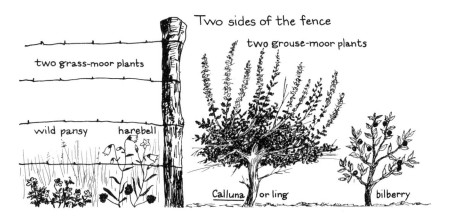

Two sides of the fence

two grass-moor plants

two grouse-moor plants

wild pansy   harebell

Calluna or ling   bilberry

Those Calluna-covered hills looked, at first glance, like wasteland, lying wild, unfenced, unwanted, cold, high, soggy, acid. It seemed as though neither man nor forests could use them.

On the contrary, this land was once covered with forest, chiefly birch, with a little pine. Its destruction may have started with the coming of the cold wet period, called the sub-Atlantic period, seven hundred to five hundred fifty years before Christ, with an excessive growth of sphagnum moss, so excessive that it enveloped trees until they toppled. The destruction may also have been started —certainly it was continued—by Iron Age farmers making clearings for their cropland and their sheep. The sheep continued the deforestation, eating seedlings, girdling birch trees. Eventually the railroad came through and burned anything that was left.

Although much of the land has been taken over by sheep and cattle, some landowners have turned the land back to the hunter— at a good profit.

The owner of the unfenced grouse moor through which we walked, deep in heather, was probably making as good an income from his land as the owner of the sheep in the fenced field where we walked among grass, pansies, harebells, buttercups, and a little heather.

On the unfenced moor the heather must be burned every few years. The burning is done when the wind carries the fire briskly past, so that the plants are not destroyed, but only mildly tip-pruned. After such a pruning they develop many new and tender tips upon which the grouse can feed.

If the heather is burned every four years it grows about ankle high. If it is burned every eight or ten years it grows about knee high. The slopes above the sheep field must have been on a ten-year schedule. We waded knee deep.

The red grouse, *Lagopus scoticus,* is at home here in Scotland, and nowhere else on earth. Such natives with greatly restricted ranges are called endemics; the red grouse is the only endemic species of bird in the British Isles. His companion on the moors, the Scottish red deer, *Cervus elaphus scoticus,* is an endemic subspecies. Because of the former land bridge to the continent, most living things have ranges extending both ways from the ends of the bridge.

No wonder that *Lagopus* is well fitted for life on the moors, especially for surviving the bitter moor winters. During a heavy snowfall the grouse sits, usually under a heather, steadily treading, so that it rises with the deepening snow. A profile cut through the snow after a heavy fall that might have been expected to bury the grouse, revealed its droppings occurring at various depths through the trodden, compacted snow. A grouse's eggs may be frosted and yet survive.

During the winter *Lagopus* feeds on green shoots on the underside of the heather that shelters him. In the spring he nibbles tender shoots on top of the shrub. (Moor burning is usually done before April 10.) In the summer this creature of simple tastes eats heather flowers, and then the forming seed-heads. Then through the fall he eats ripe seeds, and nearby berries, until the snow sends him back under the canopy.

Red deer browse on the heather, too, in the summer. In the winter they contribute to the treelessness of the heights by destroying any birch trees that may have made a start.

The red deer, by nature a creature of the open forest, has had to change its ways in order to survive on these open moors. It is reported that there are a hundred and fifty thousand red deer living in Scotland with little shelter.

This is very much a man-made landscape. Were man to turn his back on the mountains, were he to take his sheep off and stop lighting fires and burning heather to make good shooting for prosperous hunters, a quite different landscape would gradually develop.

First, the heather would invade the grassland and take it over, shading out all the pansy faces, harebells, and buttercups. Then the heather would take on a different appearance. It would lose its compact, pruned form and grow loose and leggy, three feet high. Light would find its way to the ground in many places. The wind would bring birch seeds, birds would bring seeds of the rowan tree, or mountain ash. The birch trees and the mountain ash would bring a light dappled shade. In this light shade seedling pines would thrive.

In the shade of the mature pine trees, birches could not grow, but oaks would thrive, and, at altitudes of less than a thousand feet, dominate the forest. (Above a thousand feet the birches would hold their own.) In the river valleys the alder would flourish.

The forest would have returned. The grouse moors would be gone.

While we may turn to ecologists for an understanding of the moors and for advice about their best use, we are likely to turn to our storytellers to get the flavor of the moors.

The witches of Macbeth concocted their brew near Inverness, where Macbeth's castle stood. It is easy to believe in witches there.

On another moor, in Yorkshire, Emily Brontë coughed and wrote. Charlotte Brontë said of her, "She was a native and nursling of the moors." In *Wuthering Heights* Emily showed that she was aware of the acid, preservative qualities of her moors:

We came to the chapel. . . . It lies in a hollow, between two hills; an elevated hollow, near a swamp, whose peaty moisture is said to answer all the purposes of embalming on the few corpses deposited there.

The Brontë sisters spent the long, uninterrupted years of their childhood rambling over the moors, returning always to their father's parsonage to write their many midget books; as young women they inevitably wove into their novels the strength of the moors, their harshness, and their lack of prettiness.

It was when we all suddenly, for some reason, laughed aloud on the moor, that we caught our first, and only, glimpse of the royalty of ancient lineage for whose comfort, and death, the moor was tailored. Something rust-colored, chunky, exploded with a racing motor out of the heather, buzzed up the mountain, and sank grayly into the heather again, way up there. It was as Robert Burns described it in his "Hunting Song."

> The heather was blooming, the meadows were mawn
> Our lads gaed a-hunting ae day at the dawn,
> O'er moors and o'er mosses, and mony a glen,
> At length they discovered a bonnie moor-hen.
>
> They hunted the valley, they hunted the hill,
> The best of our lads, wi' the best o' their skill;
> But still as the fairest she sat in their sight,
> Then, whirr! she was over, a mile at a flight.

Our grouse was a true Scot; the "whirr" she made was pronounced exactly as a Scotsman would say it.

GLEN

From the grouse moors about Inverness we moved southwest, following the grain of Scotland. We were traveling along one of the ancient folds that corrugate the landscape in a northeast-southwest direction, so deeply that the directional folding is apparent to the most casual map-user.

These deep folds, an extension of the folds of Norway, were shaped during the second mountain-building age of Britain. Later they were subjected to great stress, and gave before it. One particularly long crack, or rift, or fault line, developed, following the grain of the folds; then, still under stress, the two sides of the rift slipped past each other, forming a famous rift valley: the Great Glen.

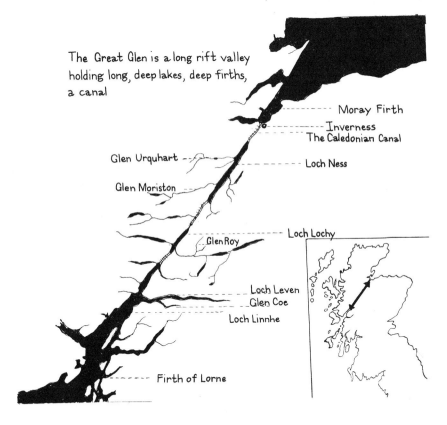

The Great Glen is a long rift valley holding long, deep lakes, deep firths, a canal

Moray Firth
Inverness
The Caledonian Canal
Glen Urquhart
Loch Ness
Glen Moriston
Loch Lochy
Glen Roy
Loch Leven
Glen Coe
Loch Linnhe
Firth of Lorne

Into this glen waters have poured from countless smaller, wilder glens, filling a host of long lakes. We stood at the bottom of the glen one day and saw the waters gushing in many a crimped and touseled waterfall down the cliff that walled the west side of our road as it followed the shores of the lakes.

This landscape cradled no subtleties. Its mountains, glens, and swift streams isolated communities and promoted clans; its bitter weather tended to make men seek warmth by fighting, or whiskey, or the hell-fire and brimstone of the United Presbyterian Church; its thin soil supported only such poor land crops as rye and barley and sheep; and its spaces were too wide and wild and deep for sounds more subtle than those of the bagpipe.

The Great Glen looked cheery enough at first, with its long stretches of lake, with dark granite castles rising from the shore among heavy masses of dark oaks. Always a part of the scene were white birches, and mountain ashes, heather, harebell, gorse, broom, and bracken. But the stories of the glen and of its clans were gloomy ones.

The gloom was gathering as we left Inverness, where Lady Macbeth had tried to wash the blood of the old king from her hands; and where the Duke of Cumberland's band had celebrated their victory by routing out and massacring the wounded Highlanders of Bonnie Prince Charlie's army.

Then, near the mouth of Glen Urquhart, the handsome birches and the bracken and the tumbling white water faced the ruins of Castle Urquhart, which had in its walls special openings for pouring hot molten lead upon wrong-clan visitors.

Harebells were drifting over the roadside when we came to the site of the church at Kilchrist, whose congregation was entirely composed of Mackenzies. On a certain Sabbath in the 1600s, the story goes, the MacDonalds crept up and set fire to the church. They left their piper to march round and round the burning building, until the flames died down.

Mountain ash throve at Fort Augustus, the place where the mighty Cumberland was so deeply offended. It seems that Cumberland had been expecting to receive the head of the conquered Prince Charlie, but was presented instead with the bleeding head of a young Edinburgh lawyer.

Further down the Great Glen was the long, narrow Loch Lochy, one mile by ten, with its "Well of the Heads." The story here concerned a certain MacDonnell, who had sent his two sons to France to be educated. He died before they came home, but just before he died he entrusted his seven brothers with the affairs of his branch of the clan—temporarily, until the sons should come home. When the sons returned, educated, the seven brothers killed them. There was, however, a faithful family bard who wrought vengeance. He had the heads of the seven murderers cut off so that he could present them to the leader of the clan, at Glengarry. For appearance's sake he washed the heads in the well beside Loch Lochy. They are carved in stone above the well.

And Glen Coe, of course, the "glen of weeping." Here occurred a famous massacre that began at dawn of February 13, 1692, with Campbell of Glenlyon and his 128 soldiers suddenly attacking the inhabitants of the glen, with whom they had been living on friendly terms. This order to attack their friends was delivered to the Campbells written on the nine of diamonds, a card known since as "The Curse of Scotland."

The length of the Great Glen teems with heather, bloodshed, harebells, and cold, cold water. It was easy to visualize lines from Walter Scott's *Lady of the Lake:*

> Instant, through copse and heath, arose
> Bonnets and spears and bended bows. . . .
>
> And every tuft of broom gives life
> To plaided warrior armed for strife. . . .
>
> That whistle garrisoned the glen
> At once with full five hundred men.

Not all the glens ran blood, of course, not those that were immortalized by Robert Burns, certainly not the one he described in "The Birks of Aberfeldy."

We came to Aberfeldy on a Saturday evening, just in time to watch the local pipers drill. Afterward we walked up the glen to the falls of Moness.

The path was embossed with the spreading roots of beech trees, mature elegant beech trees with moss and lichens and many initials on their smooth gray bark. Alongside the river ran white and loud.

Gradually the glen narrowed, until the treetops of the opposite brinks met overhead. A special richness of moss and liverwort encrusted those walls then, continually wet with the spray of the racing water. The rock face wore Marchantia, a liverwort familiar on water-sprayed rock around the world; and among the mosses there were Ptilium and Thuidium and Mnium, looking the same as they do on the walls of a canyon in Illinois or a tombstone in New England, a cove in the Smokies or a fountain in Italy.

Birch trees were few, although Burns had written of them in his poem:

> The hoary cliffs are crowned wi' flowers
> White o'er the linns the burnie pours,
> And rising, weets wi' misty showers
> > The birks of Aberfeldy.

People say Burns made a mistake. But it is possible that birches, which do not thrive in the shade of other trees, not even in the thin shade of other birches, have simply been replaced in the natural succession of plants by the more shade-tolerant beeches.

This richly furnished glen is a transitory microclimate among the windswept and fireswept hills. After a time its walls, which now confine the moist air in a pocket, will crumble. The glen will widen, and wind and fires will enter. The beeches will depart, and heather and gorse will settle in.

VOLCANIC NECK

The map of Scotland has a structure like that of a great double-decker sandwich.

The top layer, known as the Northern Highlands, is crusty and coarse-grained brown bread, well buttered with lichens.

Underneath that layer comes the top layer of filling, dark with rare, bloody meat. This is the Great Glen.

The second slice of bread is a mass of highlands called the Grampians, or Central Highlands, which form the lower, or southern, side of the Great Glen. Grouse moors cover much of this layer.

The next layer is rich, thick, and tasty. The firths have nibbled into its softness from both east and west. Most American travelers, as well as most Scotsmen (four-fifths of them live here) savor this filling, called the Midlands.

At the bottom of the sandwich is more dark bread, but not so crusty and grainy as the Highlands slice on top. This bread is called the Southern Uplands. It is the land of Sir Walter Scott.

Long ago, long before there were grouse moors, or bread, or sandwiches, or even Scotsmen, two long cracks, or rifts, cut diagonally

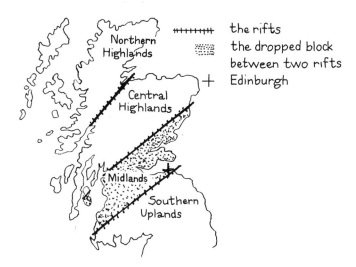

across the central mass of Scotland. Then the great block between the rifts dropped down, forming a valley. That was so long ago that there has been time for the sea to lay down sandstone in the valley; time for a swamp forest to have grown and to have been slowly changed into coal; time for yet other layers to have formed slowly and as slowly to have been eroded away.

Most important, there has been time for volcanoes to pour their molten rock into cracks; and time for the lava to have solidified into hard plugs at the volcanic openings, forming what are called volcanic necks; time for the softer rocks around the necks to have been eroded away.

Time too for a glacier to have scoured its way across the land. But the hard necks were jutting up into the glacier's path. Anyone who has ever swept snow from a walk and noticed how pebbles or bits of ice keep behind them tails of snow, which follow the direction of the broom, will be able to visualize how the glacier left stony tails streaming out from the necks.

One dramatic theater was shaped in this fashion at what is now Edinburgh, a hard, high, dark, impregnable block thrusting up out of the Midlands, ready to be surmounted by a frowning castle.

No one knows when the first castle was built on the Rock— perhaps as early as the Iron Age. But a tiny tenth-century chapel does survive on the castle grounds. It is named Margaret Chapel, after the English queen of Malcolm III Canmore—the slayer of

Macbeth. That was only one killing in a long, tortured, bloody chronicle. When the lone piper walks the old wall as the finale of the Edinburgh Festival Tattoo, the castle seems to be singing its whole wailing epic, and the strains trail down into the town at the base of the Rock.

A site for a castle

1. The molten rock solidifies in the neck of the volcano. ———

2. Erosion by water and wind wears away at the softer sedimentary layers.

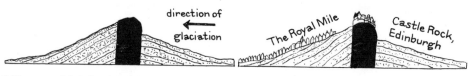

direction of glaciation

3. The great ice sheet gouges deep as it approaches, but rides over the top of the resistant volcanic neck, and leaves a long tail on the other side.

4. Men built a castle on top of the neck. A town grew down the tail.

The tail of sedimentary rock that the glacier shaped has become The Royal Mile, the historic way that a traveler follows to the top of the Rock and to the castle.

Another volcanic neck is the height where Stirling Castle made history. Another is Ailsa Craig, lifting its rounded form out of the sea to be whitened by thousands of birds. Another is Arthur's Seat, also in Edinburgh, but this one is a more complicated form, with two vents and a hard shelf. And there are others.

There are other volcanic necks elsewhere. In France there is Le Puy, topped with a chapel. In the United States there is Ship Rock, which rises starkly out of the New Mexico desert, and the Devil's Tower, which looms up in Wyoming. But not one holds a castle and a hundred tales on its top, and rises out of the center of a city.

DOWNS

The Downs are a bare-bones landscape: a thin skin of close-shorn grass and the rounded bones of the fine-textured limestone called chalk. There is no fat and no drapery, except for a few scraps of thorn-scrub and patches of woodland. The sea that built the bones has taken back a major part of them, and thereby hangs the tale of the Downs and the Weald.

During the upheaval of the Alpine period of mountain-building, that part of the floor of the sea which was one day to become southeastern England and northwestern France, was warped into parallel upfolds and downfolds, running in an east-west direction. One of the downfolds was destined to hold the Thames River and London; another was to hold Salisbury Plain. While those two downfolds were forming, a very special upfold was thrusting higher and higher between them; very special because it was to furnish England with its Box Hill, its white cliffs of Dover, its racehorse tracks and its landing fields, as well as its Kentish hop fields and apple orchards.

The sea floor that was being folded comprised several layers of rock. The uppermost layer was chalk, a thick layer of chalk. Beneath it were layers of sandstone, clay, limestone, all laid down by the sea.

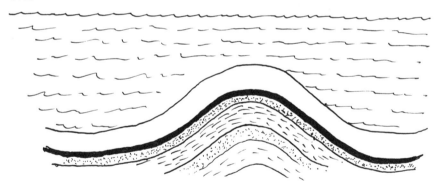

As the uplift continued the top of the fold broke the surface of the sea. An oval dome, shaped somewhat like the bottom of an over-turned rowboat, presently shone as a pure-white island. It continued to grow, and as it rose the chalk surface layer strained and cracked. It was further breached by erosion.

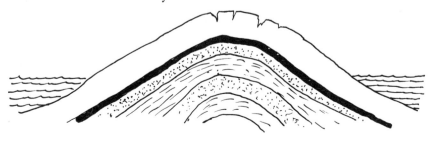

Slowly the arch of the dome disintegrated and was washed away, returning to the sea. Then the layers beneath the chalk were exposed to the forces of erosion, which lowered and partially leveled them.

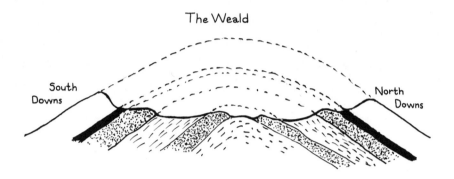

As erosion continued the rising sea level allowed an arm of the sea (now called the Straits of Dover) to cut the former dome into two parts; the eastern section became a part of France, and the western section became the southeastern part of England, with the remaining part of the chalk dome forming the North Downs and the South Downs, and the roots of the other upfolded layers forming what is known as the Weald. The drowned section lying under the Straits of Dover is so shallowly covered that the geologist A. K. Lobeck estimates that "any English cathedral standing on the sea bottom would reveal most of its steeple to passing ships."

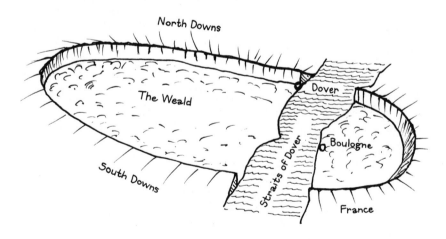

Where the edge of the Weald meets the foot of the Downs, a border of scrub makes a line separating greenness from whiteness, squared fields from wide, unfenced expanse, and a landscape with many trees from a treeless one.

The word "weald" is a Saxon one, meaning "forest" (a form of the same word as "wold," "wood," "wald"), and a part of it is forested still. On the part that the sea now covers, stumps and roots of an ancient forest have been found. The Downs, on the other hand, have long been treeless. It is suspected that this treelessness, like that of the grouse moors, is the work of man.

The Neolithic farmer must have started his clearing of the Downs about forty-five hundred years ago, using stone axes and fire. His sheep, and the sheep of succeeding farmers, have kept the area treeless, assisted by imposing numbers of rabbits, who quickly girdle any sapling. Trees come in whenever sheep and rabbits are removed.

The plants of the Downs are a hardy group. They have survived trial by wind and sun and sharp drainage, and sheep and rabbits—all on an alkaline diet. The secrets of their success give character to the Downs. A splendid place to investigate them is on top of Box Hill near Dorking, on your knees, and with a hand lens.

The dominant downland grass, called sheep's fescue, meets the sun with folded leaves. Each leaf is V-shaped in cross section and has its vulnerable openings, the stomates, on the inside of the V. This V is wider in wet weather than in dry. Some of the other grasses roll up instead of folding.

For most Downs plants the position of greatest safety from the mouths of sheep and rabbits, and from the thirsty sun, is close against the soil.

One successful way of staying close is the rosette habit. According to the count of some English botanists, 35 percent of all downland plants have it. A rosette plant claims its small domain by spreading its radiating leaves right down against the ground, pressing them firmly against the surface. Only the flowers are raised, like flags on a miniature flagpole, a signal for bees.

One rosette plant is the cowslip, *Primula veris*. This plant has a stout stalk bearing a cluster of drooping, pale-yellow flowers from its basal rosette of thick, crinkled leaves. Because it blooms in the early spring, visitors who come during "the season" may not see it making all the English meadows gay, and may not get to smell the fragrance, "like a cow's breath," which is probably responsible for its name. But a sleepless visitor may be able to procure, from one of the delightful herbalist shops, some cowslip wine or cowslip syrup, which, it is claimed, "induces quiet sleep," or a few dried cowslip leaves to slip into his tea.

Still another rosette plant, one that will bear its flowers too early for most travelers, is the pasqueflower *Anemone pulsatilla*. Its purple and gold will be gone by summer, but shocks of silky plumes will still mark the seed-heads on some warm, south-facing slopes.

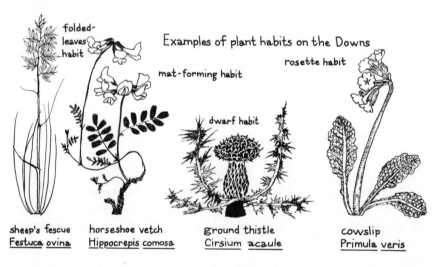

folded-leaves habit

Examples of plant habits on the Downs

mat-forming habit

rosette habit

dwarf habit

sheep's fescue	horseshoe vetch	ground thistle	cowslip
Festuca ovina	Hippocrepis comosa	Cirsium acaule	Primula veris

Almost as common as the rosette habit is the mat habit. The horseshoe vetch bears its many small, yellow, pea-shaped flowers on a dense sprawling mat, which may cover the ground with a close-clinging carpet a yard across. This particular mat can be lifted free of the ground, but many mats cannot, because they have put out roots wherever the joints of their stems touch the surface. Other plants form their mats, not of prostrate stems, but of an interwoven network of stems growing just below the surface of the soil. The mouse-ear chickweed, the bird's-foot trefoil, and the harebell are such plants.

The sun-beaten mat that is most aromatic underfoot is thyme.

Gray leaves are common on the Downs, as are narrow leaves and deep roots. Many plants hold their resting buds safely at the surface of the soil. Many are harsh or hairy or prickly to the touch. Many have deeply divided leaves that let the sun slip through. Many are impregnated with oils that help to hold onto moisture in the face of a thirsty wind. There are few annuals or biennials.

Birds come regularly to eat the seeds of the downland plants from the edge of nearby woods, where they may have already eaten the juicy fruits of hawthorns or sweetbriar roses, elderberry, privet, wayfaring tree or purging buckthorn, boxwood, spindle tree, or yew. Some of the seeds from these juicy fruits pass intact through their digestive tracts and are left on the Downs. And some do start to grow. Most of the seedlings, of course, are nipped off by rabbits as soon as they have two or three tender leaves. And if the rabbits miss them the sheep take them. And if they somehow live long enough to make bark, then the rabbits girdle them in the winter.

A few do survive, though, and surviving, they form a sort of thorny sanctuary where others may have a better chance of surviving. Even then their tender new growth is subjected to constant nibbling, relentless pruning, which shapes them into dense low forms. And so they present to hungry herbivores a massed, scrubby, twiggy, thorny, bitter formation.

This is chalk scrub.

The scrub seems most likely to get its start in valleys, but, extending under its own self-made shelter, it inches up the Downs. Its very presence indicates that the forest would return to the Downs, a forest such as that the Neolithic farmer found and leveled, if the sheep and rabbits were excluded.

First the scrub would assume a less compact form.

Soon some ash trees would poke up through the mass, presently topping it, and introducing shade to the scrub community. The thorny rose family, intolerant of shade, would grow gangling and weak, and be eliminated. So would many others.

Also in the shade of the ash trees, there might grow beech seedlings. Then the beech forest would return.

But if the chalk were too soggy for beech, as might happen in a humid valley, the ash would remain and form an ash grove. There are many ashwoods in the Cotswolds, where they flourish in the damp valleys in the oolitic limestone. Lily of the valley flourishes beneath them.

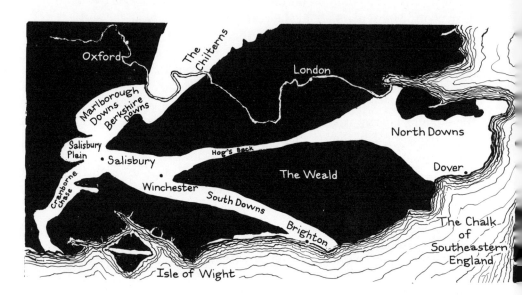

Beech, which requires sharp drainage, is sometimes perched on a steep slope, or a hill. Gilbert White, a gentle eighteenth-century priest, who described his parish in *The Natural History and Antiquities of Selborne,* started the custom of calling such a woods a "beech hanger."

The high part of the southwest consists of a vast hill of chalk, rising three hundred feet above the village, and is divided into a sheep down, the high wood, and a long hanging wood called The Hanger. The covert of this eminence is altogether beech . . .

Rudyard Kipling told stories of the Downs. Two are "Puck of Pook's Hill" and "The Knife and the Naked Chalk." He once wrote,

> Clean of officious fence or hedge,
>   Half-wild and wholly tame,
> The wise turf cloaks the white cliff edge
>   As when the Romans came.

Others have woven their plots around the Downs. But this land-scape of skin and bones needs no embellishment by imagination. The first part of its own long story is carved deep into its bones by the sea and by earth movements; the last chapters are written on its skin, by sun and rain and plants and man, and are full of puzzling erasures. Not all who read the Downs reach the same conclusions about them.

COPPICE AND POLLARD

We drove to Burnham Beeches, west of London, on a leafy summer Sunday.

We were to acquire new words that day, words for a forest in continuous use, words not coined by a botanist but hewn by a man with an ax, words that have the sound of chopping in them, "lop," and "top," "coppice," "pollard."

We parked our car on an open common, guiltily. But all the small English cars were parked there, too, helter-skelter, without any apparent rules, prohibitions, directions. Even then, that particular common could fitly have been dedicated to pilgrims kneeling rev-erently, chanting, for in its center stood a PRESENCE. An oak it was, so firmly rooted in England, so ponderously unshakable, so full of good years—of good centuries—so smilingly presenting its leaves to yet another season, that it might have been named the Churchill Oak. But, we learned, it was called (more modestly?) the Druid Oak.

The English are accustomed to such presences. While I was doing mental homage to the oak's four hundred years, and its thirty feet of girth, *they* were sitting beside their cars and having their tea and currant cake, without fuss. They seemed just glad to be there.

Then we walked into the beech forest.

It was no "cathedral forest," with long aisles below Gothic arches of branches. It was more like a fantastic, massive apple orchard, shaped by man and time.

According to the *Domesday Book*, William the Conqueror's tax-gathering survey of about 1086, the first use of this forest was for swine. The *Domesday Book* describes part of this area with the words, "there was woodland for 100 swine." The swine must have

fattened on beech mast and acorns. At the same time red deer must
have browsed on leaves and tender twigs. The appetites of swine
and cattle and deer would have kept seedlings from developing. It
was undoubtedly a rare, accidentally protected beechnut that ever
grew into a tree, perhaps one that was lodged far under the thorny
maze of a hawthorn.

In the fifteenth century someone evidently noticed the fact that
the forest was not replacing itself. Forty acres were fenced, with the
grazing animals *outside* the fence. Perhaps the purpose of the fenc-
ing was to permit the growth of understory shrubs, such as hazel,
which could be cut off at the ground—that is, "coppiced"—every
few years for firewood or for charcoal.

At about that time the cutting of branches from the trees—called
"lopping," or "pollarding"—must also have begun. After all, the lord
of the manor needed firewood for the many fireplaces of the manor
house. (His tenants needed firewood, too, and on some manors the
lopping of branches for firewood was one of the ancestral rights of
tenants, but here they had to await dispensation by the lord.)

Pollarded beeches

The pollarding was done according to certain rules. When the
forester went out to get firewood, he selected a tree that was not
more than thirty years old (if it were older, new branches might not
shoot out). Then he cut off branches about eight feet above the
ground (if the branches were removed at a lower level there was

danger that cattle would destroy the new shoots in their juicy youth). As new branches sprang from the pollarded trees, they were allowed to attain firewood size, and then they, too, were removed.

For three hundred years these thickening old trunks wore their crown of youth, curving out and upward eight feet or so above the ground.

Then came a change, and there was a new smell up at the manor house. The rich smell of wood smoke was infiltrated, and then replaced, by the thicker smell of coal, and the forester no longer needed to harvest all the good available branches. On the pollarded trees the branches began to crowd each other at the eight-foot level. By 1820 the lopping had been stopped.

In 1880 Burnham Beeches, with all rights, became the property of the Corporation of the City of London. Later still more acreage was added.

Jenny Lind came to walk here. She liked to rest against the roots of a certain great beech, and it came to be called the Jenny Lind Beech. But it finally had too great a weight of years and died. Felix Mendelssohn, it is said, also came often and rested on a certain slope. It is called, still, the Mendelssohn Slope.

By the time of the Second World War, some of the most massive arms had put on weight that was too much for the old trunks to support. The corporation, seeing that the branches would break and damage the trunks, timorously ordered some lopping. And, just as they expected, indignant citizens wrote letters to the *Times*. The citizens were just being tactfully pacified when a whole bevy of birches came out into the open, sunny places and danced into the Common. The poets loved them. The public loved them. The corporation cut them down. They wisely foresaw that these pioneer trees invading the sunny area, creating shade, and crowding, would soon change the character of the place. In dealing with the over-burdened beeches and the intrusive birches the corporation had had to assume the ecological roles that were once filled by swine, deer, cattle, and foresters; the letters to the *Times* were an added complication.

The story of the Burnham Beeches is somewhat different from that of the thriving, self-replacing beechwoods of the chalk and the limestone. Here the plant succession develops a circular form.

As with all beech forests, the layered leaf mosaics overhead permit little sunlight to filter through to the ground. These pollarded trees, in fact, seem to have leaf mosaics even more compactly layered than usual. Nevertheless, shade tolerance does not appear to be the prime factor in this forest cycle.

Sun's-eye view of the layered mosaic of a beech tree

The fallen leaves cover the ground at Burnham no more completely than they do in other beechwoods, but they cover it more deeply because they do not decay, nor are they drawn into the soil by earthworms. There are none. One year's leaves are as dry and almost as intact as two-year-old leaves, or three-year-old leaves. The bottom leaves are simply pressed together more and more compactly, until, about four inches down, they form a sort of black, stiff, undigested peatlike humus. Under this one- to two-inch layer is a bleached-looking gray-white layer, and then acid, gravelly clay. This acidity, indicated by the presence of the silver-green cushion moss, *Leucobryum,* is the decisive factor here. Where the ground is flat, as it is at Burnham, the beech forest does not seem able to regenerate itself, and no seedling beeches grow under the old trees. By contrast, on the slopes of shallow valleys, where rainwash prevents the formation of a compact layer of undecayed humus, beech seedlings are present.

Somehow, once having become established on this unlikely acid footing, the Burnham Beeches have matured, survived, and served. But they die slowly, one at a time. The death of one of these widespreading ancients lets a broad chimney of sunlight into the stand.

Then heather takes over (grassland comes if the area is pastured), thriving on the sunlight and acid soil. Presently birch trees rise through the heather, then oaks, and then beeches come again, to make their single-generation stand. But this time through they will not be recorded as swine pasture by William the Conqueror, nor will they be pollarded by the peasants for firewood. However, they will probably meet a new hazard in gases and smoke, which will infiltrate their thin leaves and their smooth bark.

Pollarding of trees was a sensible-enough practice when their unglamorous destiny was the warming of Englishmen and the cooking of their food; but for the glorious destiny of bracing a tall sailing ship against the power of the Atlantic, a different sort of conditioning was required, and a different tree—the English oak.

John Masefield tells in *Sea Life in Nelson's Time* that the building of a seventy-four-gun ship required nearly two thousand oak trees. Stout, curved branches were needed, and, especially, stout branches with sharp-angled bends called kneepieces, or ships' knees. Such branches were not formed on the narrow-topped oaks crowded closely in a natural forest; they could develop only when side branches had room to spread wide. This occurred on special plots where the oaks could stand uncrowded—about twelve to the acre. A knee that would one day serve as a strong support to the framework of a ship, or a half-timbered house, would have its beginning some spring when a side bud on a certain oak twig put forth more

A. Branches of a wide-spreading English oak
B. Centuries later

vigorous growth than the end bud on the twig. The newly angled branch would increase in girth and strength for decades, until at last it was of a size useful for harvesting. When straight timber was required it could easily be obtained from the tree trunk and upper branches.

Underneath and between these large, widespread trees, called "standards," might be grown an additional crop, "the coppice." This was most often made up of hazel, which was cut off at the ground every seven to ten years and yielded many slender straight branches of uniform size, useful for bean poles, hop vines, barrel hoops, hurdles, fences, firewood, charcoal, and, occasionally, water-divining. Under the hazels the bluebells spread, and other spring flowers.

This type of plantation, known as "coppice with standards," was a mixture of delicacy and strength, pleasing, as simple functional structures so often are. "Was" seems the right term, because well-maintained areas of this kind have become uneconomic. Spacing does not matter now, and the shrubs are allowed to grow into small trees. The new forest use entails little work and good profits; it serves primarily as a cover for pheasant and foxes, and is leased to hunters.

The practice of growing oaks may have changed, but the oak grown centuries ago in those wide-spreading branches seems little changed. It may be seen on many an old half-timbered building.

One night we slept with those oaken knees arching over us, supporting a roof as they had been doing since 1320. We arrived late at Salisbury, where we went to the George Hotel and were assigned to a room on the top floor; it was the very room where Samuel Pepys had stayed in June 1668.

The building was already three hundred years old when Pepys "lay in a silken bed" there, he records. We lay in muslin. But not until we had opened the many-paned windows in their framework of English oak and peered down into the street, where Pepys's coach had come noisily over the cobbles.

Then we lay and looked up at the heavy roof-supporting, inter-braced, curving oak beams. It was easy to imagine those wide-spreading branches upcurving over a hazel coppice, which held a drift of bluebells, or windflowers, or primroses. We knew that that massive, dark crossbeam must have once caught a thin light from a candle, then more light from whale oil, even more from kerosene, and more yet from illuminating gas.

In the dark, to the sound of rain on the pitched roof, we lay confident that the well-grown and well-selected oak boughs that had shouldered the roof for six hundred years would not fail.

BOMB CRATER

Americans may regret having no need for such picturesque terms as "moor," "heath," or "downs" to apply to features of their landscape; but there is no regret that they have not yet needed the term "bomb crater." However, even if bombs were to burst in large American cities, they would not expose anywhere layers of the past comparable to those seen in the bomb craters of London.

Back during the Alpine period of mountain-building, the setting for the craters we saw was already being prepared. While the great Wealden Dome was being unfolded across what is now southeastern England, the Straits of Dover, and the Boulognnais region of France, the accompanying downfold to the north of it was forming the London basin, a long trough extending far inland.

An arm of the sea, which was then warm, extended into this basin and received the sediment-laden waters from streams flowing out of the surrounding hills. The fine sediment was deposited in the basin and became what is now known as "London clay"; the coarser gravels were rolled up onto the shore by pounding waves to form gravel beaches (part A of the figure on the next page).

The land rose steadily, and the level of the receding sea dropped gradually below the level of the gravel-covered beaches. Cutting into the shore, the waves slowly turned those beaches into gravel-topped terraces (part B).

As the sea level continued to drop, there were times when the relative levels of land and sea remained stationary. At each such pause the waves would cut a new terrace. Finally the body of water that would be known as the Thames River was shrunk to about its present level (it was even somewhat lower for a time). The river was left to swing widely from side to side in the oversized bed that had been shaped by the sea. One particular swing that the Thames made to the north brought it to the foot of a certain gravel terrace—the one that was being shaped toward its destiny as a bomb target (part C).

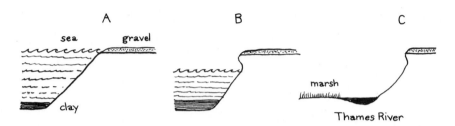

This terrace had been sculptured by a stream that was to be called Walbrook, a tributary of the Thames, into two rounded hills. And there it stood waiting, rising before the first Roman boats as they came up the river. It was high and dry, and provided a vantage point overlooking the low marshland of the opposite shore. The river swung in close, and landing was easy. Furthermore, the upper limits of the tides were at about that point. Boats could arrive on the tide and depart on the ebb. It was also the lowest point on the river that could be spanned by a bridge. The Romans built their Londinium there on the north side of the river, in A.D. 43. (The river was about fifteen feet lower in relation to the land at that time.) By A.D. 60 Tacitus was describing the city as "crowded with merchants and greatly celebrated for its commerce."

When the Romans enclosed Londinium with its first wall, the waters of the Walbrook were held back and a marsh was made out of its banks above the point at which it drained into the Thames. Later, Norman youths may have ice-skated there with bone runners tied to their feet. But eventually the marsh was drained and filled and used as an archery ground. In 1606 trees and shrubs were planted and benches were set up, and the shores of the old Walbrook became the first public park of London.

The Bank of England and the Royal Exchange surmounted one of the two hills shaped by the Walbrook, the one where the Romans had placed their Forum. The other hill, the one where the Romans raised their Temple of Venus, now holds the Cathedral of St. Paul. Between the two hills the Walbrook has been encased below ground, and its name has been given to a street.

In time the hills became encased, too, with an ever-thickening crust of stone and cement. This busy part of London, known as the City, yielded hardly a place in which a seed might lodge and grow.

Then the Germans dropped their bombs, and the bombs mixed

the present with its many pasts. The gravel of an old sea terrace, the river clay, the tools and toys of Romans, Saxons, Normans, peasants, suburban gardeners, city builders, city dwellers, were all stirred.

So the earth, cultivated by bombs and covered with a strangely assorted mulch, lay open to sun and rain, a botanical vacuum, an unoccupied ecological niche, ready.

It didn't take long. First the wind came lightly laden with winged seeds, which it had picked up on a railroad embankment some miles away. These were seeds of the plant called fireweed in America, where it blankets burned miles of the north woods. The seeds landed on the sunny ashes, the kind in which they thrive. They formed colonies, extended them by means of long underground shoots, and soon loose spikes of purple-pink flourished in every bomb crater. Near St. Paul's, the rubble-filled blocks edged by cross-sectioned buildings were full of it. In England this plant is called rosebay willow herb, or simply rosebay.

The wind also brought seeds of Oxford ragwort. We saw it in August, and the plant was still bearing its yellow flowers, but we could tell that it had been blooming for a long time. It is a sort of naturalized gypsy, first brought to Oxford from the Mediterranean for growing in a physic garden. But it quickly escaped to the walls of Oxford and by 1800 had become a common inhabitant of many old walls. Then it wandered out along the railroad tracks and perhaps occasionally hitched a ride on the cars. By 1939 it had become common on the edges of London. Then the bombs did their work, and suddenly new places were open to it, well-drained, sunny, full of ashes, resembling the volcanic slopes of its native Sicily.

We looked down into one deep gash that held a sign asking for gifts toward rebuilding Bow Bells and saw an American native, the daisy fleabane, sometimes called Canada fleabane, *Erigeron canadensis*. This plant was recorded in London as early as 1690, by John Ray. It must have traveled by boat, and then by wind. One American writer suggested that the first plant in England grew from a seed that fell from a stuffed bird. Other writers have copied his story into their writings (and now I have done it), but actually the story raises too many questions.

These three plants, fireweed, Oxford ragwort, fleabane, all wind-borne, dominated every bomb crater into which we looked. These, and bracken fern. This is the same bracken fern that fringes forests in America and appears with fireweed in the burned northwoods, the same one that is seen on the grouse moors and the heaths. This is the stout fern that happens to show a sign in a cross section of its root, a sign that, to some, is a picture of King Charles in the oak, and to others is the letter *C*, Christ's initial, which renders it a potent sign against witches. These bracken fern spores arrived on the wind, as did the seeds of other dominants.

The wind also brought willow seeds, and these grew as placidly beside the water in the crater bottom as if they were lining some rural brook where cows waded.

A. elder	D. Canadian fleabane	G. Oxford ragwort	J. Ailanthus
B. butterfly bush	E. slender foxtail grass	H. plantain	K. London plane
C. coltsfoot	F. rosebay, or fireweed	I. bracken fern	

Horses left seeds, too. These horses were brought to the craters, at first to cart away someone's salvaged household goods, later to clear rubble. While their drivers ate their lunches the horses stood with their nosebags, doubtless spilling some seeds and leaving others behind in their manure: slender foxtail grass, white clover, black medick, and oats.

And men's shoes brought seeds, as people came to hunt for something out of the past or to clear away towards the future. Their shoes brought plantain, both greater plantain, *Plantago major,* and narrow-leaved plantain, *Plantago lanceolata.* Both of these have achieved a certain fame as world travelers.

We saw a few elderberry bushes of almost tree size. Their seeds must have arrived in the digestive tracts of birds.

One shrub that we were surprised to see in the bomb craters was the butterfly bush, a common shrub in American gardens, a native of China. Probably it wandered into the craters on the wind, perhaps from a neighboring churchyard.

We had been told that commuters walking these sidewalks day after day, and mailmen, and bobbies, had scattered packetfuls of flower garden seeds and that those seeds had produced a gay display. But actually, of such plants I saw only a few small patches of sweet alyssum.

The effects of sudden fire are so obvious in the bomb crater that it is easy to forget that, in addition, the entire biological aspect of the City has been molded by the steady fires of myriad chimney pots and smokestacks, their smoke welded to the fog.

The pigeons whose breasts softly scallop the ledges of the City's man-made cliffs grow steadily more soot-colored. They are tending more and more toward the gray of their rock-dove ancestors and losing more and more of the white of their domesticated ancestors.

Certain moths are steadily developing by selection a higher percentage of dark forms. These dark moths would have been conspicuous and vulnerable against a natural habitat of lighter backgrounds, but in London it is safer to be sooty.

The City may, at a casual glance, appear to be all mechanized, modernized, industrialized, socially adjusted, but a closer look reveals that bloodthirsty hunting, lurking, sly approaches, sudden pounces, gouging, gutting, continue. Among the animals, from insects to birds to rats to man, there is business as usual. One building wore spiny armor against roosting birds on its windowsills; it also displayed a "No Loitering" sign beside its fancy door.

Sometimes the birds seem to have made better adjustment to the City than have the City men. The starlings spend the day in the country, and come to the City at evening to roost until dawn. But men, by contrast, spend their days in the City, and roost at night in the country.

One bird, the black redstart, found the City much improved by the bombs. This rare bird had been moving into London, but very slowly. Then, suddenly, an abundance of nesting sites was opened up for it in the broken, jagged, creviced walls. There was abundant food nearby, too, in the seeds of all the invading plants.

Topping all other invaders of the bombed areas rose the seedling trees, chiefly willow, tree of heaven, and the plane. In America the plane tree is called a sycamore, but in England that name seems to be reserved for the maple tree known to Americans as "sycamore maple." The tree called "London plane" is considered a hybrid between the sycamore, or American plane, and the oriental plane tree. This hybrid has endeared itself to London, not only by enduring its smoke but also by shedding patches of sooty bark and showing a smooth, clean white bark underneath.

London plane trees

The plane trees are quietly invading the bomb sites now, introducing a new element into the craters—shade. Gradually, if nature took its well-established course, the City would develop such a forest as it had when the Romans found these two hills. But nature will not be permitted to take its old established course, not in this city or any other. Two forces will oppose that. First, the smoke of London cannot be tolerated by English oaks and hornbeams. And, second, the space is rapidly being filled up by buildings, and pavements, and feet, and wheels. At present the new universal pattern of yard-goods building, offering two choices of design—vertical or horizontal stripes of glass—is taking over the bomb craters and rising high enough to dominate even St. Paul's. It may be a long time before the rich mixture of the City's many pasts is again revealed.

Now the rosebay, the butterfly bush, the Oxford ragwort, the black redstarts are all retreating. But they will return if their ecological niches are opened again, perhaps by some new blitz. Such a blitz would produce many empty niches. One can only speculate about what would come to occupy those left vacant by the disappearance of our own species.

FENS

Traveling the fifteen miles from the elevating experience of evensong in the chapel of King's College, Cambridge, to the magnificent Ely Cathedral raised high on its island, one can feel so uplifted that it is possible to go from the one height to the other without even becoming conscious of the land between: flat, low, soggy, uninspiring.

But we recovered when we came out of Ely Cathedral into the sun, bone-chilled and with necks stiff and eyes tired from looking up. Then we looked down to the flat, extensive expanse called the fenlands. Soon we learned the story of uplift recorded down there, the story of land being helped to emerge from the sea of a new, young part of England.

The story started long before the Isle of Ely existed. At first there was only a very wide river, coming down off the old limy hills on the west, flowing slowly northeast and depositing its silt on the low plain. Eventually it joined another wide river, a forerunner of the Rhine, into which the Thames had already poured itself.

Then the glaciers came, bringing clay and boulders from the north. When the ice finally retreated it left some especially high deposits of boulder clay. The largest of these would one day be called the Isle of Ely. The land sank deeper and the sea inundated the entire area, forming a bay, a great shallow bay of the shallow North Sea. At times the land rose slightly and the sea would retreat somewhat.

Plants began to grow in the shallowest parts: submerged pondweeds at first; then floating-leaved plants like water lilies taking advantage of the heaped-up remains of the pondweeds; and erect plants, such as cattails and tall reeds growing on the water lily remains; and sedges and grasses springing up wherever the debris had reached as high as the summer water level.

So far the kinds of plants and the order of their succession were not different from those in any slowly filling freshwater lake. But that was being slowly, steadily changed. The silt-filled rivers entering the area were obstructed when they arrived at a squarish, shallow bay called the Wash, the diminished representative of the former great bay. The sea tides piled up their silt across the river mouths and held the rivers back.

The Isle of Ely rose above the water. The dreaded Danish longboats passed by, and gave the town its name. "Eel-ø," they called it for the abundant eels in the waters at its feet. Ø means "island" in Danish. The name has become Ely, and the meaning is doubled because it is called the Isle of Ely. It is now only the memory of an island, surrounded completely by land.

When King Canute passed by in the early eleventh century there was already a monastery and a nunnery on the island, established there by Saint Ethelreda. An ancient song tells about it:

> Merry sungen the monkës; in Ely
> When Cnut King rowed thereby.
> Row, cnichts, near the land
> And hear we these monkës sing.

Hereward the Wake commanded the last stand against the Norman invaders on Ely. Soon afterward William the Conqueror sent the first bishop there.

None of these historic personages would have noticed that a new plant was taking over from the tall, waving reeds, taking over to such an extent that its hollow stems with their long evergreen leaves were forming large mattress-like colonies, through which little else could grow. This plant was fen sedge, or saw-sedge, *Cladium mariscus*. Its spreading is often the first indicator that the reed swamp has become fen, which is marked by the following characteristics: the plants are growing in peat that is not acid like bog peat because the water comes to it down from limestone hills (to the west and north in this case) and chalk hills (to the south); the peat has accumulated up to, or almost to, the summer water level.

On this waterlogged, unaerated accumulation of undecayed humus, the fen sedge and a few associates, if not interfered with, tend to build up humps on which certain shrubs appear. They soon form a woody tangle called fen carr, composed largely of alder buckthorn, gray sallow, common buckthorn, and a few others, similarly unattractive. It appears probable that hairy birch and black alder are the trees to succeed the carr, and that oaks would in time follow.

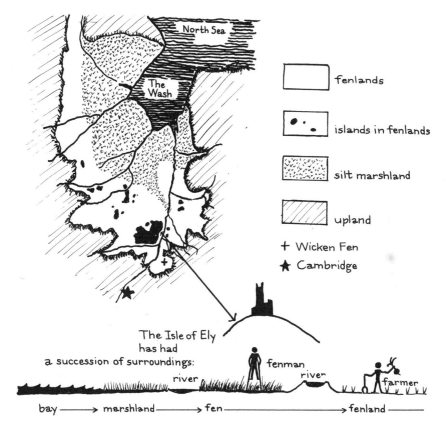

But the fens have not been permitted to proceed through the natural stages. Only in a few places, in nature preserves such as Wicken Fen, can the stages be seen now. And even there, much cutting has been necessary to reduce the tangle of carr and to preserve some areas of earlier stages.

The forces of progress have not waited for the plants to raise the fens. Men have hurried the making of plowland. Actually, the

Romans had started it, but after they left no one bothered to maintain their sea walls.

In 1631 the work of draining really began, despite the protests of the fenmen, who lived around the edges of the fen and on the islands, and cut reeds for roofing and sedges for litter, and ate plentifully from fish and waterbirds, and walked about on stilts. A straight ditch, seventy feet wide, was cut, running for twenty-one miles. Other, shorter ditches were made. They cut down the surface of the peat, and soon trouble developed because the peat shrank as it dried out under drainage. Finally it was ten feet below the silt land along the sea, and the rivers had to be lifted above the surface and banked with clay. Windmills, steam engines, diesel engines have taken their turns at pumping. Now there are squared fields of plowland and pastures. And now there are only a few relics of fens, and the broad expanse once known as the fens is called the "fen-lands."

SHINGLE

On the south coast of England we watched another sort of coastline emerging from the sea. But this emergence, unlike that of the fens, was not assisted by man, nor by plants, nor by rivers. The sea was building, all alone, the kind of pebble beach known as a shingle. This one was called Chesil Bank.

At Weymouth, near the eastern end of Chesil Bank, we were up early on a Sunday morning. We looked down from our window high in the waterfront hotel and saw that already rivers of people were flowing down to the sea for the holiday. We watched a bus pull up to the curb beside the wide sand beach. As soon as it stopped a family popped happily out, father, mother, son, and daughter. They bore deck chairs, lunch baskets, a ball, bags, newspapers. In a few moments they had set their deck chairs in a row on the sand and the father and son had started tossing a ball back and forth, while the daughter peeled to her bathing suit and went down to wade. The mother sat down firmly in the sun. Already another family was lining up its deck chairs to the right of them, and another to the left. The lines of chairs extended as far as we could see along the sand.

That sandy beach was what the sea deposited on the leeward side of a great breakwater. We had come to see what the sea brought to the windward side.

First, however, we did want to get a look at the breakwater itself, the famous Isle of Portland. We set out walking along the long, high, narrow neck of rock. Here, for generations, men have been cutting and hauling away the bottom of an ancient sea, the fine-grained limestone called oolite. This is the stone that rebuilt London after the Great Fire; that Inigo Jones, as chief architect for James I, selected from the isle (an ancient property of the Crown) for building the Great Banquet Hall at Whitehall; that Christopher Wren used for St. Paul's Cathedral, where the rain-washed whiteness of its edges and corners glow against the soot-blackened hollows.

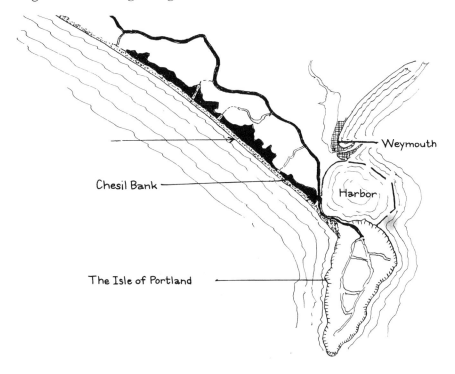

Weymouth

Chesil Bank

Harbor

The Isle of Portland

On a bare shelf of windswept rock I found a plant spreading thick stems and smooth, succulent leaves, uncrowded, unshaded, thriving. This lonely clutcher of the rock was rock samphire, *Crithmum maritimum*. In *King Lear* Shakespeare describes a gatherer of samphire:

> . . . half way down
> Hangs one that gathers samphire—dreadful trade!
> Methinks he seems no bigger than his head.

That cliff climber may have been gathering samphire for pickles, or to be used in making a sauce with butter, or for cooking to be eaten cold with bread, or as a cure for stones in the kidney. This last was logical, according to the medieval Doctrine of Signatures, because the samphire grows out of rock.

The Isle of Portland is, in fact, no longer an island. The sea has tied it to the shore with a long leash. The leash is Chesil Bank, the most famous example of shingle beach in the world.

The shingle curves in a seventeen-mile sweep from Bridport to Portland—seventeen miles of pebbles graduated by size through the action of the waves. It is said that the pebbles of Chesil Bank are graded with such accuracy that a seaman cast ashore in the darkest, stormiest night could take up a handful and, by their size, estimate his position on the beach.

We drove along the nearest road paralleling the sea that we could find. And every time we came to a crossroad of any dimension turning toward the sea, we turned and found our way back to the shingle.

At the end of the first road leading to the sea, we got out to walk and crossed the Fleet, the long body of water imprisoned by the shingle bar. I found myself alone, climbing a long hill of pebbles. Here the pebbles were all of one size, the size of hens' eggs.

I have never felt so bone clean. The smooth pebbles grated under-foot, washed bare by the waves that pushed them and sprayed them and filtered between them to the Fleet. The rain was washing me too, and rewashing those water-worn pebbles, heightening their pinks and grays and browns. The wind was slapping my wet rain-coat and leaving the taste of salt on my lips. As I climbed about on the shingle, stopping to pick up this pebble or that one, I noticed that many were of flint. I listened with pleasure to what Hardy called "the canine crunching of pebbles by the sea without" and suddenly realized how seldom the human organism is alone in such a basic, inorganic world. Even on the barest mountain top there is always a bit of lichen, and in the deadest part of Death Valley we can always find pickleweed.

I liked being the only protoplasm in sight and almost resented it when, on working back to the edge of the Fleet, I saw a band of dark, squat plants, knee high, purplish-green, thick-stemmed, dense. It was the shrubby sea blite, *Suaeda fruticosa*.

But I could not resent it for long. This was protoplasm that could really take it, tolerating not only salt water but constant punishment by the shifting, grating stones. I saw one plant that had been pushed over and partly buried when, on some wilder day, the sea must have sent a towering wave crashing over the crest of the shingle. Each pebble-pinioned branch had sent up many upright shoots, dense with the small, dark leaves, and had sent down roots as well.

The shrubby sea blite seems to thrive only in mobile sites. In this sense it is somewhat like the marram grass, that pioneer of many sand dunes, which stays only so long as the sand is shifting, and gives way before other plants when stability sets in. There are not too many performers who do their best work while the scenery is being shifted.

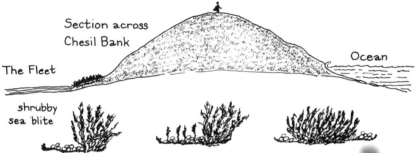

Section across Chesil Bank

The Fleet

Ocean

shrubby sea blite

1. a branch is covered with pebbles 2. shoots develop 3. the clump is extended

We met a few other plants beside the sea blite; most common were the sea campion, *Silene maritima,* and the beach pea, *Lathyrus maritimus.* We were not surprised to come at the end to bushes of tamarisk, planted by men and thriving. We have seen them as well, planted and naturalized, on the alkali flats of the Rio Grande and the bitter edges of Great Salt Lake.

HEDGEROW

There was a sunken lane in Devon that just fitted our car, snugly. Our driver called out, "Pull in your ears!" He didn't want us to have them scratched by hawthorns.

We could not see through the hedgerows. Years before, live slips or cuttings, chiefly of hawthorn, had been set out in close rows beside a cart track. Hedges of this type, which take root readily in the

English climate, are called "quickset hedges." Once the hedge was established it was pruned frequently, and sometimes its branches were interwoven. In many places the lowest branches were split and pegged to the ground to form new roots. Meanwhile the track deepened steadily, as wagons and, later, cars dug ruts and spattered mud, burying the base of the hedgerow. Our car did not contribute to the deepening of the road, nor to the heightening of the mud walls, because the lane had finally been surfaced. But even had we been riding high enough to see over the accumulation of mud, we could not have seen through the hedges. Any peek-holes that had developed were already veiled by vines: clematis (also called "shepherd's delights," "hag-ropes," "traveler's joy," "hedge feathers"), honeysuckle, or hop vines; or plugged with birds' nests.

We met a motor scooter drawing a farm cart and pulled off into a narrow space close to a barred pasture gate to let it pass. Getting out to examine the stout architecture of the hedgerow, we found

The story of the hedgerows beside a very narrow lane in Devon

1. A cart track

2. Live slips or cuttings being set in rows beside the track

3. Hedge being pruned, branches being interwoven and split and pegged down to root, wagon spattering mud

4. Cars spattering more mud

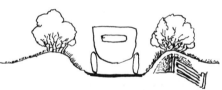

5. Lane blacktopped, no mud spattering; cut in hedgerow for pasture gate shows buried parts

6. In some places trees no longer pruned form arch over lane, pasture side is cow-pruned

that we could actually walk on it (if we didn't mind being scratched). Where the recently made pasture entrance had cut a cross section, the original bases of the hawthorns could be seen, three or four feet under the accumulated clay. The cows came to the gate to see us; and we looked over their red-brown backs to the far-flung network of hedgerows, which appeared to be holding herds of cows apart and the hills together.

A hedgerow

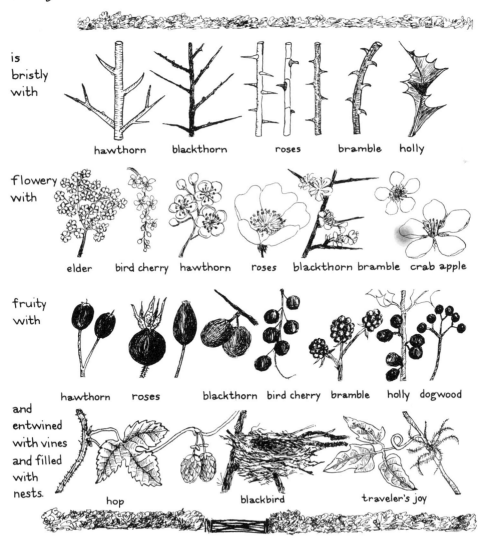

is bristly with

hawthorn blackthorn roses bramble holly

flowery with

elder bird cherry hawthorn roses blackthorn bramble crab apple

fruity with

hawthorn roses blackthorn bird cherry bramble holly dogwood

and entwined with vines and filled with nests.

hop blackbird traveler's joy

Later that morning we found ourselves to be traveling not only in a groove but in a green tunnel, with hedgerow meeting over our heads. Wider roads had been ditched, and the excavated clay had been thrown up above the bank into a ridge on which the hedgerow throve.

Usually, between the hedgerow and the road, there was the sloping bank that is called the verge. And whether the verge was shady or sunny, it was usually flower-filled, and sometimes sloped down to a different type of flora inhabiting the ditch at its base.

The hedgerow held other woody plants beside hawthorns. There were blackthorn, hazel, brambles, roses, bird cherry, elder, and sometimes holly; but the hawthorn was always dominant.

Only rarely did we see a lone hawthorn that had been allowed to attain tree size. We were watching for those lone ones because we had read about them, so deeply rooted in British history, magic, and religion. We watched for them all across Britain. And we found many, but not in the hedgerows. The most beaten, crooked ones were on the South Downs, where the sea wind had shorn and bent them. The most lonely one stood on the treelessness of Dartmoor. The most famous of all stood beside the ruins of Glastonbury Abbey.

We approached the site from the west by somewhat the same route as Joseph of Arimathea, who had provided the burial place for Jesus (Matt. 27:60), is said to have approached it. (This medieval legend is recorded in two thirteenth-century annals.) While he had come in a boat, however, we drove across croplands. But the croplands were low and flat, and they did have abundant reeds and rushes along their slow streams, indicating that they had not long been reclaimed from the sea.

Joseph climbed the hill—Wearyall Hill, it was called—leaning on his hawthorn staff, which, according to the story, was from the same tree that furnished the twigs for Christ's crown of thorns. At the top of the hill, where he and his companions rested, Joseph thrust his staff into the ground. It took root and grew.

From that time on, the tree bloomed every year at Christmas—by the old-style date, of course. When the calendar was changed the peasants put the new date to the test. Would the tree bloom? It would not. Naturally, this cast great doubt on the authenticity of the new date.

The tree throve, bearing two thick trunks. Men venerated it. Puritans disapproved. And, in the time of Elizabeth, a righteous Puritan cut down one of the two trunks. But, according to a contemporary writer, "some of the prickles flew into his eye and made him monocular."

The surviving trunk lasted until the reign of Charles I. Then, during the Rebellion, soldiers cut it down, too. By that time, however, there were several pieces of the original hawthorn growing elsewhere in Britain. One of these was brought back to Glastonbury, and that is the one we saw there. We saw others as well, one in the Oxford Botanical Garden, one in Tavistock. Our botanist-guide at Oxford said, "Yes, it produces a second blooming in the winter," and pointed out the scientific name on the label attached to the small tree, *Crataegus monogyna praecox*. *Crataegus monogyna* is the botanical name of the common hawthorn; the *praecox* is added to indicate a precocious variety of that species.

The Glastonbury thorn

On the other hand, the woman with the shopping basket who pointed out the Tavistock specimen to us, there beside the half-buried ruins of the Abbey, answered with warmth, "Of *course* it blooms at Christmas. Haven't you heard how the crown of thorns burst into bloom when Charlemagne knelt before it? And *those* twigs were all dried up. *This* tree is alive."

Of course the conversion of the hawthorn to Christianity was not an easy or always a lasting one. The tree has had too many prior attachments, commitments, enchantments.

First of all there were the fairies, especially in Ireland. Vaughn Cornish, of Surrey, who inherited a famous hawthorn and made a study of the others, in his book *Historic Thorn Trees of the British Isles* writes:

The special suitability of the solitary hawthorn as a trysting tree for "the Little People" is evident from its appearance. The lower boughs are shedded, the top rounded, the trunk gnarled, yet the height finally attained is little more than that of a bush. Hence the old hawthorn is a miniature of a monarch of the forest.

In connexion with the personality of Fairies it may be well to recall that the Fairies of primitive belief which remains in vogue among Irish peasantry in no way resemble the charming little people represented in modern pictures painted for the delight of children. The Fairies who gathered around a thorn tree were Earth Spirits, of whom, indeed, no evil thing was ever said, but this reticence was a precaution, not a tribute. The primitive belief that damage to their Trysting Tree would bring misfortune to the doer has not died out. Thus a farmer will laboriously cultivate around such a bush, and in many cases it has been impossible to persuade workmen to remove a Thorn Tree from the course of a new road or footway.

It would, of course, be dangerous to cut a branch of such a lone thorn, lest the tree bleed and scream. And one would also not dare to hang clothes to dry on the branches, lest the fairies' garments be already hanging there, invisible to mortal eye. On the Isle of Man, it is told, a peasant cut a few branches from a lone thorn in order to mend his fence. In the process he pierced his thumb with a thorn and had to have his arm amputated. On lonely moorlands of northern Yorkshire, many farms are said to have their lone thorn, on which farmers hang the placentas of their sheep and cattle.

Above all else, the hawthorn was the tree of Maypoles, springtime, and fertility. On May mornings young men and women went out to bring back armloads of its flowering branches. The *Mayflower* bore a hawthorn flower carved on its prow.

And that wasn't all the hawthorn had to do with history. From old records, old maps, and place names it appears that a lone hawthorn was often the designated meeting place of the "hundred," an ancient division of the land between the size of a county and a parish.

Accordingly, there is a place called Spelthorn, meaning "speech thorn." There is also Moot Thorn Field, a probable meeting place.

And there is Paythorne Parish, where a thorn tree marked a forest meeting ground. There is Court Thorn of Hesket-in-the-Forest, where every year the Forest Court was held and tenants from surrounding manors came to pay their annual dues. There is Anthorn (probably originally "Aynthorn" indicating its solitariness), where a local court was held. And there still is a "Judgement Thorn," in Thornhill Basin—just half a mile west of the Gallows Flat.

Badge of
King Henry VII

When Richard III fell on Bosworth Field, his crown was hidden in a hawthorn and was found and used to crown Henry Tudor, Earl of Richmond, as Henry VII. His coat of arms was a crown in a fruited thornbush. (What a prickly lot of biology has found its way to royal insignias of Britain: broom of the Plantagenets, the hawthorn and rose of the Tudors, the Scottish thistle, protected by a rampant lion's claws, and a spiky unicorn!)

The hawthorns of the hedgerow, and their associates, are all intolerant of shade. They form a canopy, spreading wide to the sun, like a row of green umbrellas. But down below, in the shade of the umbrella, are two other groups of plants that are also not shade tolerant. The vines scramble or twine to a hole in the canopy and a place in the sun. Other plants, encouraged by the shade into the formation of elongated cells that build thin, long stems, arrive at some aperture in the canopy, and spread their leaves in the sun. In this group are nettle, dead nettle, garlic mustard, and others.

But down underneath, cool and moist, with darker-green leaves, thrive the shade-tolerant ones: primrose, violets, enchanter's nightshade, and the cuckoopint.

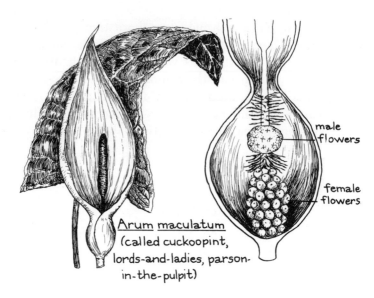

Arum maculatum
(called cuckoopint,
lords-and-ladies, parson-
in-the-pulpit)

Hardy, in *Far from the Madding Crowd*, describes this flower as

. . . the old cuckoo-pint—like an apoplectic saint in a niche of malachite.

In the shade it stands erect, lifting its pale-green sheath and exuding a fetid smell. A small fly or a midge catches that smell, flies over to the leaflike sheath, and crawls down through the narrowed neck to reach the nectar at the base of the vaselike container. Going down is easy. Downward-slanting hairs just above the female flowers delay the insect's exit until the flowers have been pollinated, probably by pollen from another cuckoopint. Then the hairs shrivel, and the fly crawls up, but not far up. Another ring of hairs delays it on the male flowers, which now have their pollen ready for travel. Then the upper ring of hairs withers and the fly takes off, probably for the nearest cuckoopint, to which it will deliver the boon of cross-pollination. This plant is also called "lords-and-ladies" and "parson in the pulpit." The last name leads one to wonder if the upright parson is, like many another, unaware of all the machinations that are going on in the church basement.

Stories and a rich assortment of country names, and superstitions, have accrued to the old, familiar hedgerows. Jacquetta Hawkes writes, in *A Land*, "Count those people fortunate who, like our-selves, have been able to keep the warp threads of the fabric long, their histories in one piece."

BUSINESS REPLY CARD

FIRST CLASS   PERMIT NO. 35   HARLAN, IOWA

POSTAGE WILL BE PAID BY ADDRESSEE

TRAVEL&LEISURE®

P.O. Box 2093
Harlan, Iowa 51593

GIVE TRAVEL & LEISURE FOR CHRISTMAS
—Save up to 43% off newsstand price

Your first gift subscription is \$24.00 for 12 issues.

\$20.00 for each additional gift.

Be sure to fill in all information below:

YOUR NAME: _____

ADDRESS _____

CITY _____ STATE _____ ZIP _____

☐ Please enter, or extend my own subscription at
these low rates

CHECK ONE:

☐ Charge to my American
Express Card account

☐ Payment enclosed

☐ Bill me

**YOU WILL NOT BE
BILLED UNTIL AFTER
JANUARY 1, 1986.**

UN351

SEND GIFT SUBSCRIPTION(S) TO:

NAME: _____

ADDRESS _____

CITY _____ STATE _____ ZIP _____

Gift card inscription "From _____"

NAME: _____

ADDRESS _____

CITY _____ STATE _____ ZIP _____

Gift card inscription "From _____"

NAME: _____

ADDRESS _____

CITY _____ STATE _____ ZIP _____

Gift card inscription "From _____"

(Attach additional sheets for extra gifts)

Add \$6 in Canada. Everywhere else, add \$25

GIFT CARDS: A gift card will be sent to you for each subscription order received before November 26 so that you can inscribe it personally. For orders received after November 26 we will send the card for you, so be sure to indicate above how you wish us to inscribe it.

Every effort will be made to begin holiday gift subscriptions with the January '86 issue. Orders not received in time will start with the next issue, or within 8-10 weeks from receipt of order.

Hedgerows would be one durable part of those long warp threads; another would be public footpaths.

PUBLIC FOOTPATHS

We had just got our hands on three amazing booklets. We wanted to believe the delights that they offered us, but being used to right-angled turns in our walking, we just couldn't.

"Listen to this!" said one of our group, brandishing the booklet called *Country Walks, First Series,* "In the directions it says:

A warning! At many points you pass fieldgates where, in wet weather, the cattle poach the soft earth into a quagmire.

Certainly *no* English farmer is going to want us to cross his fields, muddy or not."

"It's not a matter of wanting, it's a matter of immemorial custom," explained the young Englishwoman who had found the books for us.

"It just doesn't sound very likely," doubted the one who was examining *Country Walks, Third Series.* "Listen to this:

Continue straight ahead, over one golf fairway, then along the left-hand side of another.

I wonder what the golfers will have to say about that."

"They will have nothing to say," replied an American physical therapist who worked in a British hospital. "One day we followed a path like that. The golf course was really busy, and we were surprised to find signs warning the golfers to watch out because footpath-users had the right of way. It seems the footpath was crossing that field before men played golf."

"Well, what about crossing a garden?" asked the worried reader of the *First Series.* "It says here:

Leaving the road, turn right and follow the direction of a footpath sign alongside a small half-timbered house, The Rafters. The public footpath cuts straight through the garden to a pair of stiles. Cross these, continue uphill, with a hedge on the right. When the hedge bears off to the left, pass through a gap, and with the hedge now on your left go forward to a cross-track. Turn right, then alongside Ongar Hill Farm and pass between the farmhouse and a pond to a gate and a stile. At the end of the field pass through a gap in the hedge and forward still by the 50-yard waist of Owlsear Wood."

We spent a pleasant evening with those three booklets published by the London Transport Company and learned quite a bit about the ways by which we could enter places we had never hoped to enter. There were:

gaps in hedges
    iron gates
        small iron swing gates
            lych-gates
                kissing gates
                    cage-wicket gates
                        squeeze stiles
                            bar stiles
                                towpaths
                                    footbridges
                                        suspension bridges
                                            stepping-stones

and, directed a booklet at one point, "Jump the stream (it is quite shallow)."

"To tell the truth," our English girl said, "I've always suspected that a lot of footpaths grew up as the shortest distance to the nearest pub." And the pub theory did seem sound as we read the names that appeared at the centers of various plexes of footpaths, lanes, and cart tracks: The Bull, the Pheasant, the Cock and Rabbit, the Cart and Horses, the Lamb, the Rose and Crown, the Greyhound, the Green Dragon, the Red Lion, the Robin Hood.

Some of the footpaths must have been tendrils reaching out from churches, and some must have served both churches and pubs:

. . . down the slope to the crossroads and up the lane to . . . a small village of old cottages grouped between the Cock and Bottle and the church.

The most famous of the tendrils, of course, is the Pilgrims' Way, reaching out from Canterbury. Several of the "country walks" follow the route of Chaucer's pilgrims over various stretches.

The booklets offer many paths through forests:

. . . the way is now forward through beeches and yews.
. . . the track plunges down into beeches and fern.
. . . in the heart of the forest you will find an abundance of beech, oak, hornbeam and birch trees, and a dense undergrowth of hawthorn, blackthorn and bramble.

. . . wind gently uphill between hazels, holly, and beeches.

There is a promise, too, of being led to some splendid old specimens of trees:

. . . the Bear's Oak. Local tradition says that the last bear in England was killed beside this tree.
At the corner of the field is a holly tree; go *through* the tree! and turn right into the by-lane.

In time, some footpaths such as these may become roads. But that cannot be helped, and, in any case, those roads are the friendly ones, remembering much of what they had learned while they were footpaths. They have come to terms with the hills, and ride high and dry on their south-facing slopes. They accept the challenge of any crests that lie in the way, passing over with dignity for themselves and respect for the hills. In *The Old Road*, Hilaire Belloc traces the route of the Pilgrims' Way from Winchester to Canterbury. He writes:

The road had the merit of all savage trails, and of all the tracks a man still makes who is a-foot and free and can make by the shortest line for his goal: it enjoyed the hills.

The landscape has accepted these new-old roads and has woven them into its fabric, blurring and softening their edges with its own green mantle. They are on speaking terms with small streams and take them as their stepping-stones once did, mainly at places where the hills lean close to each other.

One morning, on a local bus from Guildford to Dorking, I talked with an Englishwoman sitting beside me, her lap full of market basket, about footpaths. She described with warmth the ones that she had followed all her life, and when she left the bus the man in the seat in front of me turned around and said, "I couldn't help hearing, and I do want to point out to you a path that we are about to cross. It goes to my favorite fishing spot. There, there it goes. Don't miss that one."

I didn't miss it. I came back later and followed it past a garden with rows of thriving brussels sprouts and goldenrod and huge dahlias, across a blue-green shady stream, up a bank, through a gate, across a churchyard crowded with ancient yews, around an eleventh-century church, through a stile. There I met an elderly couple with canes and stout walking shoes. They told me of a tea shop that lay ahead and asked if I knew that this path was considered a part of the Pilgrims' Way. The path led uphill between two fences enclosing vegetable plots. After another stile it widened, joining a path from the center of the town. It ran beside a fencerow of wide-spreading English oaks and hawthorns and along a high, plowed field with a view over tiled rooftops to the ridge of the North Downs. As I watched the smokes of Saturday evening rising from the houses below me it turned six o'clock, and the changes were rung on the bells in the church steeple. On that path I met coming home from town: two girls with sheets of piano music, apparently returning from their music lessons; a boy with something alive in a big bottle, evidently coming home from the river; a woman pushing a bicycle, its basket full of garden flowers; a man with a derby hat and a rolled umbrella; and several others. Everyone was using the path as a part of his daily routine, except perhaps for a young man with a loaded rucksack and a sleeping bag, who was apparently using it for an adventure.

On another day, this time following directions in the London Transport booklets, I walked down Christmas Lane, hedged with holly, and came to a wood of pollarded beech trees. On another day I followed a path, deeply cut between hills, through a small village where every house along the path had a steep flight of stairs leading down to it; and then crossed a stile into a meadow of daisies and buttercups and light-green grass, where a cow grazed and a colt came running to greet me. On other days there were other paths, all enjoyable.

Later I learned that other sections of England have their own booklets describing walks. From the booklet *Country Walks Around Saffron Walden* I followed several paths. One of the best went along the back of several gardens, with gardeners who were good enough to lean on their gates and talk a bit. One old man reported that, in his younger days, every Saturday night after tea he would take one footpath over the hill to a pub and come back late, singing loud and happy. The fencerows led him straight home, and no one heard the songs. A woman picked the biggest bunch of pansies I have ever seen, and reached them across the fence to me: "They'll take the hotel smell out of your room."

Stiles in public footpaths

Essex- a "kissing gate"

Derbyshire- a "squeeze gate" in a footpath crossing sheep pasture

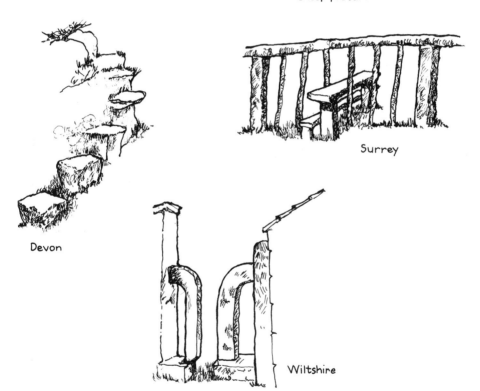

Devon

Surrey

Wiltshire

I learned of other such guides, published by the Ramblers' Association and by the Youth Hostels Association, but have not sampled those yet.

One day we discovered another method for finding footpaths, the simplest way of all, and working best from a car. In Kent we began to notice narrow, inconspicuous signs attached to a tree or fence post beside a gap in a hedge: PUBLIC FOOTPATH. The first one we tried led through a hazel coppice deep-blanketed in bluebells, then through a busy apple orchard, then beside a busy farmyard with tall, trimmed yew hedges; and more. Another path followed the high edge of the white cliffs near Dover.

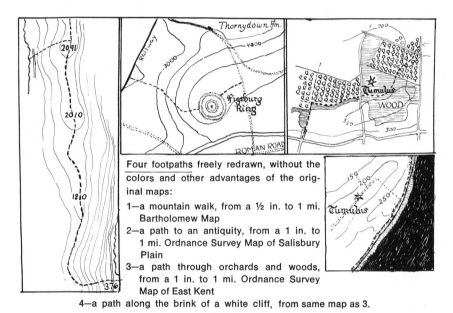

Four footpaths freely redrawn, without the colors and other advantages of the original maps:

1—a mountain walk, from a ½ in. to 1 mi. Bartholomew Map
2—a path to an antiquity, from a 1 in. to 1 mi. Ordnance Survey Map of Salisbury Plain
3—a path through orchards and woods, from a 1 in. to 1 mi. Ordnance Survey Map of East Kent
4—a path along the brink of a white cliff, from same map as 3.

Then I found that there was often a footpath leading away from a small inn or country hotel. I happened to notice our waitress of the evening taking off over the hills in the dusk and decided to follow that path in the morning. There, in the Peak District, I found one of my most delightful footpath experiences. It led through a squeeze gate to a high, rocky sheep pasture with wide views, many sheep, and a few gnomelike, sheep-pruned hawthorns.

One of the best methods of locating footpaths is by using the one-inch-to-the-mile Ordnance Survey maps. That I woke up to this method last of all was probably due to the fact that many of those maps had been around the house for so long, brought home after World War I, and had been consulted often, long before I was aware of, or would have believed in, the existence of public footpaths. The nature of the terrain is shown by contour lines and color; antiquities are marked with Old English type; the footpaths are shown with inconspicuous dotted lines. When planning walks it is wise to remember that each map tells firmly that "The representation on this map of a Road, Track, or Footpath, is no evidence of the existence of a right of way." They are taking no sides.

But many organizations and individuals are taking sides and doing battle to prevent any further loss of footpaths, through the apathy of potential users or the avarice of landowners. Watchful Britishers, realizing that some paths have been lost through disuse and the introduction of obstructions, have banded together into The Commons and Footpath Society. Meanwhile the National Trust for the Preservation of Places of Historic Interest and Natural Beauty is watching over such paths as the Pilgrims' Way. And the Council for the Preservation of Rural England is doing its part. The Chilterns' Society Rights of Way Group has set out to clear about ninety miles of overgrown paths to restore the continuity of the fifteen hundred miles of footpaths in the Chilterns. The work is done on weekends by volunteers. The Ramblers' Association, on learning that walkers had been badgered off certain paths, came out in a force of two hundred ramblers and walked the disputed paths while constables and landowners watched. On a November day in 1965 some three hundred ramblers walked five miles of paths, and, with police watching, cut five barbed wire fences as illegal obstructions on paths mentioned in an Inclosure award of 1770.

Of course, the walkers do not always win. Tom Stephenson, who had represented the walkers of several organizations for thirty years, tells in *The Countryman* quarterly magazine for summer 1969 about a famous case in 1905 concerning the paths to Stonehenge. The landowner had enclosed the site with barbed wire and charged a shilling for admission. The hearing lasted for seven days, during which the oldest inhabitants testified that they had always used the paths and had not been challenged. In that case the judge decided for the landowner.

Nevertheless, it remains true that the English footpath is surely one of the world's most steadfastly democratic phenomena. Footpaths are created by human feet to fill a variety of human needs. Fair enough is the fact that it is the feet that pass most often and/or carry the heaviest burdens (tools, firewood, full creels, market baskets, babies, books, housewares) that cast the decisive votes for the existence and direction of the paths. There is not always unanimity of opinion, of course. The feet of the elderly may cast their votes one way, usually for following the sunny contours; but the feet of the young, running uphill, may choose other ways, favoring revolutionary shortcuts, and, perhaps, winning their adoption.

One more thing about footpaths, proved by Mr. Stephenson and many others: they are defended—with spirit—by their users. There was a time when a man could be inspired by the thought of the existence of a frontier, and straighten his back and square his shoulders, even as he sat comfortably by his fire. Something of this feeling comes when one thinks about preserving the English footpath.

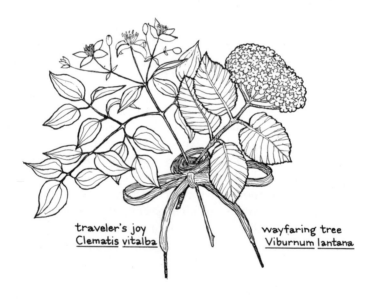

traveler's joy
Clematis vitalba

wayfaring tree
Viburnum lantana

General

The most thorough ecology of all is in *The British Isles and Their Vegetation* by A. G. Tansley (2 Volumes, Cambridge University Press, 1949). By the same author, but revised by M. C. F. Proctor, is *Britain's Green Mantle* (George Allen and Unwin Ltd., London, 1968). A good small book on ecology is *Plant Ecology* by Hilda Drabble (Edward Arnold Co., London, 1951). For an understanding of the structure of Britain there are: *A Land* by Jacquetta Hawkes (Random House, New York, 1952); and *Britain's Structure and Scenery* by L. Dudley Stamp (Collins, London, 1947). If you are lucky enough to find somewhere the set of *Cambridge County Geographies,* general editor F. H. Guillemard (Cambridge University Press, 1896), you will have a good source for any special part of England that may interest you. For a general view of the vegetation there is *British Plant Life* by W. B. Turrill (Collins, London, 1958). To read about the English flora from many angles, enjoy L. J. F. Brimble's *The Floral Year* (Macmillan, London, 1949). Do not forget the *Shell Guides,* and *The Shell Country Book* by Geoffrey Grigson (Phoenix House, Ltd., London, 1962). For areas of marked individuality there is the evergrowing list of the *Regional Books,* general editor Brian Vesey-Fitzgerald (Robert Hale, Ltd., London). The flower book to carry for identification is *Pocket Guide to Wildflowers* (McClintock and Fitter, Collins, London, 1956); the one to keep at home is *The Concise British Flora in Colour* by W. Keble Martin (Holt, Rinehart and Winston, New York, 1965).

Moor

The flavor of the moors is best tasted in novels: *The Return of the Native,* Thomas Hardy; *The Hound of the Baskervilles,* Conan Doyle; and *Wuthering Heights,* Emily Brontë. The grouse moors are covered by *Natural History of the Highlands and Islands* by F. Fraser Darling (Collins, London, 1958).

Glen

The flavor of the glens is best caught in the poetry of Robert Burns, and in the writings of Sir Walter Scott, especially in *The Lady of the Lake*.

Volcanic Neck

A graphic picturing and explanation of the site of Edinburgh is given in *The Earth's Crust* (L. Dudley Stamp, Crown, New York, 1951). A tor on Dartmoor, as well as the structure of the Downs, is also shown here, in three dimensions.

Downs

For flavor start with *Puck of Pook's Hill* by Rudyard Kipling. For ecology, read *Downs and Dunes* by Sir Edward Salisbury (Bell and Sons, London, 1952). For the loving, careful observations by a parish priest read Rev. Gilbert White's *The Natural History and Antiquities of Selborne*, 1788, republished in several forms. For the special flora read *Wild Flowers of Chalk and Limestone* by J. E. Lousley (Collins, London, 1950).

Coppice and Pollard

Englishmen have been writing about their great trees and forests for a long time. It is worthwhile consulting some of the older writings: especially the *Sylva* by John Evelyn, 1633; and *Remarks on Forest Scenery and Other Woodland Views* by John Gilpin, 1833. A study of one area of woods is a small book, *Woodland Ecology* (Ernest Neal, Harvard University Press, Cambridge, 1958). You will also want the booklet called *A Guide to Burnham Beeches*, written by A. D. C. LeSueur and published by the Corporation of London.

Bomb Crater

In the book *London's Natural History* by R. S. R. Fitter (Collins, London, 1946), read at least the chapter called "The Influence of War." Perhaps you can find a copy of the booklet *The Natural History of the City* by Fitter and J. E. Lousley, published by the Corporation of London, 1953.

Fens

To read about man's appropriation of the fenlands, see "Origin and Use of the English Peat Fens" by Kenneth Thompson, in *Scientific Monthly*, August 1957; and for a feeling of the Viking invaders, the novel, *The Long Ships*, by Frans G. Bengtsson (Knopf, New York, 1954).

Shingle

In *A Land* by Jacquetta Hawkes, read the chapter "Digression on Rocks, Soils, and Man" about the stone of Portland. In Hilda Drabble's *Plant Ecology*, read the chapter on "Shingle." (These two books are listed under *General.*)

Hedgerow

For the cult of the thorn, try to locate a copy of *Historic Thorn Trees in the British Isles* by Vaughn Cornish (Country Life Limited, London, 1941).

Public Footpaths

Three especially usable booklets are published by London Transport: *Country Walks, First Series; Second Series; Third Series.* They contain detailed maps and explicit directions. Two government pamphlets covering the legal aspects of footpaths are: *National Parks and Access to the Countryside Act,* 1949, and *Royal Commission on Common Land,* 1955–1958. For a study of the plants of the paths, see "The Vegetation of Footpaths, Sidewalks, Cart-tracks, and Gateways," by H. E. Bates, in *Journal of Ecology,* 23 (1935): 470–487. For easy cross-country walks on the chalk uplands of N. W. Essex, get the booklet *Country Walks around Saffron Walden,* obtainable from the author and publisher, Sidney E. Fisher, Saffron Waldon. For the longest footpath get *The Pennine Way,* published by the Ramblers Association, 124 Finchley Road, London. Also from the Ramblers, get *Selected Walks in the Lake District* and *Bed, Breakfast, and Bus Guide.* Above all, do not deny yourself the enjoyment of tracing the route of the Pilgrims' Way, from Winchester to Canterbury, in *The Old Road* by Hilaire Belloc (Lippincott, Philadelphia, 1911). *A Walk Through Britain* by John Hillaby (Houghton Mifflin, Boston, 1969) is an account of a walk from Land's End to John O'Groats, some 1,100 miles, and follows public footpaths for much of the way.

Index

Supplement

A PICTORIAL KEY

TO THE IDENTIFICATION

OF THE TREES

OF EUROPE

I. TO USE THE PICTORIAL KEY

1. Select a leaf from the tree to be identified. Avoid freaks.

2. Start at the top of page S-6, by choosing either or .

3. Proceed step by step, considering both choices offered at each symbol, for example or .

4. When you have made the final choice, arriving at the name of the tree, compare your leaf with the illustration, and check the shape of the tree, its growing environment, and its distribution.

NOTE: This key describes native European trees, but also includes those Asiatic trees which are most often planted or which have become naturalized in Europe. The many varieties of cultivated fruit trees seen in Europe are not included, nor are native American trees, which are also seen from time to time. In a few cases a choice between two botanical names is offered where there have been recent changes in nomenclature.

II. DISTRIBUTION

When you arrive at the name of the tree you are identifying, you will find each country in which that tree is native (of those countries included in this book) indicated at the extreme right of the illustration by one of the following symbols.

For BRITAIN
    the English daisy of green lawns

For FRANCE
    the fleur-de-lis of riversides and royalty

For ITALY
    the laurel wreath of heroes and poets

For SWITZERLAND
    the soldanella of the snow pockets

For GERMANY
    the cabbages of gardens and sauerkraut

For DENMARK
    the swan, with an ugly duckling in its wake

For NORWAY
    the glacier buttercup of the mountaintops

III. GROWING ENVIRONMENT

A simple diagram from among those that follow is shown with the leaf of each tree identified. The symbol indicates the environments in the landscape in which the tree is most likely to be seen.

 in the forest canopy

 planted in rows for crops or windbreaks

 on the upland

 in the forest understory

 on the bottomland

 at high altitudes or northern latitudes

 at the edge of the woods or in hedgerows

 near the Mediterranean

 planted in gardens

 on disturbed soil

planted or naturalized
in crowded places

 planted in parks or lawns

IV. TREE SHAPES

The shape of a tree may be modified by one or more of the following:

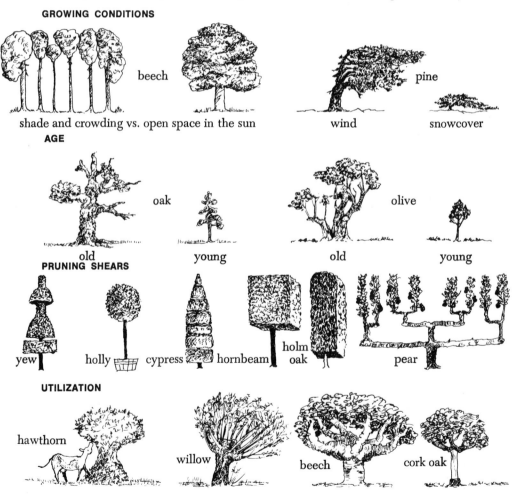

GROWING CONDITIONS

beech

pine

shade and crowding vs. open space in the sun   wind   snowcover

AGE

oak   young   olive   young

old   young   old   young

PRUNING SHEARS

yew   holly   cypress   hornbeam   holm oak   pear

UTILIZATION

hawthorn   willow   beech   cork oak

START HERE

If the tree has needles, or scales,
  go to this symbol below

If the tree has leaves,
  go to this symbol, on page S-9

 If the needles are held together in bundles or tufts, of two to many,
  go below to

If the needles are not in bundles or tufts, but are borne singly along the twig, or are scalelike, overlapping
  go, on page S-8, to

 If there are two to five needles in each bundle,
  go below to

If there are tufts composed of many needles, about an inch long
  go below to

 If the needles are deciduous,
  it is LARCH
  Larix decidua

If the needles are evergreen,
  it is CEDAR OF LEBANON
  Cedrus libani

 If there are five needles in a bundle
  it is AROLLA PINE
  Pinus cembra

If there are two needles in a bundle,
  go below to

 If the tree grows at high altitudes or in northern latitudes
  go, on page S-7, to

If the tree grows in the Mediterranean area,
  go, on page S-8, to

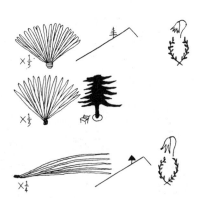

If the needles are three to five inches long, stout, stiff, with a ragged sheath,

it is AUSTRIAN PINE
Pinus nigra

If the needles are two to three inches long,

go below to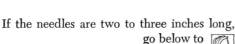

If the needles are gray-green, slightly twisted, and the branches have orange bark,

it is SCOTCH PINE
Pinus sylvestris

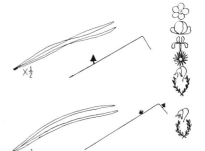

If the needles are curved, stout, dark green, and the pine is many stemmed or shrublike,

it is MUGO PINE
Pinus mugo

If the pine has a dense, flat top, with needles three to five inches long, with fringed bud scales,

it is STONE PINE
Pinus pinea

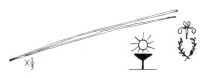

If the pine has a rounded, somewhat conical top,

go below to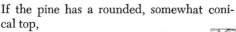

If the needles are very long, four to eight inches, and very stout, and the pine is found only in siliceous soils,

it is MARITIME PINE
Pinus pinaster

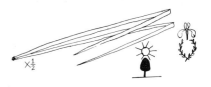

If the needles are very slender, two to four inches long, and it is found only in calcareous soils (this is the most common pine of the south coast of Europe),

it is ALEPPO PINE
Pinus halapensis

If the needles are scalelike, overlapping,
go below to

If the needles are not scalelike, but spaced
singly along the twig,
go below to

If the dense, dark tree conceals its structure
under overlapping upturned branches (a
tree often planted in cemeteries, and often
pruned),

it is ITALIAN CYPRESS
Cupressus sempervirens

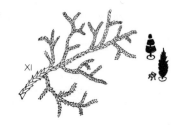

If the tree is of somewhat similar outline,
found on sunny, pastured hills, and has
spiny scales and blue berries (usually a
shrub),

it is COMMON JUNIPER
Juniperus communis
(not pictured)

If the horizontal branches are covered with
sharp, stiff, wide, leathery scales,
it is MONKEY PUZZLE TREE
Araucaria araucan

If the needles are two-ranked (like hair
divided by a comb), twigs smooth,
go below to

If the needles are stiff, radial, on rough
twigs,

it is NORWAY SPRUCE
Picea abies

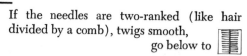

If the needles have two white stripes beneath, and notched tips,
it is WHITE FIR
Abies alba

If the needles are green beneath, twigs
green, fruit red, berrylike,
it is YEW
Taxus baccata

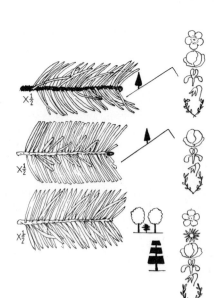

If the leaves are evergreen,
                              go below to

If the leaves are deciduous,
go, on page S-10, to

If the evergreen leaves have some points along their margins (part of the leaves on a tree may be without points),
                              go below to

If the evergreen leaves have no spiny points,
                              go below to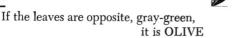

If the leaves are opposite, gray-green,
                              it is OLIVE
                                   Olea europea

If the leaves are alternate, glossy,
                              it is LAUREL
                                   Laurus nobilis

If the leaves are sharply spiny, twisted, fruit red, tree often shrublike,
                              it is HOLLY
                                   Ilex aquifolium

If the leaves are somewhat hollylike, not sharply spiny, not twisted, fruit an acorn,
                              go below to

If the bark is cork (if the tree is mature, probably the cork has been harvested from the trunk and the bases of branches), the underside of the leaves whitish, feltlike, the tree growing in siliceous soils,
                              it is CORK OAK
                                   Quercus suber

If the bark is not corky, the underside of the leaf gray or tawny, the tree growing in calcareous soils,
                              it is HOLM OAK
                                 or HOLLY OAK
                                   Quercus ilex

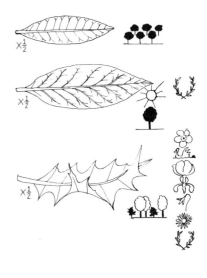

If the leaf is compound (composed of leaflets),

go below to

If the leaf is simple, not compound,

go, on page S-11, to

If the compound leaves have more than three leaflets,

go below to

If the compound leaves have only three leaflets, and long, drooping clusters of pea–blossom–shaped flowers, on a small tree,
it is GOLDEN RAIN TREE
Laburnum anagyroides

×½

If the compound leaves grow opposite each other on the twig,

go below to

If the compound leaves grow alternately along the twig,

go below to

If the leaflets all radiate from one point,
it is HORSE CHESTNUT
Aesculus hippocastanum

If the leaflets do not radiate from one point,
it is COMMON ASH
Fraxinus excelsior

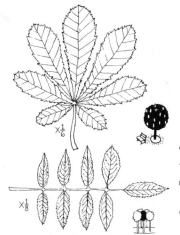

×⅙

×⅛

If the compound leaf is more than seven inches long, the leaflets without teeth, or only toothed at the base,
go, on page S-11, to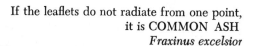

If the compound leaf is only seven inches or less, the leaflets regularly toothed,
it is MOUNTAIN ASH
Sorbus aucuparia
or *Pyrus aucuparia*

If the margins are without teeth, the terminal leaflet the longest,

it is WALNUT
Juglans regia

If there is one tooth (occasionally two) at each side of the base of each leaflet,

it is TREE OF HEAVEN
Ailanthus altissima

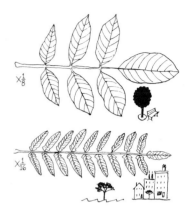

If the simple leaves grow opposite each other on the twig, and are lobed with their main veins radiating from the base,

go below to

If the simple leaves grow alternately from the twig,

go, on page S-12, to

If the leaf has teeth as well as lobes, and the paired winged seeds hang at almost right angles to each other,

it is SYCAMORE MAPLE
(called "sycamore" in Britain)
Acer pseudoplatanus

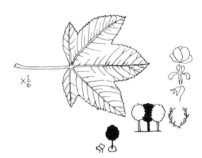

If the leaf stem shows milky juice when broken, and the winged seeds hang at a much wider angle,

go below to

If the leaf is thin, five- to seven-lobed, the lobes tapering to long points, the paired seeds looking like coat hangers,

it is NORWAY MAPLE
Acer platamoides

If the leaf is only two to four inches in diameter, the lobes rather blunt-tipped, the paired seeds almost horizontal,

it is HEDGE MAPLE
or FIELD MAPLE
Acer campestre

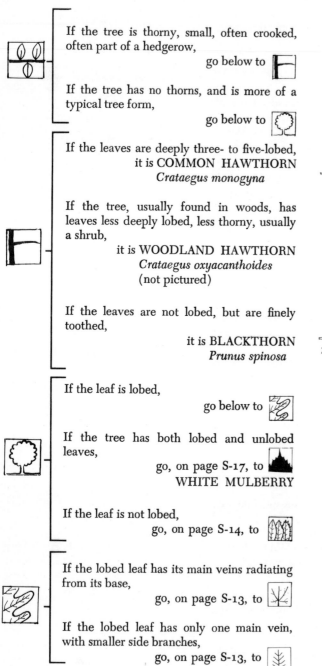

If the tree is thorny, small, often crooked, often part of a hedgerow,

go below to

If the tree has no thorns, and is more of a typical tree form,

go below to

If the leaves are deeply three- to five-lobed, it is COMMON HAWTHORN
Crataegus monogyna

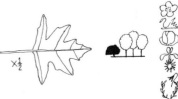

If the tree, usually found in woods, has leaves less deeply lobed, less thorny, usually a shrub,

it is WOODLAND HAWTHORN
Crataegus oxyacanthoides
(not pictured)

If the leaves are not lobed, but are finely toothed,

it is BLACKTHORN
Prunus spinosa

If the leaf is lobed,

go below to

If the tree has both lobed and unlobed leaves,

go, on page S-17, to
WHITE MULBERRY

If the leaf is not lobed,

go, on page S-14, to

If the lobed leaf has its main veins radiating from its base,

go, on page S-13, to

If the lobed leaf has only one main vein, with smaller side branches,

go, on page S-13, to

If the leaf is dark green above, and its lower surface, stem, and young twigs are covered with a snow-white felt, and the smooth gray bark is marked with diamond-shaped scars,
it is WHITE POPLAR
Populus alba

If the leaves are deeply five-lobed, without white undersurface,
go below to

If the tips of the lobes are rounded, and the leaf is the most common one in art galleries,
it is FIG
Ficus carica

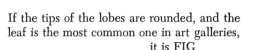

If the tips of the lobes are pointed, the bark peeling in patches, showing white underneath,
go below to

If the leaf is very deeply lobed (often to two-thirds the width of the leaf), lobes lance-shaped, trunk rugged,
it is ORIENTAL PLANE
Platanus orientalis

If the leaf is lobed less than halfway, with triangular lobes, and the trunk is erect, tall, with a rounded head of branches,
it is LONDON PLANE
Platanus acerifolia

If the lobes are toothed, tree small,
it is WILD SERVICE TREE
Sorbus torminalis
or *Pyrus torminalis*

If the lobes are not toothed,
go, on page S-14, to

If the leaf base is shaped like ear lobes, beside the very short leaf stem, and the long acorns are very long-stemmed,

it is ENGLISH OAK
Quercus robur

If the leaf base is not ear-lobed but tapering,

go below to

If the leaf is long-stemmed, acorn stemless,

it is DURMAST OAK
Quercus petraea

If the leaf has deep, acute lobes, and bristly acorn cups,

it is TURKEY OAK
Quercus cerris

If the leaf margin has one tooth terminating each vein, and veins are straight, parallel, unbranching,

go below to

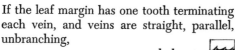

If the leaf margin has many fine teeth, and a main vein does not terminate in each tooth,

go, on page S-15, to

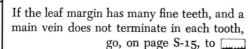

If the leaf is oval, with very small teeth, and the bark is smooth gray (probably with carved hearts and initials),

it is BEECH
Fagus sylvatica

(Often planted is a dark-leaved variety, called COPPER BEECH or PURPLE BEECH.)

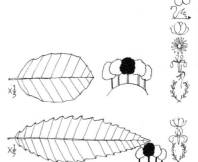

If the leaf is long, with prominent, curving teeth, and the tree has long sprays of small yellow flowers,

it is CHESTNUT
Castanea sativa

If the leaf blade is long and narrow, and the stem short,

go below to

If the leaf is not especially long and narrow,

go, on page S-16, to

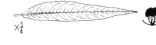

If the leaves are silky-white on both sides, finely toothed, with long pointed tips,
it is WHITE WILLOW
Salix alba

If the leaves are not silky-white on both sides,

go below to

If the twigs are long and pendulous, and the thin, long leaves whitened beneath,
it is WEEPING WILLOW
Salix babylonica

If the twigs are not pendulous, and the leaves are green on both sides,

go below to

If the twigs snap off easily at their bases, and the leaves taper very gradually toward both ends,
it is CRACK WILLOW
Salix fragilis

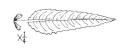

If the leaf tapers less gradually, and has two large stipules at the base of the stem, and the tree is small with almond smell and shedding bark,
it is FRENCH WILLOW
or ALMOND WILLOW
Salix triandra

If the triangular, round, or heart-shaped leaf is about as long as wide, and the leaf stem one-third to one-half as long as the blade,

go below to

If the leaf is somewhat oval,

go, on page S-18, to

If the teeth are wavy, or rounded, or blunt,

go, on page S-17, to

If the teeth are tipped with a point,

go below to

If the leaf is somewhat heart-shaped, large, soft,

go below to

If the leaf has straight, parallel side veins, hardly branching, and the tree has white, thin bark, with dark lenticels,

go, on page S-17, to

If the teeth are small, veins not prominent, base of leaf heart-shaped,

it is SMALL-LEAVED LIME
or LINDEN
Tilia cordata

If the leaf is larger, with large teeth,

go, on page S-17, to

If the leaf is asymmetrical at base, downy beneath, and young twigs are downy,
   it is LARGE-LEAVED LIME
   or LINDEN
    Tilia platyphyllos

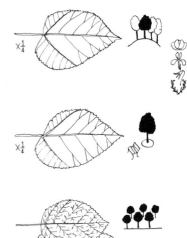

If the leaf is asymmetrical at base, but not downy beneath (a possible hybrid of the small-leaved lime and the large-leaved lime),
   it is COMMON LIME
   or LINDEN
    Tilia vulgaris

If the leaf has milky juice, the tree may have lobed or unlobed leaves, or both. Planted for silk-culture,
   it is WHITE MULBERRY
    Morus alba

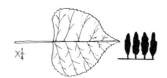

If the leaf is almost round, teeth widely spaced, blunt, irregular, the stem thin and flattened,
    it is ASPEN
    Populus tremula

If the leaf is triangular, with long tip, the tree shaped like an exclamation point,
   it is LOMBARDY POPLAR
    Populus nigra
    variety *italica*

If the leaf has a slenderly tapering tip, is doubly toothed, not downy, the branches pendulous, warty,
   it is SILVER BIRCH
    Betula pendula,
   or *Betula verrucosa*

If the leaf is less tapered, coarsely toothed, somewhat downy, the twigs not warty, not pendulous, bark darker,
   it is DOWNY BIRCH
   or BROWN BIRCH
    Betula pubescens

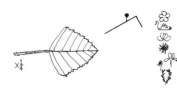

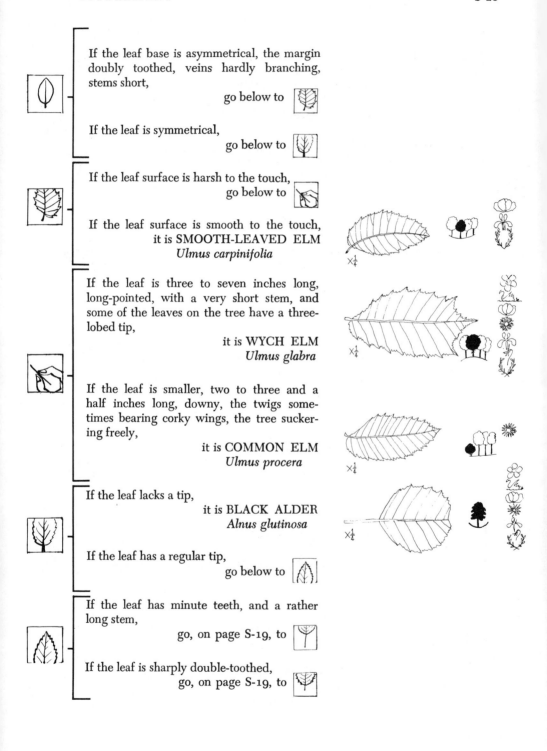

If the leaf base is asymmetrical, the margin doubly toothed, veins hardly branching, stems short,

go below to

If the leaf is symmetrical,

go below to

If the leaf surface is harsh to the touch,
go below to

If the leaf surface is smooth to the touch,
it is SMOOTH-LEAVED ELM
Ulmus carpinifolia

If the leaf is three to seven inches long, long-pointed, with a very short stem, and some of the leaves on the tree have a three-lobed tip,

it is WYCH ELM
Ulmus glabra

If the leaf is smaller, two to three and a half inches long, downy, the twigs sometimes bearing corky wings, the tree suckering freely,

it is COMMON ELM
Ulmus procera

If the leaf lacks a tip,
it is BLACK ALDER
Alnus glutinosa

If the leaf has a regular tip,
go below to

If the leaf has minute teeth, and a rather long stem,

go, on page S-19, to

If the leaf is sharply double-toothed,
go, on page S-19, to

If the leaf is white beneath, tapering to the base,

it is WHITE BEAM
Sorbus aria
or *Pyrus aria*

If the leaf is not white beneath, has straight, unbranched veins, and resembles an elm leaf, but has a symmetrical base, slightly heart-shaped,

it is HORNBEAM
Carpinus betulus

If the leaves are long with tapering tips, bases rounded or slightly heart-shaped, veins curving,

it is BIRD CHERRY
Prunus Padus

If the leaves are downy, drooping,
it is GEAN
Prunus avium

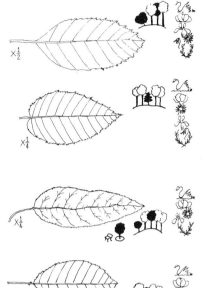

71 72 73 10 9 8 7 6 5 4 3 2 1

PUBLIC FOOTPATH